CHARLES S. PEIRCE

Essays in the Philosophy
of Science

The American Heritage Series

OSKAR PIEST, *General Editor*

[NUMBER SEVENTEEN]

CHARLES S. PEIRCE

Essays in the Philosophy of Science

CHARLES S. PEIRCE
Essays in the Philosophy of Science

Edited with an Introduction by
VINCENT TOMAS
Professor of Philosophy, Brown University

THE LIBERAL ARTS PRESS
NEW YORK

CONTENTS

ESSAYS IN THE PHILOSOPHY OF SCIENCE

NOTE ON THE TEXT

The text is that of Charles Hartshorne and Paul Weiss (eds.), *Collected Papers of Charles Sanders Peirce,* Cambridge, Mass.: Harvard University Press, Copyright 1931-1935, by the President and Fellows of Harvard College. The permission of the publishers to reprint the selections in this volume is gratefully acknowledged.

The text has been reproduced with only occasional modifications in punctuation. Footnotes, titles, and other material which are not Peirce's own are enclosed by brackets. Footnote material supplied by the present editor is marked "—Ed."

The original editors indicated in their notes where each selection was first published. To these notes the present editor has added, within parentheses, where these selections are to be found in the *Collected Papers.* The *Collected Papers* are cited throughout as *C.P.*

The first six essays in this volume comprised a series, "Illustrations of the Logic of Science," which appeared during 1877 and 1878 in *Popular Science Monthly.*

V. T.

INTRODUCTION

Charles Sanders Peirce was born in Cambridge, Massachusetts, on September 10, 1839. He died in Milford, Pennsylvania, on April 19, 1914.

After graduating from Harvard University, in 1859, Peirce was employed by the United States Coast and Geodetic Survey, from which he retired in 1891. He lectured on logic at The Johns Hopkins University during 1879-1884; and he gave some philosophical lectures at Harvard University and at the Lowell Institute in Boston. He was a voluminous writer, but during his lifetime his philosophical works appeared only as articles or reviews. Some were not published at all.

Some of Peirce's contemporaries, among them William James, Josiah Royce, John Dewey, and F. C. S. Schiller, acknowledged his influence and elaborated upon certain of his ideas. But a general appreciation of the many contributions Peirce had made to diverse fields of philosophy waited upon the publication of his *Collected Papers*, after he was dead.

The writings here collected bring together in one volume a substantial part of their author's reflections on a variety of themes in the philosophy of science: the analysis of inquiry, the logic of discovery, induction and probability, hypotheses, verifiability, laws of nature, mathematics. On these and allied subjects Peirce had some profound and original things to say.

Peirce rightfully regarded himself as being "saturated, through and through, with the spirit of the physical sciences" (1.3).[1] He was well-trained in physics and chemistry; he made his living mainly by scientific work; and he had read widely in the classics and contemporary writings of science. Nevertheless, Peirce tended to view science, as he did everything

[1] *Volume 1, paragraph 3,* of the *Collected Papers.* This convention of referring to the *Collected Papers* will be followed hereafter. Where only a page reference appears, the reference is to this book.

else, from the standpoint of logic and general (including speculative) philosophy.

From this perspective, however, Peirce did not produce works in which he expounds his conception of science in a neat and systematic manner. For example, although he alleges, of "Illustrations of the Logic of Science," that "To describe the method of scientific investigation is the object of this series of papers" (pp. 26-27), the reader will not find such a description in these essays. What he will find is a series of philosophical reflections on such concepts as inquiry, reality, meaning, probability, induction, chance, law, and so on. Peirce concentrated his attention on concepts which he took to be fundamental to a philosophical understanding of scientific method and its results; and what he actually gives is not a "description" of the method of scientific investigation, but philosophical analyses of key concepts that would have to be used in a systematic description of it.

Peirce regarded most of these writings as contributions to logic, which he conceived as the study of reasoning. Reasoning, which Peirce also calls "thought" and "inquiry," is the art of drawing inferences. Its aim is to find out, from consideration of what we already know (premises), something else that we do not know (conclusions). Reasoning or inquiry is thus a knowledge-seeking activity. Since, according to Peirce, a man knows the world to the extent that he has stable beliefs about it, another way of describing the aim of reasoning is to say that it seeks stable beliefs.

A belief is a habit, i.e., a readiness or disposition to respond in certain kinds of ways on certain kinds of occasions. There is some ambiguity as to how the word "respond" in the preceding sentence should be understood. Sometimes Peirce regards a belief-habit as a habit of action, where by "action" is meant behavior which involves movement of muscles. Hence, to say that a man believes something would be to say that he has a disposition to *behave* in certain overt ways on certain occasions. At other times Peirce tends to think of a belief-habit as a habit of expectation. He writes, "It now begins to look strongly as if perhaps all belief might involve expectation as its essence" (5.542), and he claims that the end of an explanatory hypothesis is to lead "to the establishment of a habit of positive expectation that shall not be disappointed" (p. 254). Hence, to say that a man believes something would be to say that he has a disposition to *expect* certain things on certain occasions; or, alternatively, that he has a disposition to be "surprised" if he fails to have certain experiences on certain occasions.

If we leave to one side the question about what, for Peirce, really constitutes the essence of belief, we can think of beliefs as being, on his view, complex habits of behaving and expecting. He suggests that statements of the form

Jones believes that ————

can be explicated by an indefinite number of statements of the following form:

If Jones were to undergo experiences ————
when he was actuated by motive ————, then he
would behave ———— and he would expect

————.

A belief, as above described, is *stable* or *unstable*. If a man's belief causes him to respond to circumstances in which he finds himself with actions that are frustrated and expectations that are disappointed, his belief-habit is disrupted. It is shaken off and replaced by doubt, a state of hesitancy about how to act and what to expect. The man thereby finds out that his belief was unstable. Peirce contends that until a belief is actually disrupted by experience, it will be regarded as stable, for only surprising experiences can generate genuine doubt—the "privation" of a habit.

It is obvious, however, that a belief which is stable in the sense that *it has not yet been disrupted* by experience might not be stable in the sense that *it would not be disrupted if it were tested*. The method of tenacity, which consists in one's systematically avoiding any occasion which might possibly cause one's beliefs to be disrupted, enables a person who practices it to retain his beliefs, which are then stable in the former sense. But it does not suffice to assure him that they are stable in the latter sense. The reader may be assisted to understand some of Peirce's views, especially in "The Fixation of Belief" and "How to Make Our Ideas Clear," if he bears this distinction in mind.

For instance, near the beginning of "The Fixation of Belief," Peirce writes:

> The object of reasoning [inquiry] is to find out, from the consideration of what we already know, something else which we do not know. Consequently, reasoning is good if it be such as to give true conclusions from true premisses, and not otherwise (p. 7).

A few pages later he writes:

> Hence, the sole object of inquiry [reasoning] is the settlement of opinion. We may fancy that this is not enough for us, and that we seek, not merely an opinion, but a true opinion. But put this fancy to the test, and it proves groundless; for as soon as a firm belief is reached we are entirely satisfied, whether the belief be true or false (p. 13).

In the first passage, we may understand Peirce to be asserting that the *ultimate* aim of reasoning is to arrive at beliefs which are stable in the sense that they would be "unassailable by doubt," or would not be falsifiable, however long investigation were to continue. In the second passage, we may understand him to be asserting that in pursuing our ultimate goal, we are perforce satisfied so long as we achieve beliefs which *so far* are unassailed by doubt. In traditional terminology, what we aim at is knowledge; but all that we get, from inquiry, is grounded opinion (which may be mistaken) that we *take* to be knowledge.

We may say, using a terminology that Pierce did not himself employ, that for him a stable belief is one that is verifiable in principle, and an unstable belief is one that is falsifiable in principle. A belief is verifiable in principle if it is not falsifiable, that is, if it is not such that it would be disrupted in the course of indefinitely long and scientific investigation.

To be "scientific," according to Peirce, investigation must be directed in such a way as to subject beliefs to the test of experience. Scientific investigation proceeds by the method of elimination. As it proceeds, one after another unstable belief is "surprised" and eliminated and replaced by another belief, which in its turn might be eliminated. At the limit of a long-run process of elimination, a limit the community of investigators can approach but can never reach, would be the beliefs that had not been falsified. These would be the stable beliefs, "the state of fixed belief, or perfect knowledge" (5.420). Peirce defines "truth" and "reality" in terms of stable belief. If we say that a belief we *now* have is true, we are claiming that it would not be eliminated, if and however long scientific investigation were carried on. That such claims might be mistaken is a thesis of Peirce's fallibilism. Reality—that which through investigation we seek to know—is what would be represented in perfect knowledge.

Peirce does not subscribe to the view implied by the statement, "God did not create man and then leave it to Aristotle to make him rational." He denies that man is by nature a perfectly logical animal. "We come to the full possession of our power of drawing inferences the last of all our faculties; for it is not so much a natural gift, as a long and difficult art" (p. 3). What conclusion a man will draw from given premises or data is determined by habits. A man might habitually draw conclusions according to a rule of inference which is such that, by following this rule, the man is as likely to arrive at false conclusions as at true ones. He would then have a *bad* habit of reasoning. Nevertheless, if men are motivated by the desire for truth, they will, taken collectively, shake off bad habits of reasoning and discover how they ought to reason so as ultimately to arrive at the truth.

Reasoning, on Peirce's view of it, lifts itself up by its own bootstraps in something like the way that technology does. Although he had to start with nothing but his bare hands and sticks and stones, man succeeds in making ever more intricate and more efficient precision tools. Similarly, although he must start with his primitive common-sense beliefs and habits of reasoning, man succeeds in improving both. Were men but to continue to investigate, in the long run their false beliefs and their bad habits of reasoning would be eliminated. Says Peirce:

> . . . one of the most wonderful features of reasoning and one of the most important philosophemes in the doctrine of science [is] that reasoning tends to correct itself, and the more so, the more wisely its plan is laid. Nay, it not only corrects its conclusions, it even corrects its premisses (p. 233).
>
> . . . inquiry of every type, fully carried out, has the vital power of self-correction and of growth. This is a property so deeply saturating its inmost nature that it may truly be said that there is but one thing needful for learning the truth, and that is a hearty and active desire to learn what is true. If you really want to learn the truth, you will, by however devious a path, be surely led into the way of truth, at last. No matter how erroneous your ideas of the method may be at first, you will be forced at length to correct them so long as your activity is moved by that sincere desire. Nay, no matter if you only half desire it, at first, that desire would at length conquer all others, could experience continue long enough (pp. 233-234).

Peirce's defense of this view is in part an appeal to history. He believed that the history of human inquiry discloses a gradual refinement and improvement in the methods of inquiry, culminating in the scientific method. This method "is itself a scientific result. It did not spring out of the brain of a beginner: it was a historic attainment" (p. 192); and "each chief step in science has been a lesson in logic" (p. 5).

However, his defense relies mainly on philosophical considerations. In "The Fixation of Belief," the chief such consideration is that habits of reasoning like those summed up in the method of tenacity, the method of authority, and the *a priori* method are bound to fail to establish stable beliefs. They fix beliefs not in response to the effects of objective reality on human experience, but in response to human willfulness, fiat, or preference. There is much evidence that there is no pre-established harmony between any of the latter and facts, such that beliefs grounded in them would be immune to surprise if tested. Sooner or later most beliefs adopted merely because of willfulness, the dictates of arbitrary authority, or personal preference are disrupted, and the methods themselves, therefore, become suspect. One comes to see that—

> after all, he wishes his opinions to coincide with the fact, and that there is no reason why the results of those three first methods should do so. To bring about this effect is the prerogative of the method of science (p. 29).

The reasons for Peirce's assurance that the practice of scientific method *must* eventually yield genuine knowledge are to be found scattered throughout his works and underwent modification over a span of forty years. Not all of the relevant statements are consistent with each other. Moreover, some are very obscure. As a result, it is not easy to compress his justification of science into a brief space. The following brief summary of his views on this matter will, therefore, be rough and incomplete. Despite its oversimplifications, the reader taking up Peirce for the first time may find it useful, especially if, when reading the source material itself, he watches for passages in the light of which it should be qualified.

Scientific inquiry, according to Peirce, begins when the investigator is confronted by a surprising phenomenon. As he ponders the phenomenon, explanatory hypotheses suggest themselves. A hypothesis is arrived at, Peirce holds, by reasoning. It is the conclusion of a hypothetic inference, which Peirce generally calls "abduction." It is first entertained "interrogatively" and appraised in terms of the investigator's beliefs, which are indubitable in the sense that, having so far survived the test of experience, they are not in fact doubted. Some hypotheses never pass the interrogative stage. They lack "plausibility" and are discarded as unworthy of being tested. On the other hand, a hypothesis which is "plausible" and genuinely explanatory is, other things being equal, worth testing. This is done by first deducing what would be observable under specified conditions if the hypothesis were true, and next by realizing these conditions in an experiment or experiments and observing the results. The experimental stage of inquiry employs inductive reasoning. Induction, Peirce says, is reasoning "whose business consists in testing a hypothesis already recommended" (2.755). If the results observed are surprising, i. e., different from what the deductive elucidation of the hypothesis led the investigator to expect, the process begins again.

Thus science makes use of three modes of reasoning: abduction, deduction, and induction. Of these, deduction provides no new knowledge. It is purely explicative and can only make what is already known or conjectured more distinct. We can know by deduction that, *if* certain premises are true, a certain conclusion is necessarily true; but the fountainhead of all novel premises, and so of knowledge, is abduction. Observation, Peirce holds, is a limiting case of abductive reasoning. The latter "shades off" into the former, and there is no sharp line between them. When we perceive physical objects and events, we are making what from the point of view of logical analysis would be hypothetic inferences. The only difference between perceptual judgments and abductive conclusions is that perceptual judgments are not subject to control:

> . . . we cannot form the least conception of what it would be to deny the perceptual judgment . . . . An abductive suggestion, however, is something whose truth *can* be questioned or even denied (5.186).

A mode of reasoning, Peirce holds in his earlier papers, is good or valid if from true premises it yields true conclusions as frequently as it professes to do so: either always, as deduction professes, or in a better than chance proportion of cases, as abduction and induction profess to do. In the terminology of "The Doctrine of Chances," this may be expressed as follows: The probability of a deductive conclusion is 1; the probability of an abductive or an inductive conclusion, while less than 1, is significantly greater than chance.

[The] real and sensible difference between one degree of probability and another, in which the meaning of the distinction lies, is that in the frequent employment of two different modes of inference, one will carry truth with it oftener than the other . . . in the long run, there is a real fact which corresponds to the idea of probability, and it is that a given mode of inference sometimes proves successful and sometimes not, and that in a ratio ultimately fixed . . . . We may, therefore, define the probability of a mode of argument as the proportion of cases in which it carries truth with it (pp. 62-63).

No attempt has been made to bring together in this collection Peirce's arguments that deduction is valid in the above sense.

As for abduction, Peirce claims that we know by induction that abduction is valid. Although it is conceivable that all the hypotheses that ever occurred to anyone could have been false, we know by induction that some have been true. "A man must be downright crazy to deny that science has made many true discoveries" (5.172), and every discovery was originally an abductive suggestion. This success, Peirce contends, is not a matter of mere chance:

Think of what trillions of trillions of hypotheses might be made of which one only is true; and yet after two or three or at the very most a dozen guesses, the physicist hits pretty nearly on the correct hypothesis. By chance he would not have been likely to do so in the whole time that has elapsed since the earth was solidified (5.172).

To account for the fact that man hits upon nearly true hypotheses with a frequency far above that of chance, Peirce assumed that man has a special aptitude, or "instinct," for divining the secrets of nature.

One expects that in "The Probability of Induction" Peirce will attempt to prove that the probability of an inductive conclusion is greater than chance. He writes:

Given a certain state of things [i.e., reality, or nature], required to know what proportion of all synthetic inferences relating to it will be true within a given degree of approximation . . . . [What is] the probability that our [inductive] conclusion will accord with the fact? (p. 98).

He then *seems* to argue as follows that induction is "such as must generally have led to true conclusions" (p. 104).

We reason inductively when, from the premiss that a certain proportion (from 0 to 100 per cent) of the members of a sample of a class have a predesignated character, *and* the premiss that the specimens constituting the sample were selected at random, we conclude that *approximately* the same proportion of the members of the entire class have that character. The second premiss, it should be noted, is not that the sample is random in the sense that it is *typical* or *representative* of the class as a whole. If it were, it would amount to the premiss that whatever is true of the sample is true of the whole of which it is a part, and the reasoning would be deductive. What the premiss amounts to is that the sample has been selected—

> according to a precept or method which, being applied over and over again indefinitely, would in the long run result in the drawing of any one set of instances as often as any other of the same number (2.726).

Peirce then contends that from the calculus of chances it follows that it is likely that one large sample selected at random from a class will exhibit approximately the same proportion of members having a predesignated character as another large sample similarly selected (he calls this the "rule of induction"); and that, because this is so, in the course of indefinitely repeated sampling we will, more often than not, arrive at the true proportion within a relatively small margin of error.

But no sooner does Peirce present this argument than he states:

> It appears, then, that in one sense we can, and in another we cannot, determine the probability of synthetic inference. When I reason in this way:

Ninety-nine Cretans in a hundred are liars,
But Epimenides is a Cretan;
Therefore, Epimenides is a liar;

I know that reasoning similar to that would carry truth 99 times in 100. But when I reason in the opposite direction:

Minos, Sarpedon, Rhadamanthus, Deucalion, and Epimenides are all the Cretans I can think of,
But these were all atrocious liars;
Therefore, pretty much all Cretans must have been liars;

I do not in the least know how often such reasoning would carry me right (pp. 100-101).

The concluding pages of "The Probability of Induction" are puzzling. There, as we have just noted, Peirce says that we cannot, after all, know how often inductive inferences yield true conclusions. But, at the same time, he says that we *can* know "that the processes by which our knowledge has been derived are such as must generally have led to true conclusions" (p. 104).

Evidently Peirce's view of induction was, at this time, undergoing revision. Although he never ceased to think that induction is "trustworthy," he seems now to be somewhat obscurely aware of difficulties in the view that induction can be shown to be probable in a frequency sense. But he is not yet able to formulate clearly an alternative theory.

After 1883, although the early theory now and then crops up, Peirce tends on the whole to think that probability conceived as a frequency is inapplicable to induction. Induction is now conceived to be trustworthy not in the sense that it is "probable," but in the sense that, "if it be persisted in long enough, [it] will assuredly correct any error concerning future experience into which it may temporarily lead us" (2.769). The reason is that induction ("whose business consists in testing a hypothesis already recommended") requires the exposure of hypotheses to experiential tests. That such exposure, "sufficiently persisted in," should be incapable of uncovering errors is, for Peirce, unthinkable. He maintains that the entire intellectual meaning of a hypothesis is expressible in statements describing what would be experienced under assigned conditions. Hence, a hypothesis is "a ligament of numberless possible predictions concerning future experience, so that if they fail, it fails" (p. 240). This being so, sufficiently persistent testing is bound to eliminate false hypotheses—for any hypothesis that would *never* give rise to predictions that fail is, by Peirce's definitions, true, and what it represents is real.

Peirce repeatedly insists that the validity of induction does not presuppose the truth of some principle such as Mill's Uniformity of Nature. Induction is valid whatever the constitution of the universe might be. Nothing need be supposed about it except the "negative" fact that nature does not, malignantly as it were, systematically interfere with our sampling so as to render inductive inferences in general invalid.

This does not mean, however, that Peirce lacked strong convictions about what the universe is like. When he surveyed the universe, he was impressed by the uniformities in it, which science seeks to discover and to explain; but he was equally impressed by the sheer coincidences in it, and by its "infinite specificalness." In "The Order of Nature," one of Peirce's conclusions is that the concept of a purely chance universe is self-contradictory; and, in "The Doctrine of Necessity Examined," he argues that there is no good reason for believing that every fact in the universe is precisely determined by law. According to Peirce, the universe is partly governed by laws, and it is partly not "governed" at all, but is a merely chance result, like a long run of double-sixes with a pair of honest dice.

It must be admitted that Peirce uses the word "chance" in several senses. But if we disregard some of them, and attend to *one* sense he had in mind, we can say, as he did in "The Order of Nature,"

> the chance-world . . . would be one in which there were no laws, the characters of different things being entirely independent (p. 107).

When he is using "chance" in the sense he is using it above,

Peirce points out that a "chance-world" is not necessarily a "chaos," i.e., one in which there is no "order" or "regularity." On the contrary, he argues, "nothing could be imagined more systematic" than "a thoroughly chance-world" (p. 109). So, a chance-universe might well be one in which there is "order," "system," "regularity"; but in it there would be no "law."

A universe fulfilling this description would be one that consisted of one hundred throws of a pair of dice, each of which resulted in double-sixes. A true universal proposition about this universe would be, "Every throw of a pair of dice results in double-sixes." This is the same, Peirce points out (p. 108), as to say, "There does not exist any throw of a pair of dice which does not result in double-sixes." However, this would be a "universal of fact," not a "universal of law."

Let us now make use of Peirce's "pragmatic maxim" and ask: What is the difference between two universes, each consisting of one hundred throws of a pair of dice, and about each of which it is true that "Every throw results in double-sixes," but in one of which this truth is a universal of fact, while in the other it is a universal of law?

According to Peirce, in the factual, or chance, universe the relation between the throws of the dice and the results of the throws is "constant conjunction" or "correlation," whereas in the universe of law the relation is *real connection*. In the chance universe, the regularity with which double-sixes turn up when the dice are thrown is "accidental;" in the lawful universe it is, in some sense, *necessary*. Where the regularity is the result of a "chance combination of independent elements," we are not entitled to infer that, *if* (contrary to fact) there had been an additional throw, it *would* have resulted in double-sixes. Where the regularity results from real connections, we *are* entitled to make this inference. For a genuine law, as Peirce came to say, has to do with "would-be's," and is not merely a summary of "coincidences" that were, are, or will be.

Peirce's view of the nature of laws, it is sometimes said, belongs to his "speculative period." Be this as it may, Peirce is here raising issues of considerable importance which are still being discussed. He claims that we cannot express all that is intended by a statement of law using only statements in the indicative mood, and that there are real connections in nature.

Laws, Peirce goes on to say, are "habits," to describe which we must use subjunctive conditional statements. The habit a stone has of falling to the ground when it is let go of does not consist in the fact that it *did* fall when it *was* unsupported, or that it *will* fall when it *will be* unsupported, or in the conjunction of the two. It consists in the fact that, *if it were* let go of, it *would* fall. This subjunctive conditional statement remains true and represents a reality even when it is false that the stone is let go of, so that the stone *did* not and *will* not ever fall to the ground.

Peirce has now arrived at the stage where he rejects the view he set forth in 1878 in "How to Make Our Ideas Clear," namely:

> the question of what would occur under circumstances which do not actually arise is not a question of fact, but only of the most perspicuous arrangement of them (p. 45).

He now holds that the question is not about what did or will happen, but about whether it would be wise "to engage in any line of conduct whose successful issue depended" upon what *would* happen if contrary-to-fact conditions were realized (5.453).

To see the significance of this change, assume that it is false that there will be an atomic war. On this assumption, a true universal of fact about our world is, "Every atomic war results in the annihilation of all mankind," i.e., "There is no atomic war which does not result in the annihilation of all mankind." But another true universal of fact, on the same assumption, is, "Every atomic war enhances the happiness of all mankind," i.e., "There is no atomic war which does not enhance the happiness of all mankind." Now we, who are in our world, and who do not know whether it is one about which it is true or false that there will be an atomic war, may raise the question what would happen if there were one. On the view of 1878, the question is one of "nomenclature," not a question of fact. On the later view, the question is about whether it would be wise to engage in a line of conduct whose successful issue depends upon what we take to be the *laws* of our world, i.e., upon what *would* happen *if* there were an atomic war.

About now Peirce also modifies his earlier concept of probability, and states that the meaning of the statement, "The probability, that if a die be thrown from a dice box it will turn up a number divisible by three, is one-third," is "that the die has a certain 'would-be'; and to say that a die has a 'would-be' is to say that it has a property, quite analogous to any *habit* that a man might have" (p. 79).

In this introduction, "How to Make Our Ideas Clear" has been mentioned only casually. Yet it is possibly the best known and most influential of Peirce's papers. When William James launched pragmatism upon the world, he acknowledged his debt to this paper. Ever since, Peirce has been known as the founder of pragmatism.

When seen in its original setting, as part of an extended work on the logic of science, it is clear that in 1878 Peirce introduced the pragmatic maxim mainly so that it might be used to clear up the concepts of reality and of probability. In later years, when pragmatism as a system, a universally applicable therapeutic method, or a theory of truth had become popular, Peirce sought to disassociate himself from it. In 1905 he wrote:

So then, the writer, finding his bantling "pragmatism" so promoted [to "literary clutches"], feels that it is time to kiss this child good-by and relinquish it to its higher destiny; while to save the precise purpose of expressing the original definition, he begs to announce the birth of the word "pragmaticism," which is ugly enough to be safe from kidnappers (5.414).

VINCENT TOMAS

SELECTED BIBLIOGRAPHY

COLLECTIONS OF PEIRCE'S WORKS

Buchler, Justus (ed.). *The Philosophy of Peirce: Selected Writings*. New York and London, 1940.

Cohen, Morris R. (ed.). *Chance, Love, and Logic*. With a supplementary essay by John Dewey. New York, 1923.

Hartshorne, Charles, and Weiss, Paul (eds.). *Collected Papers of Charles Sanders Peirce*. 6 vols. Cambridge, Mass., 1931-1935. (Volumes 7-8, edited by Arthur W. Burks, are now in preparation.)

COLLATERAL READING

Buchler, Justus. *Charles Peirce's Empiricism*. London, 1939.

Feibleman, James. *An Introduction to Peirce's Philosophy*. New York and London, 1946.

Gallie, W. B. *Peirce and Pragmatism*. Harmondsworth, 1952.

Goudge, Thomas A. *The Thought of C. S. Peirce*. Toronto, 1950.

Thompson, Manley. *The Pragmatic Philosophy of C. S. Peirce*. Chicago, 1953.

Wiener, Philip P., and Young, Frederic H. (eds.). *Studies in the Philosophy of C. S. Peirce*. Cambridge, Mass., 1952.

BIBLIOGRAPHIES

A "tentative bibliography" of Peirce's papers is published as an appendix in Cohen (ed.), *Chance, Love, and Logic,* and "some additions" to it are published in Wiener and Young (eds.), *Studies in the Philosophy of C. S. Peirce*, Appendix V.

ESSAYS IN THE PHILOSOPHY
OF SCIENCE

THE FIXATION OF BELIEF [1]

I [SCIENCE AND LOGIC]

Few persons care to study logic, because everybody conceives himself to be proficient enough in the art of reasoning already. But I observe that this satisfaction is limited to one's own ratiocination, and does not extend to that of other men.

We come to the full possession of our power of drawing inferences, the last of all our faculties; for it is not so much a natural gift as a long and difficult art. The history of its practice would make a grand subject for a book. The medieval schoolmen, following the Romans, made logic the earliest of a boy's studies after grammar, as being very easy. So it was as they understood it. Its fundamental principle, according to

[1] [*Popular Science Monthly*, XII (1877), 1-15; with corrections and notes from several revised versions, one of which was intended as Chapter 5 of the "Grand Logic" of 1893 and another of which was intended as Essay VII of the "Search for a Method" of 1893. (In *C.P.*, V, 223-247.)

[About 1903, the following introduction was attached to this and the following paper: "The two chapters composing this Essay ['My Plea for Pragmatism'] were first published, without any title for the whole [they appeared with a title] in the *Popular Science Monthly* for November 1877 and January 1878. A French version by the author (the second having in fact been first written in French on board a steamer in September 1877) appeared in the *Revue philosophique*, Vols. VI and VII. They received as little attention as they laid claim to; but some years later the potent pen of Professor James brought their chief thesis to the attention of the philosophic world (pressing it, indeed, further than the tether of their author would reach, who continues to acknowledge, not indeed the Existence, but yet the Reality, of the Absolute, nearly as it has been set forth, for example, by Royce in his *The World and the Individual*, a work not free from faults of logic, yet valid in the main). The doctrine of this pair of chapters had already for some years been known among friends of the writer by the name he had proposed for it, which was 'Pragmatism.'"]

them, was, that all knowledge rests either on [2] authority or reason; but that whatever is deduced by reason depends ultimately on a premiss derived from authority. Accordingly, as soon as a boy was perfect in the syllogistic procedure, his intellectual kit of tools was held to be complete.

To Roger Bacon,[3] that remarkable mind who in the middle of the thirteenth century was almost a scientific man, the schoolmen's conception of reasoning appeared only an obstacle to truth. He saw that experience alone teaches anything— a proposition which to us seems easy to understand, because a distinct conception of experience has been handed down to us from former generations; which to him likewise [4] seemed perfectly clear, because its difficulties had not yet unfolded themselves. Of all kinds of experience, the best, he thought, was interior illumination, which teaches many things about Nature which the external senses could never discover, such as the transubstantiation of bread.

Four centuries later, the more celebrated Bacon, in the first book of his *Novum Organum,* gave his clear account of experience as something which must be open to verification and re-examination. But, superior as Lord Bacon's conception is to earlier notions, a modern reader who is not in awe of his grandiloquence is chiefly struck by the inadequacy of his view of scientific procedure. That we have only to make some crude experiments, to draw up briefs of the results in certain blank forms, to go through these by rule, checking off everything disproved and setting down the alternatives, and that thus in a few years physical science would be finished up— what an idea! "He wrote on science like a Lord Chancellor," [5] indeed, as Harvey, a genuine man of science said.[6]

The early scientists, Copernicus, Tycho Brahe, Kepler,

---

2 ["On" and "either" originally transposed.]
3 [See his *Opus Majus,* pars VI.]
4 [Originally "also."]
5 Cf. J. Aubrey's *Brief Lives* (Oxford ed. 1898), I, 299.
6 ["as . . . said" added *c.* 1910.]

Galileo, Harvey,[7] and Gilbert, had methods more like those of their modern brethren. Kepler undertook to draw a curve through the places of Mars,[8] and to state the times occupied by the planet in describing the different parts of that curve;[9] but perhaps[10] his greatest service to science was in impressing on men's minds that this was the thing to be done if they wished to improve astronomy; that they were not to content themselves with inquiring whether one system of epicycles was better than another but that they were to sit down to the figures and find out what the curve, in truth, was. He accomplished this by his incomparable energy and courage, blundering along in the most inconceivable way (to us), from one irrational hypothesis to another, until, after trying twenty-two of these, he fell, by the mere exhaustion of his invention, upon the orbit which a mind well furnished with the weapons of modern logic would have tried almost at the outset.[11]

In the same way, every work of science great enough to be well[12] remembered for a few generations affords some exemplification of the defective state of the art of reasoning of the time when it was written; and each chief step in science has been a lesson in logic. It was so when Lavoisier and his contemporaries took up the study of Chemistry. The old chemist's maxim had been, "Lege, lege, lege, labora, ora, et relege." Lavoisier's method was not to read and pray, but to dream that some long and complicated chemical process would have a certain effect, to put it into practice with dull patience, after

7 [Not in the original.]

8 Not quite so, but as nearly so as can be told in a few words.

9 ["and . . . curve" added c. 1910.]

10 ["but perhaps," originally "and."]

11 I am ashamed at being obliged to confess that this volume contains a very false and foolish remark about Kepler. When I wrote it, I had never studied the original book as I have since. It is now my deliberate opinion that it is the most marvelous piece of inductive reasoning I have been able to find.—1893. [Peirce partially rectifies this error c. 1910 by deleting the expression "in . . . us."]

12 [Not in original.]

its inevitable failure, to dream that with some modification it would have another result, and to end by publishing the last dream as a fact: his way was to carry his mind into his laboratory, and literally [13] to make of his alembics and cucurbits instruments of thought, giving a new conception of reasoning as something which was to be done with one's eyes open, in [14] manipulating real things instead of words and fancies.

The Darwinian controversy is, in large part, a question of logic. Mr. Darwin proposed to apply the statistical method to biology.[15] The same thing has been done in a widely different branch of science, the theory of gases. Though unable to say what the movements of any particular molecule of gas would be on a certain hypothesis regarding the constitution of this class of bodies, Clausius and Maxwell were yet able, eight years before the publication of Darwin's immortal work,[16] by the application of the doctrine of probabilities, to predict that in the long run such and such a proportion of the molecules would, under given circumstances, acquire such and such velocities; that there would take place, every second, such and such a relative [17] number of collisions, etc.; and from these propositions were able to deduce certain properties of gases, especially in regard to their heat-relations. In like manner, Darwin, while unable to say what the operation of variation and natural selection in any individual case will be, demonstrates that in the long run they will, or would,[18] adapt animals to their circumstances. Whether or not existing animal forms are due to such action, or what position the theory ought to take, forms the subject of a discussion in which questions of fact and questions of logic are curiously interlaced.

13 [Not in original.]

14 [Originally "by."]

15 What he did, a most instructive illustration of the logic of science, will be described in another chapter [where?]; and we now know what was authoritatively denied when I first suggested it, that he took a hint from Malthus' book on Population.—1903.

16 ["eight . . . work" inserted c. 1910.]

17 [Not in original.]

18 ["or would" not in the original.]

II [GUIDING PRINCIPLES]

The object of reasoning is to find out, from the consideration of what we already know, something else which we do not know. Consequently, reasoning is good if it be such as to [1] give a true conclusion from true premises, and not otherwise. Thus, the question of validity is purely one of fact and not of thinking. A being the facts stated in the [2] premises and B being that concluded,[3] the question is, whether these facts are really so related that if A were B would generally be.[4] If so, the inference is valid; if not, not. It is not in the least the question whether, when the premises are accepted by the mind, we feel an impulse to accept the conclusion also. It is true that we do generally reason correctly by nature. But that is an accident; the true conclusion would remain true if we had no impulse to accept it; and the false one would remain false, though we could not resist the tendency to believe in it.

We are, doubtless, in the main logical animals, but we are not perfectly so. Most of us, for example, are naturally more sanguine and hopeful than logic would justify. We seem to be so constituted that in the absence of any facts to go upon we are happy and self-satisfied; so that the effect of experience is continually to contract our hopes and aspirations. Yet a lifetime of the application of this corrective does not usually eradicate our sanguine disposition. Where hope is unchecked by any experience, it is likely that our optimism is extravagant. Logicality in regard to practical matters (if this be understood, not in the old sense, but as consisting in a wise union of security with fruitfulness of reasoning [5]) is the most useful quality an animal can possess, and might, therefore, result from the action of natural selection; but outside of these

1 I.e., be dominated by such a habit as generally to give.—1903.
2 ["facts . . . the" not in original.]
3 [Originally "the conclusion."]
4 ["A . . . be," originally "A is B is."]
5 [The portion within the parentheses was inserted c. 1910.]

it is probably of more advantage to the animal to have his mind filled with pleasing and encouraging visions, independently of their truth; and thus, upon unpractical subjects, natural selection might occasion a fallacious tendency of thought.[6]

That which determines us, from given premisses, to draw one inference rather than another, is some habit of mind, whether it be constitutional or acquired. The habit is good or otherwise, according as it produces true conclusions from true premisses or not; and an inference is regarded as valid or not, without reference to the truth or falsity of its conclusion specially, but according as the habit which determines it is such as to produce true conclusions in general or not. The particular habit of mind which governs this or that inference may be formulated in a proposition whose truth depends on the validity of the inferences which the habit determines; and such a formula is called a *guiding principle* of inference. Suppose, for example, that we observe that a rotating disk of copper quickly comes to rest when placed between the poles of a magnet, and we infer that this will happen with every disk of copper. The guiding principle is, that what is true of one piece of copper is true of another. Such a guiding principle with regard to copper would be much safer than with regard to many other substances—brass, for example.

A book might be written to signalize all the most important of these guiding principles of reasoning. It would probably be, we must confess, of no service to a person whose thought is directed wholly to practical subjects, and whose activity moves along thoroughly-beaten paths. The problems that[7] present themselves to such a mind are matters of routine which he has learned once for all to handle in learning his business. But let a man venture into an unfamiliar field, or where his results are not continually checked by experience,

[6] Let us not, however, be cocksure that natural selection is the only factor of evolution; and until this momentous proposition has been much better proved than as yet it has been, let it not blind us to the force [of] very sound reasoning.—1903.

[7] [Originally "which."]

and all history shows that the most masculine intellect will ofttimes lose his orientation and waste his efforts in directions which bring him no nearer to his goal, or even carry him entirely astray. He is like a ship in the open sea, with no one on board who understands the rules of navigation. And in such a case some general study of the guiding principles of reasoning would be sure to be found useful.

The subject could hardly be treated, however, without being first limited; since almost any fact may serve as a guiding principle. But it so happens that there exists a division among facts, such that in one class are all those which are absolutely essential as guiding principles, while in the others are all which have any other interest as objects of research. This division is between those which are necessarily taken for granted in asking why [8] a certain conclusion is thought to follow [9] from certain premises, and those which are not implied in such a [10] question. A moment's thought will show that a variety of facts are already assumed when the logical question is first asked. It is implied, for instance, that there are such states of mind as doubt and belief—that a passage from one to the other is possible, the object of thought remaining the same, and that this transition is subject to some rules by [11] which all minds are alike bound. As these are facts which we must already know before we can have any clear conception of reasoning at all, it cannot be supposed to be any longer of much interest to inquire into their truth or falsity. On the other hand, it is easy to believe that those rules of reasoning which are deduced from the very idea of the process are the ones which are the most essential; and, indeed, that so long as it conforms to these it will, at least, not lead to false conclusions from true premises. In point of fact, the importance of what may be deduced from the assumptions involved in the logical question turns out to be greater than might be sup-

[8] [Originally "whether."]
[9] ["is . . . follow," originally "follows."]
[10] ["such a" originally "that."]
[11] ["by" originally at the end of the sentence.]

posed, and this for reasons which it is difficult to exhibit at the outset. The only one which I shall here mention is, that conceptions which are really products of logical reflection, without being readily seen to be so, mingle with our ordinary thoughts, and are frequently the causes of great confusion. This is the case, for example, with the conception of quality. A quality, as such, is never an object of observation. We can see that a thing is blue or green, but the quality of being blue and the quality of being green are not things which we see; they are products of logical reflections. The truth is, that common-sense, or thought as it first emerges above the level of the narrowly practical, is deeply imbued with that bad logical quality to which the epithet *metaphysical* is commonly applied; and nothing can clear it up but a severe course of logic.

III [DOUBT AND BELIEF]

We generally know when we wish to ask a question and when we wish to pronounce a judgment, for there is a dissimilarity between the sensation of doubting and that of believing.

But this is not all which distinguishes doubt from belief. There is a practical difference. Our beliefs guide our desires and shape our actions. The Assassins, or followers of the Old Man of the Mountain, used to rush into death at his least command, because they believed that obedience to him would insure everlasting felicity. Had they doubted this, they would not have acted as they did. So it is with every belief, according to its degree. The feeling of believing is a more or less sure indication of there being established in our nature some habit which will determine our actions.[1] Doubt never has such an effect.

1 Let us recall the nature of a sign and ask ourselves how we can know that a feeling of any sort is a sign that we have a habit implanted within us. We can understand one habit by likening it to another habit. But to

Nor must we overlook a third point of difference. Doubt is an uneasy and dissatisfied state from which we struggle to free ourselves and pass into the state of belief; [2] while the latter is a calm and satisfactory state which we do not wish to avoid, or to change to a belief in anything else.[3] On the contrary, we cling tenaciously, not merely to believing, but to believing just what we do believe.

Thus, both doubt and belief have positive effects upon us, though very different ones. Belief does not make us act at once, but puts us into such a condition that we shall behave in some [4] certain way, when the occasion arises. Doubt has not the least such active [5] effect,[6] but stimulates us to inquiry [7] until it is destroyed. This reminds us of the irritation

---

understand what any habit is, there must be some habit of which we are directly conscious in its generality. That is to say, we must have a certain generality in our direct consciousness. Bishop Berkeley and a great many clear thinkers laugh at the idea of our being able to imagine a triangle that is neither equilateral, isosceles, nor scalene. They seem to think the object of imagination must be precisely determinate in every respect. But it seems certain that something general we must imagine. I do not intend, in this book, to go into questions of psychology. It is not necessary for us to know in detail how our thinking is done, but only how it can be done. Still, I may as well say, at once, that I think our direct consciousness covers a duration of time, although only an infinitely brief duration. At any rate, I can see no way of escaping the proposition that to attach any general significance to a sign and to know that we do attach a general significance to it, we must have a direct imagination of something not in all respects determinate.—1893.

2 In this, it is like any other stimulus. It is true that just as men may, for the sake of the pleasures of the table, like to be hungry and take means to make themselves so, although hunger always involves a desire to fill the stomach, so for the sake of the pleasures of inquiry, men may like to seek out doubts. Yet, for all that, doubt essentially involves a struggle to escape it.—1893.

3 I am not speaking of secondary effects occasionally produced by the interference of other impulses. ["secondary . . . produced by" changed in 1910 to "accidental . . . superinduced by reflexion or . . ."]

4 [Originally "a."]

5 ["such active" not in the original.]

6 ["Of this sort" originally followed "effect."]

7 [Originally "action."]

of a nerve and the reflex action produced thereby; while for the analogue of belief, in the nervous system, we must look to what are called nervous associations—for example, to that habit of the nerves in consequence of which the smell of a peach will make the mouth water.[8]

IV   [THE END OF INQUIRY]

The irritation of doubt causes a struggle to attain a state of belief. I shall term this struggle *Inquiry*, though it must be admitted that this is sometimes not a very apt designation.

The irritation of doubt is the only immediate motive for the struggle to attain belief. It is certainly best for us that our beliefs should be such as may truly guide our actions so as to satisfy our desires; and this reflection will make us reject every [1] belief which does not seem to have been so formed as to insure this result. But it will only do so by creating a doubt in the place of that belief.[2] With the doubt, therefore,

---

[8] Doubt, however, is not usually hesitancy about what is to be done then and there. It is anticipated hesitancy about what I shall do hereafter, or a feigned hesitancy about a fictitious state of things. It is the power of making believe we hesitate, together with the pregnant fact that the decision upon the merely make-believe dilemma goes toward forming a bona fide habit that will be operative in a real emergency. It is these two things in conjunction that constitute us intellectual beings.

Every answer to a question that has any meaning is a decision as to how we would act under imagined circumstances, or how the world would be expected to react upon our senses. Thus, suppose I am told that if two straight lines in one plane are cut by a third making the sum of the internal angles on one side less than two right angles, then those lines if sufficiently produced will meet on the side on which the said sum is less than two right angles. This means to me that if I had two lines drawn on a plane and wished to find where they would meet, I could draw a third line cutting them and ascertaining on which side the sum of the two interval angles was less than two right angles, and should lengthen the lines on that side. In like manner, all doubt is a state of hesitancy about an imagined state of things.—1893.

[1] [Originally "any."]

[2] Unless, indeed, it leads us to modify our desires.—1903.

the struggle begins, and with the cessation of doubt it ends. Hence, the sole object of inquiry is the settlement of opinion. We may fancy that this is not enough for us, and that we seek, not merely an opinion, but a true opinion. But put this fancy to the test, and it proves groundless; for as soon as a firm belief is reached we are entirely satisfied, whether the belief be true or false. And it is clear that nothing out of the sphere of our knowledge can be our object, for nothing which does not affect the mind can be the motive for mental effort. The most that can be maintained is, that we seek for a belief that we shall *think* to be true. But we think each one of our beliefs to be true, and, indeed, it is mere tautology to say so.[3]

That the settlement of opinion is the sole end of inquiry is a very important proposition. It sweeps away, at once, various vague and erroneous conceptions of proof. A few of these may be noticed here.

1. Some philosophers have imagined that to start an inquiry it was only necessary to utter a question whether orally or by setting [4] it down upon paper, and have even recommended us to begin our studies with questioning everything! But the mere putting of a proposition into the interrogative form does not stimulate the mind to any struggle after belief. There must be a real and living doubt, and without this all discussion is idle.[5]

[3] For truth is neither more nor less than that character of a proposition which consists in this, that belief in the proposition would, with sufficient experience and reflection, lead us to such conduct as would tend to satisfy the desires we should then have. To say that truth means more than this is to say that it has no meaning at all.—1903.

[4] ["whether . . . setting" originally "or set."]

[5] So long as we cannot put our fingers on our erroneous opinions, they remain our opinions, still. It will be wholesome enough for us to make a general review of the causes of our beliefs; and the result will be that most of them have been taken upon trust and have been held since we were too young to discriminate the credible from the incredible. Such reflections may awaken real doubts about some of our positions. But in cases where no real doubt exists in our minds inquiry will be an idle farce, a mere whitewashing commission which were better let alone. This fault in philosophy was very widespread in those ages in which Disputa-

2. It is a very common idea that a demonstration must rest on some ultimate and absolutely indubitable propositions. These, according to one school, are first principles of a general nature; according to another, are first sensations. But, in point of fact, an inquiry, to have that completely satisfactory result called demonstration, has only to start with propositions perfectly free from all actual doubt. If the premisses are not in fact doubted at all, they cannot be more satisfactory than they are.[6]

3. Some people seem to love to argue a point after all the world is fully convinced of it. But no further advance can be made. When doubt ceases, mental action on the subject comes to an end; and, if it did go on, it would be without a purpose.[7]

V   [METHODS OF FIXING BELIEF]

If the settlement of opinion is the sole object of inquiry, and if belief is of the nature of a habit, why should we not attain the desired end, by taking as [1] answer to a question any [2] we may fancy, and constantly reiterating it to ourselves,

---

tions were the principal exercises in the universities; that is, from their rise in the thirteenth century down to the middle of the eighteenth, and even to this day in some Catholic institutions. But since those disputations went out of vogue, this philosophic disease is less virulent.—1893.

[6] We have to acknowledge that doubts about them may spring up later; but we can find no propositions which are not subject to this contingency. We ought to construct our theories so as to provide for such discoveries; first, by making them rest on as great a variety of different considerations as possible, and second, by leaving room for the modifications which cannot be foreseen but which are pretty sure to prove needful. Some systems are much more open to this criticism than others. All those which repose heavily upon an "inconceivability of the opposite" have proved particularly fragile and short-lived. Those, however, which rest upon positive evidences and which avoid insisting upon the absolute precision of their dogmas are hard to destroy.—1893.

[7] Except that of self-criticism. Insert here a section upon self-control and the analogy between Moral and Rational self-control.—1903.

[1] [Originally "any."]

[2] [Originally "which."]

dwelling on all which may conduce to that belief, and learning to turn with contempt and hatred from anything that [3] might disturb it? This simple and direct method is really pursued by many men. I remember once being entreated not to read a certain newspaper lest it might change my opinion upon free-trade. "Lest I might be entrapped by its fallacies and misstatements," was the form of expression. "You are not," my friend said, "a special student of political economy. You might, therefore, easily be deceived by fallacious arguments upon the subject. You might, then, if you read this paper, be led to believe in protection. But you admit that free-trade is the true doctrine; and you do not wish to believe what is not true." I have often known this system to be deliberately adopted. Still oftener, the instinctive dislike of an undecided state of mind, exaggerated into a vague dread of doubt, makes men cling spasmodically to the views they already take. The man feels that, if he only holds to his belief without wavering, it will be entirely satisfactory. Nor can it be denied that a steady and immovable faith yields great peace of mind. It may, indeed, give rise to inconveniences, as if a man should resolutely continue to believe that fire would not burn him, or that he would be eternally damned if he received his *ingesta* otherwise than through a stomach-pump. But then the man who adopts this method will not allow that its inconveniences are greater than its advantages. He will say, "I hold steadfastly to the truth, and the truth is always wholesome." And in many cases it may very well be that the pleasure he derives from his calm faith overbalances any inconveniences resulting from its deceptive character. Thus, if it be true that death is annihilation, then the man who believes that he will certainly go straight to heaven when he dies, provided he have fulfilled certain simple observances in this life, has a cheap pleasure which will not be followed by the least disappointment.[4] A similar consideration seems to have weight

---

[3] [Originally "which."]

[4] Although it certainly may be that it will cause a line of conduct leading to pains that deeper reflection would have avoided.—1903.

with many persons in religious topics, for we frequently hear it said, "Oh, I could not believe so-and-so, because I should be wretched if I did." When an ostrich buries its head in the sand as danger approaches, it very likely takes the happiest course. It hides the danger, and then calmly says there is no danger; and, if it feels perfectly sure there is none, why should it raise its head to see? A man may go through life, systematically keeping out of view all that might cause a change in his opinions, and if he only succeeds—basing his method, as he does, on two fundamental psychological laws—I do not see what can be said against his doing so. It would be an egotistical impertinence to object that his procedure is irrational, for that only amounts to saying that his method of settling belief is not ours. He does not propose to himself to be rational, and, indeed, will often talk with scorn of man's weak and illusive reason. So let him think as he pleases.

But this method of fixing belief, which may be called the method of tenacity, will be unable to hold its ground in practice. The social impulse is against it. The man who adopts it will find that other men think differently from him, and it will be apt to occur to him, in some saner moment, that their opinions are quite as good as his own, and this will shake his confidence in his belief. This conception, that another man's thought or sentiment may be equivalent to one's own, is a distinctly new step, and a highly important one. It arises from an impulse too strong in man to be suppressed, without danger of destroying the human species. Unless we make ourselves hermits, we shall necessarily influence each other's opinions; so that the problem becomes how to fix belief, not in the individual merely, but in the community.

Let the will of the state act, then, instead of that of the individual. Let an institution be created which shall have for its object to keep correct doctrines before the attention of the people, to reiterate them perpetually, and to teach them to the young; having at the same time power to prevent contrary doctrines from being taught, advocated, or expressed. Let all possible causes of a change of mind be removed from men's apprehensions. Let them be kept ignorant, lest they should learn of some reason to think otherwise than they do. Let their passions be enlisted, so that they may regard private and unusual opinions with hatred and horror. Then, let all men who reject the established belief be terrified into silence. Let the people turn out and tar-and-feather such men, or let inquisitions be made into the manner of thinking of suspected persons, and when they are found guilty of forbidden beliefs, let them be subjected to some signal punishment. When complete agreement could not otherwise be reached, a general massacre of all who have not thought in a certain way has proved a very effective means of settling opinion in a country.[5] If the power to do this be wanting, let a list of opinions be drawn up, to which no man of the least independence of thought can assent, and let the faithful be required to accept all these propositions, in order to segregate them as radically as possible from the influence of the rest of the world.

This method has, from the earliest times, been one of the chief means of upholding correct theological and political doctrines, and of preserving their universal or catholic character. In Rome, especially, it has been practised from the days of Numa Pompilius to those of Pius Nonus.[6] This is the most perfect example in history; but wherever there is a priesthood —and no religion has been without one—this method has been

[5] [The reference here is to the Massacre of St. Bartholomew.—Ed.]

[6] [Both men are noted for their strong influence on the shaping of religious institutions. Numa Pompilius (?715-672 B.C.) was the second king of Rome. Legend has credited him with establishing the major religious institutions, which in turn became an important instrument in forming the way of life in early Rome, and in setting the Romans off from their neighbors. Today it seems more probable that these institutions were the result of a long process of religious and social development.

[Pius Nonus, Pius IX (Giovanni Maria Mastai-Ferretti, 1792-1878), pope 1846-1878. He exerted a strong conservative influence on the teachings of the Catholic Church and for a long time determined its attitude toward social institutions and development. He proclaimed the dogma of the immaculate conception of the Virgin Mary. He strongly opposed the influence of modernism on ecclesiastical life and claimed for the Church the control of all culture and all science.—Ed.]

more or less made use of. Wherever there is an aristocracy, or a guild, or any association of a class of men whose interests depend, or are supposed to depend, on certain propositions, there will be inevitably found some traces of this natural product of social feeling. Cruelties always accompany this system; and when it is consistently carried out, they become atrocities of the most horrible kind in the eyes of any rational man. Nor should this occasion surprise, for the officer of a society does not feel justified in surrendering the interests of that society for the sake of mercy, as he might his own private interests. It is natural, therefore, that sympathy and fellowship should thus produce a most ruthless power.

In judging this method of fixing belief, which may be called the method of authority, we must, in the first place, allow its immeasurable mental and moral superiority to the method of tenacity. Its success is proportionately greater; and, in fact, it has over and over again worked the most majestic results. The mere structures of stone which it has caused to be put together —in Siam, for example, in Egypt, and in Europe—have many of them a sublimity hardly more than rivaled by the greatest works of Nature. And, except the geological epochs, there are no periods of time so vast as those which are measured by some of these organized faiths.[7] If we scrutinize the matter closely,

---

[7] Unify them in the sense of Alexander Pope's *Universal Prayer,* and who is the individual whose conceit shall stand up and place his dictum against theirs? These faiths lay claim to divine authorship; and it is true that men have no more *invented* them, than the birds have invented their songs. It is a relapse toward the method of tenacity that segregates them and blinds the ecclesiastic to the value of anything but hatred. Every distinctive creed was as a historical fact invented to harm somebody. Still, the upshot has, on the whole, been success unparalleled. If slavery of opinion is natural and wholesome for men, then slaves they ought to remain.

Every such system was first established by some individual legislator or prophet; and once established it grew of itself. But within this principle of growth lurk germs of decay. The power of individualism becomes extinct; the organization alone has life. Now, in the course of ages old questions pass out of mind: new questions become urgent. The sea advances or recedes; some horde which has always lived by conquest happens to

we shall find that there has not been one of their creeds which has remained always the same; yet the change is so slow as to be imperceptible during one person's life, so that individual belief remains sensibly fixed. For the mass of mankind, then, there is perhaps no better method than this. If it is their highest impulse to be intellectual slaves, then slaves they ought to remain.

But no institution can undertake to regulate opinions upon every subject. Only the most important ones can be attended to, and on the rest men's minds must be left to the action of natural causes. This imperfection will be no source of weakness so long as men are in such a state of culture that one opinion does not influence another—that is, so long as they cannot put two and two together. But in the most priest-ridden states some individuals will be found who are raised above that condition. These men possess a wider sort of social feeling; they see that men in other countries and in other ages have held to very different doctrines from those which they themselves have been brought up to believe; and they cannot help seeing that it is the mere accident of their having been taught as they have, and of their having been surrounded with

---

make a conquest of consequence to the world at large. In one way or another, commerce is diverted from its ancient roads. Such change brings novel experiences and new ideas. Men begin to rebel at doings of the authorities to which in former times they would have submitted. Questions never before raised come up for decision; yet an individual legislator would no longer be listened to. Never has the instinct of rulers failed to see that the summoning of a council of the people was a measure fraught with peril to authority. Yet however they strive to avoid it, they in effect invoke public opinion, which is a momentous appeal to a new method of settling opinion. Disturbances occur; knots of men discuss the state of affairs; and a suspicion is kindled, which runs about like a train of gun powder, that the Dicta [which] men have been reverencing originated in caprice, in the pertinacity of some busybody, in the schemes of an ambitious man, or in other influences which are seen to edify a delibera- tive assembly. Men now begin to demand that, as the power which maintains the belief has become no longer capricious but public and methodical, so the propositions to be believed shall be determined in a public and methodical manner.—1893.

the manners and associations they have, that has caused them
to believe as they do and not far differently. Nor can their
candour [8] resist the reflection that there is no reason to rate
their own views at a higher value than those of other nations
and other centuries; thus giving [9] rise to doubts in their minds.

They will further perceive that such doubts as these must
exist in their minds with reference to every belief which seems
to be determined by the caprice either of themselves or of
those who originated the popular opinions. The willful ad-
herence to a belief, and the arbitrary forcing of it upon others,
must, therefore, both be given up. A different [10] new method
of settling opinions must be adopted, that [11] shall not only
produce an impulse to believe, but shall also decide what
proposition it is which is to be believed. Let the action of
natural preferences be unimpeded, then, and under their influence let men, conversing together and regarding matters in
different lights, gradually develop beliefs in harmony with
natural causes. This method resembles that by which conceptions of art have been brought to maturity. The most
perfect example of it is to be found in the history of metaphysical philosophy. Systems of this sort have not usually
rested upon any observed facts, at least not in any great degree.
They have been chiefly adopted because their fundamental
propositions seemed "agreeable to reason." This is an apt expression; it does not mean that which agrees with experience,
but that which we find ourselves inclined to believe. Plato, for
example, finds it agreeable to reason that the distances of the
celestial spheres from one another should be proportional to
the different lengths of strings which produce harmonious
chords. Many philosophers have been led to their main conclusions by considerations like this; [12] but this is the lowest and

---

8 ["Nor . . . candour" originally "And their candor cannot."]

9 ["thus giving" originally "and this gives."]

10 ["A different" originally "And a."]

11 [Originally "which."]

12 Let us see in what manner a few of the greatest philosophers have
undertaken to settle opinion, and what their success has been. Descartes,

least developed form which the method takes, for it is clear that another man might find Kepler's theory, that the celestial spheres are proportional to the inscribed and circumscribed spheres of the different regular solids, more agreeable to *his* reason. But the shock of opinions will soon lead men to rest

who would have a man begin by doubting everything, remarks that there is one thing he will find himself unable to doubt, and that is, that he does doubt; and when he reflects that he doubts, he can no longer doubt that he exists. Then, because he is all the while doubting whether there are any such things as shape and motion, Descartes thinks he must be persuaded that shape and motion do not belong to his nature, or anything else but consciousness. This is taking it for granted that nothing in his nature lies hidden beneath the surface. Next, Descartes asks the doubter to remark that he has the idea of a Being, in the highest degree intelligent, powerful, and perfect. Now a Being would not have these qualities unless he existed necessarily and eternally. By existing necessarily he means existing by virtue of the existence of the idea. Consequently, all doubt as to the existence of this Being must cease. This plainly supposes that belief is to be fixed by what men find in their minds. He is reasoning like this: I find it written in the volume of my mind that there is something X, which is such a sort of thing that the moment it is written down it exists. Plainly, he is aiming at a kind of truth which saying so can make to be so. He gives two further proofs of God's existence. Descartes makes God easier to know than anything else; for whatever we think He is, He is. He fails to remark that this is precisely the definition of a *figment*. In particular, God cannot be a deceiver; whence it follows, that whatever we quite clearly and distinctly think to be true about any subject, must *be* true. Accordingly, if people will thoroughly discuss a subject, and quite clearly and distinctly make up their minds what they think about it, the desired settlement of the question will be reached. I may remark that the world has pretty thoroughly deliberated upon that theory and has quite distinctly come to the conclusion that it is utter nonsense; whence that judgment is indisputably right.

Many critics have told me that I misrepresent the *a priori* philosophers, when I represent them as adopting whatever opinion there seems to be a natural inclination to adopt. But nobody can say the above does not accurately define the position of Descartes, and upon what does he repose except natural ways of thinking? Perhaps I shall be told however, that since Kant, that vice has been cured. Kant's great boast is that he critically examines into our natural inclinations toward certain opinions. An opinion that something is *universally* true clearly goes further than experience can warrant. An opinion that something is *necessarily* true (that is, not merely is true in the existing state of things, but would be true in

on preferences of a far more universal nature. Take, for example, the doctrine that man only acts selfishly—that is, from the consideration that acting in one way will afford him more

---

every state of things) equally goes further than experience will warrant. Those remarks had been made by Leibniz and admitted by Hume; and Kant reiterates them. Though they are propositions of a nominalistic cast, they can hardly be denied. I may add that whatever is held to be precisely true goes further than experience can possibly warrant. Accepting those criteria of the origin of ideas, Kant proceeds to reason as follows: Geometrical propositions are held to be universally true. Hence, they are not given by experience. Consequently, it must be owing to an inward necessity of man's nature that he sees everything in space. Ergo, the sum of the angles of a triangle will be equal to two right angles for all the objects of our vision. Just that, and nothing more, is Kant's line of thought. But the dry-rot of reason in the seminaries has gone to the point where such stuff is held to be admirable argumentation. I might go through the *Critic of the Pure Reason*, section by section, and show that the thought throughout is precisely of this character. He everywhere shows that ordinary objects, such as trees and gold-pieces, involve elements not contained in the first presentations of sense. But we cannot persuade ourselves to give up the reality of trees and gold-pieces. There is a general inward insistence upon them, and that is the warrant for swallowing the entire bolus of general belief about them. This is merely accepting without question a belief as soon as it is shown to please a great many people very much. When he comes to the ideas of God, Freedom, and Immortality, he hesitates; because people who think only of bread and butter, pleasure and power, are indifferent to those ideas. He subjects these ideas to a different kind of examination, and finally admits them upon grounds which appear to the seminarists more or less suspicious, but which in the eyes of laboratorists are infinitely stronger than the grounds upon which he has accepted space, time, and causality. Those last grounds amount to nothing but this, that what there is a very decided and general inclination to believe must be true. Had Kant merely said, I shall adopt for the present the belief that the three angles of a triangle are equal to two right angles because nobody but brother Lambert and some Italian has ever called it in question, his attitude would be well enough. But on the contrary, he and those who today represent his school distinctly maintain the proposition is *proved*, and the Lambertists *refuted*, by what comes merely to general disinclination to think with them.

As for Hegel, who led Germany for a generation, he recognizes clearly what he is about. He simply launches his boat into the current of thought and allows himself to be carried wherever the current leads. He himself calls his method *dialectic*, meaning that a frank discussion of the difficul-

pleasure than acting in another. This rests on no fact in the world, but it has had a wide acceptance as being the only reasonable theory.[13]

This method is far more intellectual and respectable from the point of view of reason than either of the others which we have noticed. Indeed, as long as no better method can be applied, it ought to be followed, since it is then the expression of instinct which must be the ultimate cause of belief in all cases.[14] But its failure has been the most manifest. It makes of inquiry something similar to the development of taste; but

---

ties to which any opinion spontaneously gives rise will lead to modification after modification until a tenable position is attained. This is a distinct profession of faith in the method of inclinations.

Other philosophers appeal to "the test of inconceivability of the opposite," to "presuppositions" (by which they mean *Voraussetzungen,* properly translated, *postulates*), and other devices; but all these are but so many systems of rummaging the garret of the skull to find an enduring opinion about the Universe.

When we pass from the perusal of works upholding the method of authority to those of the philosophers, we not only find ourselves in a vastly higher intellectual atmosphere, but also in a clearer, freer, brighter, and more refreshing moral atmosphere. All this, however, is beside the one significant question of whether the method succeeds in fixing men's opinions. The projects of these authors are most persuasive. One dare swear they should succeed. But in point of fact, up to date they decidedly do not; and the outlook in this direction is most discouraging. The difficulty is that the opinions which today seem most unshakable are found tomorrow to be out of fashion. They are really far more changeable than they appear to a hasty reader to be; since the phrases made to dress out defunct opinions are worn at second hand by their successors.

We still talk of "cause and effect" although, in the mechanical world, the opinion that phrase was meant to express has been shelved long ago. We now know that the acceleration of a particle at any instant depends upon its position relative to other particles at that same instant; while the old idea was that the past affects the future, while the future does not affect the past. So the "law of demand and supply" has utterly different meanings with different economists.—1893.

13 An acceptance whose real support has been the opinion that pleasure is the only ultimate good. But this opinion, or even the opinion that pleasure *per se* is any good at all, is only tenable so long as he who holds it remains without any distinct idea of what he means by "good."—1903.

14 [This sentence inserted *c.* 1910.]

taste, unfortunately, is always more or less a matter of fashion, and accordingly metaphysicians have never come to any fixed agreement, but the pendulum has swung backward and forward between a more material and a more spiritual philosophy, from the earliest times to the latest. And so from this, which has been called the *a priori* method, we are driven, in Lord Bacon's phrase, to a true induction. We have examined into this *a priori* method as something which promised to deliver our opinions from their accidental and capricious element. But development, while it is a process which eliminates the effect of some casual circumstances, only magnifies that of others. This method, therefore, does not differ in a very essential way from that of authority. The government may not have lifted its finger to influence my convictions; I may have been left outwardly quite free to choose, we will say, between monogamy and polygamy, and, appealing to my conscience only, I may have concluded that the latter practice is in itself licentious. But when I come to see that the chief obstacle to the spread of Christianity among a people of as high culture as the Hindoos has been a conviction of the immorality of our way of treating women, I cannot help seeing that, though governments do not interfere, sentiments in their development will be very greatly determined by accidental causes. Now, there are some people, among whom I must suppose that my reader is to be found, who, when they see that any belief of theirs is determined by any circumstance extraneous to the facts, will from that moment not merely admit in words that that belief is doubtful, but will experience a real doubt of it, so that it ceases in some degree at least [15] to be a belief.

To satisfy our doubts, therefore, it is necessary that a method should be found by which our beliefs may be determined [16] by nothing human, but by some external permanency—by something upon which our thinking has no effect.[17] Some

[15] ["in . . . least" inserted *c.* 1910.]

[16] [Originally "caused."]

[17] But which, on the other hand, unceasingly tends to influence thought; or in other words, by something Real.—1903.

mystics imagine that they have such a method in a private inspiration from on high. But that is only a form of the method of tenacity, in which the conception of truth as something public is not yet developed. Our external permanency would not be external, in our sense, if it was restricted in its influence to one individual. It must be something which affects, or might affect, every man. And, though these affections are necessarily as various as are individual conditions, yet the method must be such that the ultimate conclusion of every man shall be the same.[18] Such is the method of science. Its fundamental hypothesis, restated in more familiar language, is this: There are Real things, whose characters are entirely independent of our opinions about them; those Reals [19] affect our senses according to regular laws, and, though our sensations are as different as are our relations to the objects, yet, by taking advantage of the laws of perception, we can ascertain by reasoning how things really and truly [20] are; and any man, if he have sufficient experience and he [21] reason enough about it, will be led to the one True conclusion. The new conception here involved is that of Reality. It may be asked how I know that there are any Reals.[22] If this hypothesis is the sole support of my method of inquiry, my method of inquiry must not be used to support my hypothesis. The reply is this: 1. If investigation cannot be regarded as proving that there are Real things, it at least does not lead to a contrary conclusion; but the method and the conception on which it is based remain ever in harmony. No doubts of the method, therefore, necessarily arise from its practice, as is the case with all the others. 2. The feeling which gives rise to any method of fixing belief is a dissatisfaction at two repugnant propositions. But here already is a vague concession that there is some

18 Or would be the same if inquiry were sufficiently persisted in.—1903.
19 [Originally "realities."]
20 ["and truly" not in the original.]
21 [Not in the original.]
22 [Originally "realities."]

one thing which a proposition should represent.[23] Nobody, therefore, can really doubt that there are Reals,[24] for,[25] if he did, doubt would not be a source of dissatisfaction. The hypothesis, therefore, is one which every mind admits. So that the social impulse does not cause men [26] to doubt it. 3. Everybody uses the scientific method about a great many things, and only ceases to use it when he does not know how to apply it. 4. Experience of the method has not led us [27] to doubt it, but, on the contrary, scientific investigation has had the most wonderful triumphs in the way of settling opinion. These afford the explanation of my not doubting the method or the hypothesis which it supposes; and not having any doubt, nor believing that anybody else whom I could influence has, it would be the merest babble for me to say more about it. If there be anybody with a living doubt upon the subject let him consider it.[28]

To describe the method of scientific investigation is the ob-

23 [Originally "to which a proposition should conform."]
24 [Originally "realities."]
25 [Originally "or."]
26 [Originally "me."]
27 [Originally "me."]
28 Changes of opinion are brought about by events beyond human control. All mankind were so firmly of opinion that heavy bodies must fall faster than light ones, that any other view was scouted as absurd, eccentric, and probably insincere. Yet as soon as some of the absurd and eccentric men could succeed in inducing some of the adherents of common sense to look at their experiments—no easy task—it became apparent that nature would not follow human opinion, however unanimous. So there was nothing for it but human opinion must move to nature's position. That was a lesson in humility. A few men, the small band of laboratory men, began to see that they had to abandon the pride of an opinion assumed absolutely final in any respect, and to use all their endeavors to yield as unresistingly as possible to the overwhelming tide of experience, which must master them at last, and to listen to what nature seems to be telling us. The trial of this method of experience in natural science for these three centuries—though bitterly detested by the majority of men—encourages us to hope that we are approaching nearer and nearer to an opinion which is not destined to be broken down—though we cannot expect ever quite to reach that ideal goal.—1893.

ject of this series of papers. At present I have only room to notice some points of contrast between it and other methods of fixing belief.

This is the only one of the four methods which presents any distinction of a right and a wrong way. If I adopt the method of tenacity, and shut myself out from all influences, whatever I think necessary to doing this, is necessary according to that method. So with the method of authority: the state may try to put down heresy by means which, from a scientific point of view, seem very ill-calculated to accomplish its purposes; but the only test *on that method* is what the state thinks; so that it cannot pursue the method wrongly. So with the *a priori* method. The very essence of it is to think as one is inclined to think. All metaphysicians will be sure to do that, however they may be inclined to judge each other to be perversely wrong. The Hegelian system recognizes every natural tendency of thought as logical, although it be certain to be abolished by counter-tendencies. Hegel thinks there is a regular system in the succession of these tendencies, in consequence of which, after drifting one way and the other for a long time, opinion will at last go right. And it is true that metaphysicians do [29] get the right ideas at last; Hegel's system of Nature represents tolerably the science of his [30] day; and one may be sure that whatever scientific investigation shall have [31] put out of doubt will presently receive *a priori* demonstration on the part of the metaphysicians. But with the scientific method the case is different. I may start with known and observed facts to proceed to the unknown; and yet the rules which I follow in doing so may not be such as investigation would approve. The test of whether I am truly following the method is not an immediate appeal to my feelings and purposes, but, on the contrary, itself involves the application of the method. Hence it is that bad reasoning as well as good reasoning is possible; and this fact is the foundation of the practical side of logic.

[29] [Not in the original.]
[30] [Originally "that."]
[31] [Originally "has" (instead of "shall have").]

It is not to be supposed that the first three methods of settling opinion present no advantage whatever over the scientific method. On the contrary, each has some peculiar convenience of its own. The *a priori* method is distinguished for its comfortable conclusions. It is the nature of the process to adopt whatever belief we are inclined to, and there are certain flatteries to the vanity of man which we all believe by nature, until we are awakened from our pleasing dream by [32] rough facts. The method of authority will always govern the mass of mankind; and those who wield the various forms of organized force in the state will never be convinced that dangerous reasoning ought not to be suppressed in some way. If liberty of speech is to be untrammeled from the grosser forms of constraint, the uniformity of opinion will be secured by a moral terrorism to which the respectability of society will give its thorough approval. Following the method of authority is the path of peace. Certain non-conformities are permitted; certain others (considered unsafe) are forbidden. These are different in different countries and in different ages; but, wherever you are, let it be known that you seriously hold a tabooed belief, and you may be perfectly sure of being treated with a cruelty less brutal but more refined than hunting you like a wolf. Thus, the greatest intellectual benefactors of mankind have never dared, and dare not now, to utter the whole of their thought; and thus a shade of *prima facie* doubt is cast upon every proposition which is considered essential to the security of society. Singularly enough, the persecution does not all come from without; but a man torments himself and is oftentimes most distressed at finding himself believing propositions which he has been brought up to regard with aversion. The peaceful and sympathetic man will, therefore, find it hard to resist the temptation to submit his opinions to authority. But most of all I admire the method of tenacity for its strength, simplicity, and directness. Men who pursue it are distinguished for their decision of character, which becomes very easy with such a mental rule. They do not waste time in

[32] ["Some" deleted in 1893.]

trying to make up their minds what they want, but, fastening like lightning upon whatever alternative comes first, they hold to it to the end, whatever happens, without an instant's irresolution. This is one of the splendid qualities which generally accompany brilliant, unlasting success. It is impossible not to envy the man who can dismiss reason, although we know how it must turn out at last.

Such are the advantages which the other methods of settling opinion have over scientific investigation. A man should consider well of them; and then he should consider that, after all, he wishes his opinions to coincide with the fact, and that there is no reason why the results of those three first [33] methods should do so. To bring about this effect is the prerogative of the method of science. Upon such considerations he has to make his choice—a choice which is far more than the adoption of any intellectual opinion, which is one of the ruling decisions of his life, to which, when once made, he is bound to adhere. The force of habit will sometimes cause a man to hold on to old beliefs, after he is in a condition to see that they have no sound basis. But reflection upon the state of the case will overcome these habits, and he ought to allow reflection its full weight. People sometimes shrink from doing this, having an idea that beliefs are wholesome which they cannot help feeling rest on nothing. But let such persons suppose an analogous though different case from their own. Let them ask themselves what they would say to a reformed Mussulman who should hesitate to give up his old notions in regard to the relations of the sexes; or to a reformed Catholic who should still shrink from reading the Bible. Would they not say that these persons ought to consider the matter fully, and clearly understand the new doctrine, and then ought to embrace it, in its entirety? But, above all, let it be considered that what is more wholesome than any particular belief is integrity of belief, and that to avoid looking into the support of any belief from a fear that it may turn out rotten is quite as immoral as it is disadvantageous. The person who confesses that there is such a

[33] [Not in the original.]

thing as truth, which is distinguished from falsehood simply by this, that if acted on it should, on full consideration, carry [34] us to the point we aim at and not astray, and then, though convinced of this, dares not know the truth and seeks to avoid it, is in a sorry state of mind indeed.

[35] Yes, the other methods do have their merits: a clear logical conscience does cost something—just as any virtue, just as all that we cherish, costs us dear. But we should not desire it to be otherwise. The genius of a man's logical method should be loved and reverenced as his bride, whom he has chosen from all the world. He need not contemn the others; on the contrary, he may honor them deeply, and in doing so he only honors her the more. But she is the one that he has chosen, and he knows that he was right in making that choice. And having made it, he will work and fight for her, and will not complain that there are blows to take, hoping that there may be as many and as hard to give, and will strive to be the worthy knight and champion of her from the blaze of whose splendors he draws his inspiration and his courage.

[34] ["should . . . carry" originally "will carry."]
[35] Delete the remainder.—Marginal note, 1893, 1903.

II

HOW TO MAKE OUR IDEAS CLEAR [1]

I [CLEARNESS AND DISTINCTNESS]

Whoever has looked into a modern treatise on logic of the common sort,[2] will doubtless remember the two distinctions between *clear* and *obscure* conceptions, and between *distinct* and *confused* conceptions. They have lain in the books now for nigh two centuries, unimproved and unmodified, and are generally reckoned by logicians as among the gems of their doctrine.

A clear idea is defined as one which is so apprehended that it will be recognized wherever it is met with, and so that no other will be mistaken for it. If it fails of this clearness, it is said to be obscure.

This is rather a neat bit of philosophical terminology; yet, since it is clearness that they were defining, I wish the logicians had made their definition a little more plain. Never to fail to recognize an idea, and under no circumstances to mistake another for it, let it come in how recondite a form it may, would indeed imply such prodigious force and clearness of intellect as is seldom met with in this world. On the other hand, merely to have such an acquaintance with the idea as to have become familiar with it, and to have lost all hesitancy in recognizing it in ordinary cases, hardly seems to deserve the name of clearness of apprehension, since after all it only amounts to a subjective feeling of mastery which may be en-

1 [*Popular Science Monthly*, XII (1878), 286-302; with corrections and notes from revised versions, one of which was intended as Ch. 16 of the "Grand Logic" of 1893 and as Essay IX of the "Search for a Method" of 1893. (In *C.P.* V, 248-271).]

2 One of the treatises upon logic dating from *L'Art de Penser* of the Port Royalists down to very recent times.—1893.

tirely mistaken. I take it, however, that when the logicians speak of "clearness," they mean nothing more than such a familiarity with an idea, since they regard the quality as but a small merit, which needs to be supplemented by another, which they call *distinctness*.

A distinct idea is defined as one which contains nothing which is not clear. This is technical language; by the *contents* of an idea logicians understand whatever is contained in its definition. So that an idea is *distinctly* apprehended, according to them, when we can give a precise definition of it, in abstract terms. Here the professional logicians leave the subject; and I would not have troubled the reader with what they have to say, if it were not such a striking example of how they have been slumbering through ages of intellectual activity, listlessly disregarding the enginery of modern thought, and never dreaming of applying its lessons to the improvement of logic. It is easy to show that the doctrine that familiar use and abstract distinctness make the perfection of apprehension has its only true place in philosophies which have long been extinct; and it is now time to formulate the method of attaining to a more perfect clearness of thought, such as we see and admire in the thinkers of our own time.

When Descartes set about the reconstruction of philosophy, his first step was to (theoretically) permit scepticism and to discard the practice of the schoolmen of looking to authority as the ultimate source of truth. That done, he sought a more natural fountain of true principles, and thought he found [3] it in the human mind; thus passing, in the directest way, from the method of authority to that of apriority, as described in my first paper. Self-consciousness was to furnish us with our fundamental truths, and to decide what was agreeable to reason. But since, evidently, not all ideas are true, he was led to note, as the first condition of infallibility, that they must be clear. The distinction between an idea *seeming* clear and really being so, never occurred to him. Trusting to introspec-

[3] ["thought he found" originally "professed to find."]

tion, as he did, even for a knowledge of external things, why should he question its testimony in respect to the contents of our own minds? But then, I suppose, seeing men, who seemed to be quite clear and positive, holding opposite opinions upon fundamental principles, he was further led to say that clearness of ideas is not sufficient, but that they need also to be distinct, i.e., to have nothing unclear about them. What he probably meant by this (for he did not explain himself with precision) was, that they must sustain the test of dialectical examination; that they must not only seem clear at the outset, but that discussion must never be able to bring to light points of obscurity connected with them.

Such was the distinction of Descartes, and one sees that it was precisely on the level of his philosophy. It was somewhat developed by Leibniz. This great and singular genius was as remarkable for what he failed to see as for what he saw. That a piece of mechanism could not do work perpetually without being fed with power in some form, was a thing perfectly apparent to him; yet he did not understand that the machinery of the mind can only transform knowledge, but never originate it, unless it be fed with facts of observation. He thus missed the most essential point of the Cartesian philosophy, which is, that to accept propositions which seem perfectly evident to us is a thing which, whether it be logical or illogical, we cannot help doing. Instead of regarding the matter in this way, he sought to reduce the first principles of science to two classes, those which cannot be denied without self-contradiction, and those which result from the principle of sufficient reason (of which more anon),[4] and was apparently unaware of the great difference between his position and that of Descartes.[5] So he

---

[4] ["two . . . anon" originally "formulas which cannot be denied without self-contradiction."]

[5] He was, however, above all, one of the minds that grow; while at first he was an extreme nominalist, like Hobbes, and dabbled in the nonsensical and impotent *Ars magna* of Raymond Lully, he subsequently embraced the law of continuity and other doctrines opposed to nominalism. I speak here of his earlier views.—1903.

reverted to the old trivialities [6] of logic; and, above all, abstract definitions played a great part in his philosophy. It was quite natural, therefore, that on observing that the method of Descartes labored under the difficulty that we may seem to ourselves to have clear apprehensions of ideas which in truth are very hazy, no better remedy occurred to him than to require an abstract definition of every important term. Accordingly, in adopting the distinction of *clear* and *distinct* notions, he described the latter quality as the clear apprehension of everything contained in the definition; and the books have ever since copied his words.[7] There is no danger that his chimerical scheme will ever again be over-valued. Nothing new can ever be learned by analyzing definitions. Nevertheless, our existing beliefs can be set in order by this process, and order is an essential element of intellectual economy, as of every other. It may be acknowledged, therefore, that the books are right in making familiarity with a notion the first step toward clearness of apprehension, and the defining of it the second. But in omitting all mention of any higher perspicuity of thought, they simply mirror a philosophy which was exploded a hundred years ago. That much-admired "ornament of logic"—the doctrine of clearness and distinctness—may be pretty enough, but it is high time to relegate to our cabinet of curiosities the antique *bijou,* and to wear about us something better adapted to modern uses.

[8] The very first lesson that we have a right to demand that logic shall teach us is, how to make our ideas clear; and a most important one it is, depreciated only by minds who stand in need of it. To know what we think, to be masters of our own meaning, will make a solid foundation for great and weighty thought. It is most easily learned by those whose ideas are meagre and restricted; and far happier they than

---

[6] [Originally "formalities."]

[7] [Cf. his "Meditationes de cognitione," *Die Philosophischen Schriften von Leibniz,* her. von C. I. Gerhardt, Bd. IV, S. 422-427; *Nouveaux Essais,* II, 29.]

[8] Delete this paragraph.—1903.

such as wallow helplessly in a rich mud of conceptions. A nation, it is true, may, in the course of generations, overcome the disadvantage of an excessive wealth of language and its natural concomitant, a vast, unfathomable deep of ideas. We may see it in history, slowly perfecting its literary forms, sloughing at length its metaphysics, and, by virtue of the untirable patience which is often a compensation, attaining great excellence in every branch of mental acquirement. The page of history is not yet unrolled that [9] is to tell us whether such a people will or will not in the long run prevail over one whose ideas (like the words of their language) are few, but which possesses a wonderful mastery over those which it has. For an individual, however, there can be no question that a few clear ideas are worth more than many confused ones. A young man would hardly be persuaded to sacrifice the greater part of his thoughts to save the rest; and the muddled head is the least apt to see the necessity of such a sacrifice. Him we can usually only commiserate, as a person with a congenital defect. Time will help him, but intellectual maturity with regard to clearness is apt to [10] come rather late. This seems [11] an unfortunate arrangement of Nature, inasmuch as clearness is of less use to a man settled in life, whose errors have in great measure had their effect, than it would be to one whose path lay [12] before him. It is terrible to see how a single unclear idea, a single formula without meaning, lurking in a young man's head, will sometimes act like an obstruction of inert matter in an artery, hindering the nutrition of the brain, and condemning its victim to pine away in the fullness of his intellectual vigor and in the midst of intellectual plenty. Many a man has cherished for years as his hobby some vague shadow of an idea, too meaningless to be positively false; he has, nevertheless, passionately loved it, has made it his companion by day and by night, and has given to it his strength and his life,

9 [Originally "which."]
10 ["is apt to" not in the original.]
11 ["This seems" not in the original, replacing a semicolon.]
12 [Originally "lies."]

leaving all other occupations for its sake and in short has lived
with it and for it, until it has become, as it were, flesh of his
flesh and bone of his bone; and then he has waked up some
bright morning to find it gone, clean vanished away like the
beautiful Melusina of the fable, and the essence of his life
gone with it. I have myself known such a man; and who can
tell how many histories of circle-squarers, metaphysicians,
astrologers, and what not, may not be told in the old German
[French!] story?

II [THE PRAGMATIC MAXIM]

The principles set forth in the first part of this essay [1] lead,
at once, to a method of reaching a clearness of thought of [2]
higher grade than the "distinctness" of the logicians. It was
there noticed [3] that the action of thought is excited by the
irritation of doubt, and ceases when belief is attained; so that
the production of belief is the sole function of thought. All
these words, however, are too strong for my purpose. It is as if
I had described the phenomena as they appear under a mental
microscope. Doubt and Belief, as the words are commonly
employed, relate to religious or other grave discussions. But
here I use them to designate the starting of any question, no
matter how small or how great, and the resolution of it. If,
for instance, in a horse-car, I pull out my purse and find a five-
cent nickel and five coppers, I decide, while my hand is going
to the purse, in which way I will pay my fare. To call such a
question Doubt, and my decision Belief, is certainly to use
words very disproportionate to the occasion. To speak of such
a doubt as causing an irritation which needs to be appeased,
suggests a temper which is uncomfortable to the verge of insanity. Yet, looking at the matter minutely, it must be admitted that, if there is the least hesitation as to whether I

1 ["part . . . essay" originally "of these papers."]
2 ["a far," followed "of" in the original.]
3 [Originally "We have there found."]

shall pay the five coppers or the nickel (as there will be sure to be, unless I act from some previously contracted habit in the matter), though irritation is too strong a word, yet I am excited to such small mental activity as may be necessary to deciding how I shall act. Most frequently doubts arise from some indecision, however momentary, in our action. Sometimes it is not so. I have, for example, to wait in a railway-station, and to pass the time I read the advertisements on the walls. I compare the advantages of different trains and different routes which I never expect to take, merely fancying myself to be in a state of hesitancy, because I am bored with having nothing to trouble me. Feigned hesitancy, whether feigned for mere amusement or with a lofty purpose, plays a great part in the production of scientific inquiry. However the doubt may originate, it stimulates the mind to an activity which may be slight or energetic, calm or turbulent. Images pass rapidly through consciousness, one incessantly melting into another, until at last, when all is over—it may be in a fraction of a second, in an hour, or after long years—we find ourselves decided as to how we should act under such circumstances as those which occasioned our hesitation. In other words, we have attained belief.

In this process we observe two sorts of elements of consciousness, the distinction between which may best be made clear by means of an illustration. In a piece of music there are the separate notes, and there is the air. A single tone may be prolonged for an hour or a day, and it exists as perfectly in each second of that time as in the whole taken together; so that, as long as it is sounding, it might be present to a sense from which everything in the past was as completely absent as the future itself. But it is different with the air, the performance of which occupies a certain time, during the portions of which only portions of it are played. It consists in an orderliness in the succession of sounds which strike the ear at different times; and to perceive it there must be some continuity of consciousness which makes the events of a lapse of time present to us. We certainly only perceive the air by hearing the separate notes; yet we cannot be said to directly hear it, for we hear only what is present at the instant, and an orderliness of succession cannot exist in an instant. These two sorts of objects, what we are *immediately* conscious of and what we are *mediately* conscious of, are found in all consciousness. Some elements (the sensations) are completely present at every instant so long as they last, while others (like thought) are actions having beginning, middle, and end, and consist in a congruence in the succession of sensations which flow through the mind. They cannot be immediately present to us, but must cover some portion of the past or future. Thought is a thread of melody running through the succession of our sensations.

We may add that just as a piece of music may be written in parts, each part having its own air, so various systems of relationship of succession subsist together between the same sensations. These different systems are distinguished by having different motives, ideas, or functions. Thought is only one such system, for its sole motive, idea, and function is to produce belief, and whatever does not concern that purpose belongs to some other system of relations. The action of thinking may incidentally have other results; it may serve to amuse us, for example, and among *dilettanti* it is not rare to find those who have so perverted thought to the purposes of pleasure that it seems to vex them to think that the questions upon which they delight to exercise it may ever get finally settled; and a positive discovery which takes a favorite subject out of the arena of literary debate is met with ill-concealed dislike. This disposition is the very debauchery of thought. But the soul and meaning of thought, abstracted from the other elements which accompany it, though it may be voluntarily thwarted, can never be made to direct itself toward anything but the production of belief. Thought in action has for its only possible motive the attainment of thought at rest; and whatever does not refer to belief is no part of the thought itself.

And what, then, is belief? It is the demi-cadence which

closes a musical phrase in the symphony of our intellectual
life. We have seen that it has just three properties: First, it is
something that we are aware of; second, it appeases the irritation of doubt; and, third, it involves the establishment in our
nature of a rule of action, or, say for short, a *habit*. As it appeases the irritation of doubt, which is the motive for thinking, thought relaxes, and comes to rest for a moment when
belief is reached. But, since belief is a rule for action, the application of which involves further doubt and further thought,
at the same time that it is a stopping-place, it is also a new
starting-place for thought. That is why I have permitted myself to call it thought at rest, although thought is essentially
an action. The *final* upshot of thinking is the exercise of voli-
tion, and of this thought no longer forms a part; but belief is
only a stadium of mental action, an effect upon our nature due
to thought, which will influence future thinking.

The essence of belief is the establishment of a habit; and
different beliefs are distinguished by the different modes of
action to which they give rise. If beliefs do not differ in this
respect, if they appease the same doubt by producing the same
rule of action, then no mere differences in the manner of consciousness of them can make them different beliefs, any more
than playing a tune in different keys is playing different tunes.
Imaginary distinctions are often drawn between beliefs which
differ only in their mode of expression;—the wrangling which
ensues is real enough, however. To believe that any objects are
arranged among themselves ⁴ as in Fig. 1 [p. 40], and to believe
that they are arranged [as] in Fig. 2, are one and the same
belief; yet it is conceivable that a man should assert one proposition and deny the other. Such false distinctions do as much
harm as the confusion of beliefs really different, and are
among the pitfalls of which we ought constantly to beware,
especially when we are upon metaphysical ground. One singular deception of this sort, which often occurs, is to mistake the
sensation produced by our own unclearness of thought for a

---

⁴ ["among themselves" not in the original.]

character of the object we are thinking. Instead of perceiving that the obscurity is purely subjective, we fancy that we contemplate a quality of the object which is essentially mysterious; and if our conception be afterward presented to us in a clear form we do not recognize it as the same, owing to the

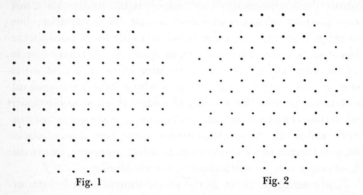

Fig. 1   Fig. 2

absence of the feeling of unintelligibility. So long as this deception lasts, it obviously puts an impassable barrier in the way of perspicuous thinking; so that it equally interests the opponents of rational thought to perpetuate it, and its adherents to guard against it.

Another such deception is to mistake a mere difference in the grammatical construction of two words for a distinction between the ideas they express. In this pedantic age, when the general mob of writers attend so much more to words than to things, this error is common enough. When I just said that thought is an *action,* and that it consists in a *relation,* although a person performs an action but not a relation, which can only be the result of an action, yet there was no inconsistency in what I said, but only a grammatical vagueness.

From all these sophisms we shall be perfectly safe so long as we reflect that the whole function of thought is to produce habits of action; and that whatever there is connected with a thought, but irrelevant to its purpose, is an accretion to it, but no part of it. If there be a unity among our sensations which has no reference to how we shall act on a given occasion, as when we listen to a piece of music, why we do not call that thinking. To develop its meaning, we have, therefore, simply to determine what habits it produces, for what a thing means is simply what habits it involves. Now, the identity of a habit depends on how it might lead us to act, not merely under such circumstances as are likely to arise, but under such as might possibly occur, no matter how improbable they may be.[5] What the habit is depends on *when* and *how* it causes us to act. As for the *when*, every stimulus to action is derived from perception; as for the *how*, every purpose of action is to produce some sensible result. Thus, we come down to what is tangible and conceivably [6] practical, as the root of every real distinction of thought, no matter how subtle it may be; and there is no distinction of meaning so fine as to consist in anything but a possible difference of practice.

To see what this principle leads to, consider in the light of it such a doctrine as that of transubstantiation. The Protestant churches generally hold that the elements of the sacrament are flesh and blood only in a tropical sense; they nourish our souls as meat and the juice of it would our bodies. But the Catholics maintain that they are literally just meat and blood; [7] although they possess all the sensible qualities of wafer-cakes and diluted wine. But we can have no conception of wine except what may enter into a belief, either—

1. That this, that, or the other, is wine; or,
2. That wine possesses certain properties.

Such beliefs are nothing but self-notifications that we should, upon occasion, act in regard to such things as we believe to be wine according to the qualities which we believe wine to possess. The occasion of such action would be some sensible perception, the motive of it to produce some sensible result. Thus our action has exclusive reference to what affects the

5 [No matter if contrary to all previous experience.—Marginal note, 1893.]
6 [Not in the original.]
7 ["meat and blood" originally "that."]

senses, our habit has the same bearing as our action, our belief the same as our habit, our conception the same as our belief; and we can consequently mean nothing by wine but what has certain effects, direct or indirect, upon our senses; and to talk of something as having all the sensible characters of wine, yet being in reality blood, is senseless jargon. Now, it is not my object to pursue the theological question; and having used it as a logical example I drop it, without caring to anticipate the theologian's reply. I only desire to point out how impossible it is that we should have an idea in our minds which relates to anything but conceived sensible effects of things. Our idea of anything *is* our idea of its sensible effects; and if we fancy that we have any other we deceive ourselves, and mistake a mere sensation accompanying the thought for a part of the thought itself. It is absurd to say that thought has any meaning unrelated to its only function. It is foolish for Catholics and Protestants to fancy themselves in disagreement about the elements of the sacrament, if they agree in regard to all their sensible effects, here and [8] hereafter.

It appears, then, that the rule for attaining the third grade of clearness of apprehension is as follows: Consider what effects, that [9] might conceivably have practical bearings, we conceive the object of our conception to have. Then, our conception of these effects is the whole of our conception of the object.[10, 11, 12]

[8] [Originally "or."]

[9] [Originally "which."]

[10] Long addition refuting what comes next.—1903. [This seems to refer to the following, which was written ten years earlier on a different sheet.]

[11] Before we undertake to apply this rule, let us reflect a little upon what it implies. It has been said to be a sceptical and materialistic principle. But it is only an application of the sole principle of logic which was recommended by Jesus; "Ye may know them by their fruits," and it is very intimately allied with the ideas of the gospel. We must certainly guard ourselves against understanding this rule in too individualistic a sense. To say that man accomplishes nothing but that to which his endeavors are directed would be a cruel condemnation of the great bulk of mankind, who never have leisure to labor for anything but the necessities

III [SOME APPLICATIONS OF THE
PRAGMATIC MAXIM]

Let us illustrate this rule by some examples; and, to begin
with the simplest one possible, let us ask what we mean by
calling a thing *hard*. Evidently that it will not be scratched
by many other substances. The whole conception of this quality, as of every other, lies in its conceived effects. There is ab-

---

of life for themselves and their families. But, without directly striving for
it, far less comprehending it, they perform all that civilization requires,
and bring forth another generation to advance history another step. Their
fruit is, therefore, collective; it is the achievement of the whole people.
What is it, then, that the whole people is about, what is this civilization
that is the outcome of history, but is never completed? We cannot expect
to attain a complete conception of it; but we can see that it is a gradual
process, that it involves a realization of ideas in man's consciousness and
in his works, and that it takes place by virtue of man's capacity for learning, and by experience continually pouring upon him ideas he has not
yet acquired. We may say that it is the process whereby man, with all
his miserable littleness, becomes gradually more and more imbued with
the Spirit of God, in which Nature and History are rife. We are also told
to believe in a world to come; but the idea is itself too vague to contrib-
ute much to the perspicuity of ordinary ideas. It is a common observation
that those who dwell continually upon their expectations are apt to become oblivious to the requirements of their actual station. The great
principle of logic is self-surrender, which does not mean that self is to lay
low for the sake of an ultimate triumph. It may turn out so; but that
must not be the governing purpose.

When we come to study the great principle of continuity and see how
all is fluid and every point directly partakes the being of every other, it
will appear that individualism and falsity are one and the same. Meantime, we know that man is not whole as long as he is single, that he is
essentially a possible member of society. Especially, one man's experience
is nothing, if it stands alone. If he sees what others cannot, we call it
hallucination. It is not "my" experience, but "our" experience that has to
be thought of; and this "us" has indefinite possibilities.

Neither must we understand the practical in any low and sordid sense.
Individual action is a means and not our end. Individual pleasure is not
our end; we are all putting our shoulders to the wheel for an end that
none of us can catch more than a glimpse at—that which the generations

solutely no difference between a hard thing and a soft thing so long as they are not brought to the test. Suppose, then, that a diamond could be crystallized in the midst of a cushion of soft cotton, and should remain there until it was finally burned up. Would it be false to say that that diamond was soft? This

---

are working out. But we can see that the development of embodied ideas is what it will consist in.—1893.

12 Note that in these three lines one finds, "conceivably," "conceive," "conception," "conception," "conception." Now I find there are many people who detect the authorship of my unsigned screeds; and I doubt not that one of the marks of my style by which they do so is my inordinate reluctance to repeat a word. This employment five times over of derivates of *concipere* must then have had a purpose. In point of fact it had two. One was to show that I was speaking of meaning in no other sense than that of *intellectual purport*. The other was to avoid all danger of being understood as attempting to explain a concept by percepts, images, schemata, or by anything but concepts. I did not, therefore, mean to say that acts, which are more strictly singular than anything, could constitute the purport, or adequate proper interpretation, of any symbol. I compared action to the finale of the symphony of thought, belief being a demicadence. Nobody conceives that the few bars at the end of a musical movement are the *purpose* of the movement. They may be called its upshot. But the figure obviously would not bear detailed application. I only mention it to show that the suspicion I myself expressed (Baldwin's *Dictionary* Article, *Pragmatism*) after a too hasty rereading of the forgotten magazine paper, that it expressed a stoic, that is, a nominalistic, materialistic, and utterly philistine state of thought, was quite mistaken.

No doubt, Pragmaticism makes thought ultimately *apply* to action exclusively—to *conceived* action. But between admitting that and either saying that it makes thought, in the sense of the purport of symbols, to consist in acts, or saying that the true ultimate purpose of thinking is action, there is much the same difference as there is between saying that the artist-painter's living art is applied to dabbing paint upon canvas, and saying that that art-life consists in dabbing paint, or that its ultimate aim is dabbing paint. Pragmaticism makes thinking to consist in the living inferential metaboly of symbols whose purport lies in conditional general resolutions to act. As for the ultimate purpose of thought, which must be the purpose of everything, it is beyond human comprehension; but according to the stage of approach which my thought has made to it—with aid from many persons, among whom I may mention Royce (in his *World and Individual*), Schiller (in his *Riddles of the Sphinx*) as well, by the way, as the famous poet [Friedrich Schiller] (in his *Aesthetische Briefe*), Henry James the elder (in his *Substance and Shadow* and in his conversa-

seems a foolish question, and would be so, in fact, except in the realm of logic. There such questions are often of the greatest utility as serving to bring logical principles into sharper relief than real discussions ever could. In studying logic we must not put them aside with hasty answers, but must consider them with attentive care, in order to make out the principles involved. We may, in the present case, modify our question, and ask what prevents us from saying that all hard bodies remain perfectly soft until they are touched, when their hardness increases with the pressure until they are scratched. Reflection will show that the reply is this: there would be no *falsity* in such modes of speech. They would involve a modification of our present usage of speech with regard to the words hard and soft, but not of their meanings. For they represent no fact to be different from what it is; only they involve arrangements of facts which would be exceedingly maladroit. This leads us to remark that the question of what would occur under circumstances which do not actually arise is not a question of fact, but only of the most perspicuous arrangement of them. For example, the question of free-will and fate in its simplest form, stripped of verbiage, is something like this: I have done something of which I am ashamed; could I, by an effort of the will, have resisted the temptation, and done otherwise? The philosophical reply is, that this is not a question of fact, but only of the arrangement of facts. Arranging them so as to exhibit what is particularly pertinent to my question—

---

tions), together with Swedenborg himself—it is by the indefinite replication of self-control upon self-control that the *vir* is begotten, and by action, through thought, he grows an esthetic ideal, not for the behoof of his own poor noddle merely, but as the share which God permits him to have in the work of creation.

This ideal, by modifying the rules of self-control modifies action, and so experience too—both the man's own and that of others, and this centrifugal movement thus rebounds in a new centripetal movement, and so on; and the whole is a bit of what has been going on, we may presume, for a time in comparison with which the sum of the geological ages is as the surface of an electron in comparison with that of a planet.—From "Consequences of Pragmaticism," 1906.

namely, that I ought to blame myself for having done wrong —it is perfectly true to say that, if I had willed to do otherwise than I did, I should have done otherwise. On the other hand, arranging the facts so as to exhibit another important consideration, it is equally true that, when a temptation has once been allowed to work, it will, if it has a certain force, produce its effect, let me struggle how I may. There is no objection to a contradiction in what would result from a false supposition. The *reductio ad absurdum* consists in showing that contradictory results would follow from a hypothesis which is consequently judged to be false. Many questions are involved in the free-will discussion, and I am far from desiring to say that both sides are equally right. On the contrary, I am of opinion that one side denies important facts, and that the other does not. But what I do say is, that the above single question was the origin of the whole doubt; that, had it not been for this question, the controversy would never have arisen; and that this question is perfectly solved in the manner which I have indicated.

Let us next seek a clear idea of Weight. This is another very easy case. To say that a body is heavy means simply that, in the absence of opposing force, it will fall. This (neglecting certain specifications of how it will fall, etc., which exist in the mind of the physicist who uses the word) is evidently the whole conception of weight. It is a fair question whether some particular facts may not *account* for gravity; but what we mean by the force itself is completely involved in its effects.

This leads us to undertake an account of the idea of Force in general. This is the great conception which, developed in the early part of the seventeenth century from the rude idea of a cause, and constantly improved upon since, has shown us how to explain all the changes of motion which bodies experience, and how to think about all physical phenomena; which has given birth to modern science, and changed the face of the globe; and which, aside from its more special uses, has played a principal part in directing the course of modern thought, and in furthering modern social development. It is, therefore, worth some pains to comprehend it. According to our rule, we must begin by asking what is the immediate use of thinking about force; and the answer is, that we thus account for changes of motion. If bodies were left to themselves, without the intervention of forces, every motion would continue unchanged both in velocity and in direction. Furthermore, change of motion never takes place abruptly; if its direction is changed, it is always through a curve without angles; if its

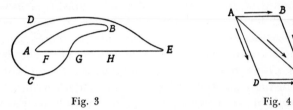

Fig. 3   Fig. 4

velocity alters, it is by degrees. The gradual changes which are constantly taking place are conceived by geometers to be compounded together according to the rules of the parallelogram of forces. If the reader does not already know what this is, he will find it, I hope, to his advantage to endeavor to follow the following explanation; but if mathematics are insupportable to him, pray let him skip three paragraphs rather than that we should part company here.

A *path* is a line whose beginning and end are distinguished. Two paths are considered to be equivalent, which, beginning at the same point, lead to the same point. Thus the two paths, *A B C D E* and *A F G H E* (Fig. 3), are equivalent. Paths which do *not* begin at the same point are considered to be equivalent, provided that, on moving either of them without turning it, but keeping it always parallel to its original position, when its beginning coincides with that of the other path, the ends also coincide. Paths are considered as geometrically added together, when one begins where the other ends; thus the path *A E* is conceived to be a sum of *A B, B C, C D,* and *D E*. In the parallelogram of Fig. 4 the diagonal *A C* is the sum of *A B* and *B C;* or, since *A D* is geometrically equivalent to *B C, A C* is the geometrical sum of *A B* and *A D*.

All this is purely conventional. It simply amounts to this: that we choose to call paths having the relations I have described equal or added. But, though it is a convention, it is a convention with a good reason. The rule for geometrical addition may be applied not only to paths, but to any other things which can be represented by paths. Now, as a path is determined by the varying direction and distance of the point which moves over it from the starting-point, it follows that anything which from its beginning to its end is determined by a varying direction and a varying magnitude is capable of being represented by a line. Accordingly, *velocities* may be represented by lines, for they have only directions and rates. The same thing is true of *accelerations,* or changes of velocities. This is evident enough in the case of velocities; and it becomes evident for accelerations if we consider that precisely what velocities are to positions—namely, states of change of them—that accelerations are to velocities.

The so-called "parallelogram of forces" is simply a rule for compounding accelerations. The rule is, to represent the accelerations by paths, and then to geometrically add the paths. The geometers, however, not only use the "parallelogram of forces" to compound different accelerations, but also to resolve one acceleration into a sum of several. Let *A B* (Fig. 5) be the

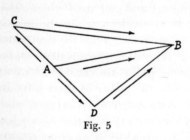

Fig. 5

path which represents a certain acceleration—say, such a change in the motion of a body that at the end of one second the body will, under the influence of that change, be in a position different from what it would have had if its motion had continued unchanged such that a path equivalent to *A B* would lead from the latter position to the former. This acceleration may be considered as the sum of the accelerations represented by *A C* and *C B*. It may also be considered as the sum of the very different accelerations represented by *A D* and

D B, where *A D* is almost the opposite of *A C*. And it is clear that there is an immense variety of ways in which *A B* might be resolved into the sum of two accelerations.

After this tedious explanation, which I hope, in view of the extraordinary interest of the conception of force, may not have exhausted the reader's patience, we are prepared at last to state the grand fact which this conception embodies. This fact is that if the actual changes of motion which the different particles of bodies experience are each resolved in its appropriate way, each component acceleration is precisely such as is prescribed by a certain law of Nature, according to which bodies, in the relative positions which the bodies in question actually have at the moment,[13] always receive certain accelerations, which, being compounded by geometrical addition, give the acceleration which the body actually experiences.

This is the only fact which the idea of force represents, and whoever will take the trouble clearly to apprehend what this fact is, perfectly comprehends what force is. Whether we ought to say that a force *is* an acceleration, or that it *causes* an acceleration, is a mere question of propriety of language, which has no more to do with our real meaning than the difference between the French idiom *"Il fait froid"* and its English equivalent *"It is cold."* Yet it is surprising to see how this simple affair has muddled men's minds. In how many profound treatises is not force spoken of as a "mysterious entity," which seems to be only a way of confessing that the author despairs of ever getting a clear notion of what the word means! In a recent admired work on *Analytic Mechanics*[14] it is stated that we understand precisely the effect of force, but what force itself is we do not understand! This is simply a self-contradiction. The idea which the word force excites in our minds has no other function than to affect our actions, and these actions can have no reference to force otherwise than through its effects. Consequently, if we know what the effects of force are,

---

[13] Possibly the velocities also have to be taken into account.

[14] [Kirchhoff's *Vorlesungen über math. Physik*, Bd. I, Vorrede.]

we are acquainted with every fact which is implied in saying that a force exists, and there is nothing more to know. The truth is, there is some vague notion afloat that a question may mean something which the mind cannot conceive; and when some hair-splitting philosophers have been confronted with the absurdity of such a view, they have invented an empty distinction between positive and negative conceptions, in the attempt to give their non-idea a form not obviously nonsensical. The nullity of it is sufficiently plain from the considerations given a few pages back; and, apart from those considerations, the quibbling character of the distinction must have struck every mind accustomed to real thinking.

IV [REALITY]

Let us now approach the subject of logic, and consider a conception which particularly concerns it, that of *reality*. Taking clearness in the sense of familiarity, no idea could be clearer than this. Every child uses it with perfect confidence, never dreaming that he does not understand it. As for clearness in its second grade, however, it would probably puzzle most men, even among those of a reflective turn of mind, to give an abstract definition of the real. Yet such a definition may perhaps be reached by considering the points of difference between reality and its opposite, fiction. A figment is a product of somebody's imagination; it has such characters as his thought impresses upon it. That those [1] characters are independent of how you or I think is an external reality. There are, however, phenomena within our own minds, dependent upon our thought, which are at the same time real in the sense that we really think them. But though their characters depend on how we think, they do not depend on what we think those characters to be. Thus, a dream has a real existence as a mental phenomenon, if somebody has really dreamt it; that

---

1 [Probably "whose."—Ed.]

he dreamt so and so, does not depend on what anybody thinks was dreamt, but is completely independent of all opinion on the subject. On the other hand, considering, not the fact of dreaming, but the thing dreamt, it retains its peculiarities by virtue of no other fact than that it was dreamt to possess them. Thus we may define the real as that whose characters are independent of what anybody may think them to be.

But, however satisfactory such a definition may be found, it would be a great mistake to suppose that it makes the idea of reality perfectly clear. Here, then, let us apply our rules. According to them, reality, like every other quality, consists in the peculiar sensible effects which things partaking of it produce. The only effect which real things have is to cause belief, for all the sensations which they excite emerge into consciousness in the form of beliefs. The question therefore is, how is true belief (or belief in the real) distinguished from false belief (or belief in fiction). Now, as we have seen in the former paper, the ideas of truth and falsehood, in their full development, appertain exclusively to the experiential [2] method of settling opinion. A person who arbitrarily chooses the propositions which he will adopt can use the word truth only to emphasize the expression of his determination to hold on to his choice. Of course, the method of tenacity never prevailed exclusively; reason is too natural to men for that. But in the literature of the dark ages we find some fine examples of it. When Scotus Erigena is commenting upon a poetical passage in which hellebore is spoken of as having caused the death of Socrates, he does not hesitate to inform the inquiring reader that Helleborus and Socrates were two eminent Greek philosophers, and that the latter, having been overcome in argument by the former, took the matter to heart and died of it! What sort of an idea of truth could a man have who could adopt and teach, without the qualification of a perhaps, an opinion taken so entirely at random? The real spirit of Socrates, who I hope would have been delighted to have been

2 [Originally "scientific."]

"overcome in argument," because he would have learned something by it, is in curious contrast with the naïve idea of the glossist, for whom (as for "the born missionary" of today) [3] discussion would seem to have been simply a struggle. When philosophy began to awake from its long slumber, and before theology completely dominated it, the practice seems to have been for each professor to seize upon any philosophical position he found unoccupied and which seemed a strong one, to intrench himself in it, and to sally forth from time to time to give battle to the others. Thus, even the scanty records we possess of those disputes enable us to make out a dozen or more opinions held by different teachers at one time concerning the question of nominalism and realism. Read the opening part of the *Historia Calamitatum* of Abelard,[4] who was certainly as philosophical as any of his contemporaries, and see the spirit of combat which it breathes. For him, the truth is simply his particular stronghold. When the method of authority prevailed, the truth meant little more than the Catholic faith. All the efforts of the scholastic doctors are directed toward harmonizing their faith in Aristotle and their faith in the Church, and one may search their ponderous folios through without finding an argument which goes any further. It is noticeable that where different faiths flourish side by side, renegades are looked upon with contempt even by the party whose belief they adopt; so completely has the idea of loyalty replaced that of truth-seeking. Since the time of Descartes, the defect in the conception of truth has been less apparent. Still, it will sometimes strike a scientific man that the philosophers have been less intent on finding out what the facts are, than on inquiring what belief is most in harmony with their system. It is hard to convince a follower of the *a priori* method by adducing facts; but show him that an opinion he is defending is inconsistent with what he has laid down elsewhere, and he will be very apt to retract it. These minds do not seem

---

[3] [The parenthetized phrase was not in the original.]

[4] [*Patrologiae Cursus, series Latina*, Vol. 178 (1855), pp. 114 et seq.—Ed.]

to believe that disputation is ever to cease; they seem to think that the opinion which is natural for one man is not so for another, and that belief will, consequently, never be settled. In contenting themselves with fixing their own opinions by a method which would lead another man to a different result, they betray their feeble hold of the conception of what truth is.

On the other hand, all the followers of science are animated by a cheerful hope [5] that the processes of investigation, if only pushed far enough, will give one certain solution to each [6] question to which they apply it.[7] One man may investigate the velocity of light by studying the transits of Venus and the aberration of the stars; another by the oppositions of Mars and the eclipses of Jupiter's satellites; a third by the method of Fizeau; a fourth by that of Foucault; a fifth by the motions of the curves of Lissajoux; a sixth, a seventh, an eighth, and a ninth, may follow the different methods of comparing the measures of statical and dynamical electricity. They may at first obtain different results, but, as each perfects his method and his processes, the results are found to move [8] steadily together toward a destined centre. So with all scientific research. Different minds may set out with the most antagonistic views, but the progress of investigation carries them by a force outside of themselves to one and the same conclusion. This activity of thought by which we are carried, not where we wish, but to a fore-ordained goal, is like the operation of destiny. No modification of the point of view taken, no selection of other facts for study, no natural bent of mind even, can enable a man to escape the predestinate opinion. This great hope [9] is embodied in the conception of truth and reality. The opinion which is fated [10] to be ultimately agreed to by all

---

5 ["are . . . hope" originally "are fully persuaded."]

6 [Originally "every."]

7 ["apply it" originally "can be applied."]

8 ["are . . . move" originally "will move."]

9 [Originally "law."]

10 Fate means merely that which is sure to come true, and can nohow be avoided. It is a superstition to suppose that a certain sort of events are

who investigate, is what we mean by the truth, and the object represented in this opinion is the real. That is the way I would explain reality.

But it may be said that this view is directly opposed to the abstract definition which we have given of reality, inasmuch as it makes the characters of the real depend on what is ultimately thought about them. But the answer to this is that, on the one hand, reality is independent, not necessarily of thought in general, but only of what you or I or any finite number of men may think about it; and that, on the other hand, though the object of the final opinion depends on what that opinion is, yet what that opinion is does not depend on what you or I or any man thinks. Our perversity and that of others may indefinitely postpone the settlement of opinion; it might even conceivably cause an arbitrary proposition to be universally accepted as long as the human race should last. Yet even that would not change the nature of the belief, which alone could be the result of investigation carried sufficiently far; and if, after the extinction of our race, another should arise with faculties and disposition for investigation, that true opinion must be the one which they would ultimately come to. "Truth crushed to earth shall rise again," and the opinion which would finally result from investigation does not depend on how anybody may actually think. But the reality of that which is real does depend on the real fact that investigation is destined to lead, at last, if continued long enough, to a belief in it.

But I may be asked what I have to say to all the minute facts of history, forgotten never to be recovered, to the lost books of the ancients, to the buried secrets:

> Full many a gem of purest ray serene
>   The dark, unfathomed caves of ocean bear;
> Full many a flower is born to blush unseen,
>   And waste its sweetness on the desert air.

---

ever fated, and it is another to suppose that the word fate can never be freed from its superstitious taint. We are all fated to die.

Do these things not really exist because they are hopelessly beyond the reach of our knowledge? And then, after the universe is dead (according to the prediction of some scientists), and all life has ceased forever, will not the shock of atoms continue though there will be no mind to know it? To this I reply that, though in no possible state of knowledge can any number be great enough to express the relation between the amount of what rests unknown to the amount of the known, yet it is unphilosophical to suppose that, with regard to any given question (which has any clear meaning), investigation would not bring forth a solution of it, if it were carried far enough. Who would have said, a few years ago, that we could ever know of what substances stars are made whose light may have been longer in reaching us than the human race has existed? Who can be sure of what we shall not know in a few hundred years? Who can guess what would be the result of continuing the pursuit of science for ten thousand years, with the activity of the last hundred? And if it were to go on for a million, or a billion, or any number of years you please, how is it possible to say that there is any question which might not ultimately be solved?

But it may be objected, "Why make so much of these remote considerations, especially when it is your principle that only practical distinctions have a meaning?" Well, I must confess that it makes very little difference whether we say that a stone on the bottom of the ocean, in complete darkness, is brilliant or not—that is to say, that it *probably* makes no difference, remembering always that that stone *may* be fished up tomorrow. But that there are gems at the bottom of the sea, flowers in the untraveled desert, etc., are propositions which, like that about a diamond being hard when it is not pressed, concern much more the arrangement of our language than they do the meaning of our ideas.

It seems to me, however, that we have, by the application of our rule, reached so clear an apprehension of what we mean by reality, and of the fact which the idea rests on, that we should not, perhaps, be making a pretension so presumptuous as it would be singular, if we were to offer a metaphysical theory of existence for universal acceptance among those who employ the scientific method of fixing belief. However, as metaphysics is a subject much more curious than useful, the knowledge of which, like that of a sunken reef, serves chiefly to enable us to keep clear of it, I will not trouble the reader with any more Ontology at this moment. I have already been led much further into that path than I should have desired; and I have given the reader such a dose of mathematics, psychology, and all that is most abstruse, that I fear he may already have left me, and that what I am now writing is for the compositor and proof-reader exclusively. I trusted to the importance of the subject. There is no royal road to logic, and really valuable ideas can only be had at the price of close attention. But I know that in the matter of ideas the public prefer the cheap and nasty; and in my next paper I am going to return to the easily intelligible, and not wander from it again. The reader who has been at the pains of wading through this paper, shall be rewarded in the next one by seeing how beautifully what has been developed in this tedious way can be applied to the ascertainment of the rules of scientific reasoning.

We have, hitherto, not crossed the threshold of scientific logic. It is certainly important to know how to make our ideas clear, but they may be ever so clear without being true. How to make them so, we have next to study. How to give birth to those vital and procreative ideas which multiply into a thousand forms and diffuse themselves everywhere, advancing civilization and making the dignity of man, is an art not yet reduced to rules, but of the secret of which the history of science affords some hints.

III

THE DOCTRINE OF CHANCES [1]

I [CONTINUITY AND THE FORMATION OF CONCEPTS]

It is a common observation that a science first begins to be exact when it is quantitatively treated. What are called the exact sciences are no others than the mathematical ones. Chemists reasoned vaguely until Lavoisier showed them how to apply the balance to the verification of their theories, when chemistry leaped suddenly into the position of the most perfect of the classificatory sciences. It has thus become so precise and certain that we usually think of it along with optics, thermotics, and electrics. But these are studies of general laws, while chemistry considers merely the relation and classification of certain objects; and belongs, in reality, in the same category as systematic botany and zoölogy. Compare it with these last, however, and the advantage that it derives from its quantitative treatment is very evident.[2]

The rudest numerical scales, such as that by which the mineralogists distinguish the different degrees of hardness, are found useful. The mere counting of pistils and stamens suf-

---

[1] [*Popular Science Monthly*, XII (1878), 604-15; with corrections of 1893 and a note of 1910; intended as Ch. 18 of the "Grand Logic" (1893), and as Essay X of the "Search for a Method" (1893). (In *C.P.*, II, 389-414.)]

[2] This characterization of chemistry now sounds antiquated indeed; and yet it was justified by the general state of mind of chemists at that day, as is shown by the fact that only a few months before, van't Hoff had put forth a statement of the law of mass-action as something absolutely new to science. I am satisfied by considerable search after pertinent facts that no distinction between different allied sciences can represent any truth of fact other than a difference between what habitually passes in the minds, and moves the investigations of the two general bodies of the cultivators of those sciences at the time to which the distinction refers.—1910.

ficed to bring botany out of total chaos into some kind of
form. It is not, however, so much from *counting* as from *meas-*
uring, not so much from the conception of number as from
that of continuous quantity, that the advantage of mathematical treatment comes. Number, after all, only serves to pin
us down to a precision in our thoughts which, however bene-
ficial, can seldom lead to lofty conceptions, and frequently
descends to pettiness. Of those two faculties of which Bacon
speaks,[3] that which marks differences and that which notes
resemblances, the employment of number can only aid the
lesser one; and the excessive use of it must tend to narrow the
powers of the mind. But the conception of continuous quantity has a great office to fulfill, independently of any attempt
at precision. Far from tending to the exaggeration of differences, it is the direct instrument of the finest generalizations.
When a naturalist wishes to study a species, he collects a considerable number of specimens more or less similar. In contemplating them, he observes certain ones which are more or
less alike in some particular respect. They all have, for instance, a certain S-shaped marking. He observes that they are
not *precisely* alike, in this respect; the S has not precisely the
same shape, but the differences are such as to lead him to believe that forms could be found intermediate between any two
of those he possesses. He, now, finds other forms apparently
quite dissimilar—say a marking in the form of a C—and the
question is, whether he can find intermediate ones which will
connect these latter with the others. This he often succeeds in
doing in cases where it would at first be thought impossible;
whereas, he sometimes finds those which differ, at first glance,
much less, to be separated in Nature by the non-occurrence of
intermediaries. In this way, he builds up from the study of
Nature a new general conception of the character in question.
He obtains, for example, an idea of a leaf which includes
every part of the flower, and an idea of a vertebra which in-

[3] [*Novum Organum,* Bk. II, Aphorism XXVII.]

cludes the skull. I surely need not say much to show what a logical engine is here. It is the essence of the method of the naturalist. How he applies it first to one character, and then to another, and finally obtains a notion of a species of animals, the differences between whose members, however great, are confined within limits, is a matter which does not here concern us. The whole method of classification must be considered later; but, at present, I only desire to point out that it is by taking advantage of the idea of continuity, or the passage from one form to another by insensible degrees,[4] that the naturalist builds his conceptions. Now, the naturalists are the great builders of conceptions; there is no other branch of science where so much of this work is done as in theirs; and we must, in great measure, take them for our teachers in this important part of logic. And it will be found everywhere that the idea of continuity [5] is a powerful aid to the formation of true and fruitful conceptions. By means of it, the greatest differences are broken down and resolved into differences of degree, and the incessant application of it is of the greatest value in broadening our conceptions. I propose to make a great use of this idea [6] in the present series of papers; and the particular series of important fallacies, which, arising from a neglect of it,[7] have desolated philosophy, must further on be closely studied. At present, I simply call the reader's attention to the utility of this conception.

In studies of numbers, the idea of continuity is so indispensable, that it is perpetually introduced even where there is no continuity in fact, as where we say that there are in the

---

4 "Or rather of an idea that continuity suggests—that of limitless intermediation; i.e., of a series between every two members of which there is another member of it"—to be substituted for the phrase "or . . . degrees."—1893.

5 For "continuity" substitute "limitless intermediation, the business of reasoning."—1893.

6 "And others that are involved in that of continuity."—1893.

7 For "neglect of" substitute "want of close study of these concepts."—1893.

United States 10.7 inhabitants per square mile, or that in New York 14.72 persons live in the average house.[8] Another example is that law of the distribution of errors which Quetelet, Galton, and others, have applied with so much success to the study of biological and social matters. This application of continuity to cases where it does not really exist illustrates, also, another point which will hereafter demand a separate study, namely, the great utility which fictions sometimes have in science.

II [THE PROBLEM OF PROBABILITY]

The theory of probabilities is simply the science of logic quantitatively treated. There are two conceivable certainties with reference to any hypothesis, the certainty of its truth and the certainty of its falsity. The numbers *one* and *zero* are appropriated, in this calculus, to marking these extremes of knowledge; while fractions having values intermediate between them indicate, as we may vaguely say, the degrees in which the evidence leans toward one or the other. The general problem of probabilities is, from a given state of facts, to determine the numerical probability of a possible fact. This is the same as to inquire how much the given facts are worth, considered as evidence to prove the possible fact. Thus the problem of probabilities is simply the general problem of logic.

Probability is a continuous quantity, so that great advantages may be expected from this mode of studying logic. Some writers have gone so far as to maintain that, by means of the calculus of chances, every solid inference may be represented by legitimate arithmetical operations upon the numbers given

[8] This mode of thought is so familiarly associated with all exact numerical consideration, that the phrase appropriate to it is imitated by shallow writers in order to produce the appearance of exactitude where none exists. Certain newspapers, which affect a learned tone, talk of "the average man," when they simply mean *most men*, and have no idea of striking an average.

in the premisses. If this be, indeed, true, the great problem of logic, how it is that the observation of one fact can give us knowledge of another independent fact, is reduced to a mere question of arithmetic. It seems proper to examine this pretension before undertaking any more recondite solution of the paradox.

But, unfortunately, writers on probabilities are not agreed in regard to this result. This branch of mathematics is the only one, I believe, in which good writers frequently get results entirely erroneous. In elementary geometry the reasoning is frequently fallacious, but erroneous conclusions are avoided; but it may be doubted if there is a single extensive treatise on probabilities in existence which does not contain solutions absolutely indefensible. This is partly owing to the want of any regular method of procedure; for the subject involves too many subtilities to make it easy to put its problems into equations without such an aid. But, beyond this, the fundamental principles of its calculus are more or less in dispute. In regard to that class of questions to which it is chiefly applied for practical purposes, there is comparatively little doubt; but in regard to others to which it has been sought to extend it, opinion is somewhat unsettled.

This last class of difficulties can only be entirely overcome by making the idea of probability perfectly clear in our minds in the way set forth in our last paper.

III [ON DEGREES OF PROBABILITY]

To get a clear idea of what we mean by probability, we have to consider what real and sensible difference there is between one degree of probability and another.

The character of probability belongs primarily, without doubt, to certain inferences. Locke [1] explains it as follows: After remarking that the mathematician positively knows that

---

[1] [Locke, *Essay Concerning Human Understanding*. Bk. IV, Ch. 15, §1.]

the sum of the three angles of a triangle is equal to two right angles because he apprehends the geometrical proof, he thus continues: "But another man who never took the pains to observe the demonstration, hearing a mathematician, a man of credit, affirm the three angles of a triangle to be equal to two right ones, *assents* to it; i.e., receives it for true. In which case the foundation of his assent is the probability of the thing, the proof being such as, for the most part, carries truth with it; the man on whose testimony he receives it not being wont to affirm anything contrary to, or besides his knowledge, especially in matters of this kind." The celebrated *Essay Concerning Human Understanding* contains many passages which, like this one, make the first steps in profound analyses which are not further developed. It was shown in the first of these papers that the validity of an inference does not depend on any tendency of the mind to accept it, however strong such tendency may be; but consists in the real fact that, when premisses like those of the argument in question are true, conclusions related to them like that of this argument are also true. It was remarked that in a logical mind an argument is always conceived as a member of a *genus* of arguments all constructed in the same way, and such that, when their premisses are real facts, their conclusions are so also. If the argument is demonstrative, then this is always so; if it is only probable, then it is for the most part so. As Locke says, the probable argument is *"such as* for the most part carries truth with it."

According to this, that real and sensible difference between one degree of probability and another, in which the meaning of the distinction lies, is that in the frequent employment of two different modes of inference, one will carry truth with it oftener than the other. It is evident that this is the only difference there is in the existing fact. Having certain premisses, a man draws a certain conclusion, and as far as this inference alone is concerned the only possible practical question is whether that conclusion is true or not, and between existence and non-existence there is no middle term. "Being only is and nothing is altogether not," said Parmenides; and this is in strict accordance with the analysis of the conception of reality given in the last paper. For we found that the distinction of reality and fiction depends on the supposition that sufficient investigation would cause one opinion to be universally received and all others to be rejected. That presupposition, involved in the very conceptions of reality and figment, involves a complete sundering of the two. It is the heaven-and-hell idea in the domain of thought. But, in the long run, there is a real fact which corresponds to the idea of probability, and it is that a given mode of inference sometimes proves successful and sometimes not, and that in a ratio ultimately fixed. As we go on drawing inference after inference of the given kind, during the first ten or hundred cases the ratio of successes may be expected to show considerable fluctuations; but when we come into the thousands and millions, these fluctuations become less and less; and if we continue long enough, the ratio will approximate toward a fixed limit. We may, therefore, define the probability of a mode of argument as the proportion of cases in which it carries truth with it.

The inference from the premiss, A, to the conclusion, B, depends, as we have seen, on the guiding principle, that if a fact of the class A is true, a fact of the class B is true. The probability consists of the fraction whose numerator is the number of times in which both A and B are true, and whose denominator is the total number of times in which A is true, whether B is so or not. Instead of speaking of this as the probability of the inference, there is not the slightest objection to calling it the probability that, if A happens, B happens. But to speak of the probability of the event B, without naming the condition, really has no meaning at all. It is true that when it is perfectly obvious what condition is meant, the ellipsis may be permitted. But we should avoid contracting the habit of using language in this way (universal as the habit is), because it gives rise to a vague way of thinking, as if the action of causation might either determine an event to happen or determine it not to happen, or leave it more or less free to happen or not, so as to give rise to an *inherent* chance in regard to its occurrence. It is quite clear to me that some of the worst and most persistent errors in the use of the doctrine of chances have arisen from this vicious mode of expression.[2]

IV [THREE LOGICAL SENTIMENTS]

But there remains an important point to be cleared up. According to what has been said, the idea of probability essentially belongs to a kind of inference which is repeated indefinitely. An individual inference must be either true or false, and can show no effect of probability; and, therefore, in reference to a single case considered in itself, probability can have no meaning. Yet if a man had to choose between drawing a card from a pack containing twenty-five red cards and a black one, or from a pack containing twenty-five black cards and a red one, and if the drawing of a red card were destined to transport him to eternal felicity, and that of a black one to consign him to everlasting woe, it would be folly to deny that he ought to prefer the pack containing the larger proportion of red cards, although, from the nature of the risk, it could not be repeated. It is not easy to reconcile this with our analysis of the conception of chance. But suppose he should choose the red pack, and should draw the wrong card, what consolation would he have? He might say that he had acted in accordance with reason, but that would only show that his reason was absolutely worthless. And if he should choose the right card, how could he regard it as anything but a happy accident? He could not say that if he had drawn from the other pack, he might have drawn the wrong one, because an hypothetical proposition such as, "if A, then B," means nothing with reference to a single case. Truth consists in the exist-

2 The conception of probability here set forth is substantially that first developed by Mr. Venn, in his *Logic of Chance*. Of course, a vague apprehension of the idea had always existed, but the problem was to make it perfectly clear, and to him belongs the credit of first doing this.

ence of a real fact corresponding to the true proposition. Corresponding to the proposition, "if A, then B," there may be the fact that *whenever* such an event as A happens, such an event as B happens. But in the case supposed, which has no parallel as far as this man is concerned, there would be no real fact whose existence could give any truth to the statement that, if he had drawn from the other pack, he might have drawn a black card. Indeed, since the validity of an inference consists in the truth of the hypothetical proposition that *if* the premisses be true the conclusion will also be true, and since the only real fact which can correspond to such a proposition is that whenever the antecedent is true the consequent is so also, it follows that there can be no sense in reasoning in an isolated case at all.

These considerations appear, at first sight, to dispose of the difficulty mentioned. Yet the case of the other side is not yet exhausted. Although probability will probably manifest its effect in, say, a thousand risks, by a certain proportion between the numbers of successes and failures, yet this, as we have seen, is only to say that it certainly will, at length, do so. Now the number of risks, the number of probable inferences, which a man draws in his whole life, is a finite one, and he cannot be absolutely *certain* that the mean result will accord with the probabilities at all. Taking all his risks collectively, then, it cannot be certain that they will not fail, and his case does not differ, except in degree, from the one last supposed. It is an indubitable result of the theory of probabilities that every gambler, if he continues long enough, must ultimately be ruined. Suppose he tries the martingale, which some believe infallible, and which is, as I am informed, disallowed in the gambling-houses. In this method of playing, he first bets say $1; if he loses it he bets $2; if he loses that he bets $4; if he loses that he bets $8; if he then gains he has lost $1 + 2 + 4 = 7$, and he has gained $1 more; and no matter how many bets he loses, the first one he gains will make him $1 richer than he was in the beginning. In that way, he will probably gain at first; but, at last, the time will come when the run of luck is so against him that he will not have money enough to double, and must, therefore, let his bet go. This will *probably* happen before he has won as much as he had in the first place, so that this run against him will leave him poorer than he began; some time or other it will be sure to happen. It is true that there is always a possibility of his winning any sum the bank can pay, and we thus come upon a celebrated paradox that, though he is certain to be ruined, the value of his expectation calculated according to the usual rules (which omit this consideration) is large. But, whether a gambler plays in this way or any other, the same thing is true, namely, that if [he] plays long enough he will be sure some time to have such a run against him as to exhaust his entire fortune. The same thing is true of an insurance company. Let the directors take the utmost pains to be independent of great conflagrations and pestilences, their actuaries can tell them that, according to the doctrine of chances, the time must come, at last, when their losses will bring them to a stop. They may tide over such a crisis by extraordinary means, but then they will start again in a weakened state, and the same thing will happen again all the sooner. An actuary might be inclined to deny this, because he knows that the expectation of his company is large, or perhaps (neglecting the interest upon money) is infinite. But calculations of expectations leave out of account the circumstance now under consideration, which reverses the whole thing. However, I must not be understood as saying that insurance is on this account unsound, more than other kinds of business. All human affairs rest upon probabilities, and the same thing is true everywhere. If man were immortal he could be perfectly sure of seeing the day when everything in which he had trusted should betray his trust, and, in short, of coming eventually to hopeless misery. He would break down, at last, as every great fortune, as every dynasty, as every civilization does. In place of this we have death.

But what, without death, would happen to every man, with death must happen to some man. At the same time, death makes the number of our risks, of our inferences, finite, and so makes their mean result uncertain. The very idea of probability and of reasoning rests on the assumption that this number is indefinitely great. We are thus landed in the same difficulty as before, and I can see but one solution of it. It seems to me that we are driven to this, that logicality inexorably requires that our interests shall *not* be limited. They must not stop at our own fate, but must embrace the whole community. This community, again, must not be limited, but must extend to all races of beings with whom we can come into immediate or mediate intellectual relation. It must reach, however vaguely, beyond this geological epoch, beyond all bounds. He who would not sacrifice his own soul to save the whole world, is, as it seems to me, illogical in all his inferences, collectively. Logic is rooted in the social principle.

To be logical men should not be selfish; and, in point of fact, they are not so selfish as they are thought. The willful prosecution of one's desires is a different thing from selfishness. The miser is not selfish; his money does him no good, and he cares for what shall become of it after his death. We are constantly speaking of *our* possessions on the Pacific, and of *our* destiny as a republic, where no personal interests are involved, in a way which shows that we have wider ones. We discuss with anxiety the possible exhaustion of coal in some hundreds of years, or the cooling-off of the sun in some millions, and show in the most popular of all religious tenets that we can conceive the possibility of a man's descending into hell for the salvation of his fellows.

Now, it is not necessary for logicality that a man should himself be capable of the heroism of self-sacrifice. It is sufficient that he should recognize the possibility of it, should perceive that only that man's inferences who has it are really logical, and should consequently regard his own as being only so far valid as they would be accepted by the hero. So far as he thus refers his inferences to that standard, he becomes identified with such a mind.

This makes logicality attainable enough. Sometimes we can personally attain to heroism. The soldier who runs to scale a wall knows that he will probably be shot, but that is not all he cares for. He also knows that if all the regiment, with whom in feeling he identifies himself, rush forward at once, the fort will be taken. In other cases we can only imitate the virtue. The man whom we have supposed as having to draw from the two packs, who if he is not a logician will draw from the red pack from mere habit, will see, if he is logician enough, that he cannot be logical so long as he is concerned only with his own fate, but that that man who should care equally for what was to happen to all possible cases of the sort could act logically, and would draw from the pack with the most red cards, and thus, though incapable himself of such sublimity, our logician would imitate the effect of that man's courage in order to share his logicality.

But all this requires a conceived identification of one's interests with those of an unlimited community. Now, there exist no reasons, and a later discussion will show that there can be no reasons, for thinking that the human race, or any intellectual race, will exist forever. On the other hand, there can be no reason against it,[1] and, fortunately, as the whole requirement is that we should have certain sentiments, there is nothing in the facts to forbid our having a *hope,* or calm and cheerful wish, that the community may last beyond any assignable date.

It may seem strange that I should put forward three sentiments, namely, interest in an indefinite community, recognition of the possibility of this interest being made supreme, and hope in the unlimited continuance of intellectual activity, as indispensable requirements of logic. Yet, when we consider that logic depends on a mere struggle to escape doubt, which, as it terminates in action, must begin in emotion, and that, furthermore, the only cause of our planting ourselves on reason is that other methods of escaping doubt fail on account

[1] I do not here admit an absolutely unknowable. Evidence could show us what would probably be the case after any given lapse of time; and though a subsequent time might be assigned which that evidence might not cover, yet further evidence would cover it.

of the social impulse, why should we wonder to find social sentiment presupposed in reasoning? As for the other two sentiments which I find necessary, they are so only as supports and accessories of that. It interests me to notice that these three sentiments seem to be pretty much the same as that famous trio of Charity, Faith, and Hope, which, in the estimation of St. Paul, are the finest and greatest of spiritual gifts. Neither Old nor New Testament is a textbook of the logic of science, but the latter is certainly the highest existing authority in regard to the dispositions of heart which a man ought to have.

V [FUNDAMENTAL RULES FOR THE CALCULATION OF CHANCES]

Such average statistical numbers as the number of inhabitants per square mile, the average number of deaths per week, the number of convictions per indictment, or, generally speaking, the numbers of x's per y, where the x's are a class of things some or all of which are connected with another class of things, their y's, I term *relative numbers*. Of the two classes of things to which a relative number refers, that one of which it is a number may be called its *relate*, and that one *per* which the numeration is made may be called its *correlate*.

Probability is a kind of relative number; namely, it is the ratio of the number of arguments of a certain genus which carry truth with them to the total number of arguments of that genus, and the rules for the calculation of probabilities are very easily derived from this consideration. They may all be given here, since they are extremely simple, and it is sometimes convenient to know something of the elementary rules of calculation of chances.

Rule I. *Direct Calculation.*—To calculate, directly, any relative number, say for instance the number of passengers in the average trip of a street-car, we must proceed as follows:

Count the number of passengers for each trip; add all these

numbers, and divide by the number of trips. There are cases in which this rule may be simplified. Suppose we wish to know the number of inhabitants to a dwelling in New York. The same person cannot inhabit two dwellings. If he divide his time between two dwellings he ought to be counted a half-inhabitant of each. In this case we have only to divide the total number of the inhabitants of New York by the number of their dwellings, without the necessity of counting separately those which inhabit each one. A similar proceeding will apply wherever each individual relate belongs to one individual correlate exclusively. If we want the number of x's per y, and no x belongs to more than one y, we have only to divide the whole number of x's of y's by the number of y's. Such a method would, of course, fail if applied to finding the average number of street-car passengers per trip. We could not divide the total number of travelers by the number of trips, since many of them would have made many passages.

To find the probability that from a given class of premisses, A, a given class of conclusions, B, follows, it is simply necessary to ascertain what proportion of the times in which premisses of that class are true the appropriate conclusions are also true. In other words, it is the number of cases of the occurrence of both the events A and B, divided by the total number of cases of the occurrence of the event A.

Rule II. *Addition of Relative Numbers.*—Given two relative numbers having the same correlate, say the number of x's per y, and the number of z's per y, it is required to find the number of x's and z's together per y. If there is nothing which is at once an x and a z to the same y, the sum of the two given numbers would give the required number. Suppose, for example, that we had given the average number of friends that men have, and the average number of enemies, the sum of these two is the average number of persons interested in a man. On the other hand, it plainly would not do to add the average number of persons having constitutional diseases to the average number over military age, and to the average number exempted by each special cause from military service, in order to get the average number exempt in any way, since many are exempt in two or more ways at once.

This rule applies directly to probabilities, given the probability that two different and mutually exclusive events will happen under the same supposed set of circumstances. Given, for instance, the probability that if A then B, and also the probability that if A then C, then the sum of these two probabilities is the probability that if A then either B or C, so long as there is no event which belongs at once to the two classes B and C.

Rule III. *Multiplication of Relative Numbers.*—Suppose that we have given the relative number of x's per y; also the relative number of z's per x of y; or, to take a concrete example, suppose that we have given, first, the average number of children in families living in New York; and, second, the average number of teeth in the head of a New York child—then the product of these two numbers would give the average number of children's teeth in a New York family. But this mode of reckoning will only apply in general under two restrictions. In the first place, it would not be true if the same child could belong to different families, for in that case those children who belonged to several different families might have an exceptionally large or small number of teeth, which would affect the average number of children's teeth in a family more than it would affect the average number of teeth in a child's head. In the second place, the rule would not be true if different children could share the same teeth, the average number of children's teeth being in that case evidently something different from the average number of teeth belonging to a child.

In order to apply this rule to probabilities, we must proceed as follows: Suppose that we have given the probability that the conclusion B follows from the premiss A, B and A representing as usual certain classes of propositions. Suppose that we also knew the probability of an inference in which B should be the premiss, and a proposition of a third kind, C, the conclusion. Here, then, we have the materials for the ap-

plication of this rule. We have, first, the relative number of
B's per A. We next should have the relative number of C's
per B following from A. But the classes of propositions being
so selected that the probability of C following from any B in
general is just the same as the probability of C's following from
one of those B's which is deducible from an A, the two probabilities may be multiplied together, in order to give the probability of C following from A. The same restrictions exist as
before. It might happen that the probability that B follows
from A was affected by certain propositions of the class B following from several different propositions of the class A. But,
practically speaking, all these restrictions are of very little
consequence, and it is usually recognized as a principle universally true that the probability that, if A is true, B is, multiplied by the probability that, if B is true, C is, gives the probability that, if A is true, C is.

There is a rule supplementary to this, of which great use is
made. It is not universally valid, and the greatest caution has
to be exercised in making use of it—a double care, first, never
to use it when it will involve serious error; and, second, never
to fail to take advantage of it in cases in which it can be employed. This rule depends upon the fact that in very many
cases the probability that C is true if B is, is substantially the
same as the probability that C is true if A is. Suppose, for example, we have the average number of males among the children born in New York; suppose that we also have the average number of children born in the winter months among
those born in New York. Now, we may assume without doubt,
at least as a closely approximate proposition (and no very nice
calculation would be in place in regard to probabilities), that
the proportion of males among all the children born in New
York is the same as the proportion of males born in summer
in New York; and, therefore, if the names of all the children
born during a year were put into an urn, we might multiply
the probability that any name drawn would be the name of
a male child by the probability that it would be the name of
a child born in summer, in order to obtain the probability

that it would be the name of a male child born in summer. The question of probability, in the treatises upon the subject, have usually been such as relate to balls drawn from urns, and games of cards, and so on, in which the question of the *independence* of events, as it is called—that is to say, the question of whether the probability of C, under the hypothesis B, is the same as its probability under the hypothesis A—has been very simple; but, in the application of probabilities to the ordinary questions of life, it is often an exceedingly nice question whether two events may be considered as independent with sufficient accuracy or not. In all calculations about cards it is assumed that the cards are thoroughly shuffled, which makes one deal quite independent of another. In point of fact the cards seldom are, in practice, shuffled sufficiently to make this true; thus, in a game of whist, in which the cards have fallen in sets of four of the same suit, and are so gathered up, they will lie more or less in sets of four of the same suit, and this will be true even after they are shuffled. At least some traces of this arrangement will remain, in consequence of which the number of "short suits," as they are called—that is to say, the number of hands in which the cards are very unequally divided in regard to suit—is smaller than the calculation would make it to be; so that, when there is a misdeal, where the cards, being thrown about the table, get very thoroughly shuffled, it is a common saying that in the hands next dealt out there are generally short suits. A few years ago, a friend of mine, who plays whist a great deal, was so good as to count the number of spades dealt to him in 165 hands, in which the cards had been, if anything, shuffled better than usual. According to calculation, there should have been 85 of these hands in which my friend held either three or four spades, but in point of fact there were 94, showing the influence of imperfect shuffling.

According to the view here taken, these are the only fundamental rules for the calculation of chances. An additional one, derived from a different conception of probability, is given in some treatises, which if it be sound might be made the basis of a theory of reasoning. Being, as I believe it is, absolutely absurd, the consideration of it serves to bring us to the true theory; and it is for the sake of this discussion, which must be postponed to the next number, that I have brought the doctrine of chances to the reader's attention at this early stage of our studies of the logic of science.

VI [NOTES ON THE DOCTRINE OF CHANCES] [1]

On reperusing this article after the lapse of a full generation, it strikes me as making two points that were worth making. The better made of the two had been still better made ten years before in my three articles in the [*Journal of Speculative Philosophy*] Vol. 2. This point is that no man can be logical whose supreme desire is the well-being of himself or of any other existing person or collection of persons. The other good point is that probability never properly refers immediately to a single event, but exclusively to the happening of a given kind of event on any occasion of a given kind. So far all is well. But when I come to define probability, I repeatedly say that it is the quotient of the *number* of occurrences of the event divided by the *number* of occurrences of the occasion. Now this is manifestly wrong, for probability relates to the future; and how can I say how many times a given die will be thrown in the future? To be sure I might, immediately after my throw, put the die in strong nitric acid, and dissolve it, but this suggestion only puts the preposterous character of the definition in a still stronger light. For it is plain that, if probability be the ratio of the occurrences of the specific event to the occurrences of the generic occasion, it is the ratio that there *would be* in the long run, and has nothing to do with any supposed cessation of the occasions. This long run can be nothing but an endlessly long run; and even if it be correct to speak of an infinite "number," yet $\frac{\infty}{\infty}$ (infinity divided by infinity) has certainly, *in itself*, no definite value.

1 [1910.]

But we have not yet come to the end of the flaws in the definition, since no notice whatever has been taken of two conditions which require the strictest precautions in all experiments to determine the probability of a specific event on a generic occasion. Namely, in the first place we must limit our endeavors strictly to counting occurrences of the right genus of occasion and carefully resist all other motives for counting them, and strive to take them just as they would ordinarily occur. In the next place, it must be known that the occurrence of the specific event on one occasion will have no tendency to produce or to prevent the occurrence of the same event upon any other of the occurrences of the generic occasion. In the third place, after the probability has been ascertained, we must remember that this probability cannot be relied upon at any future time unless we have adequate grounds for believing that it has not too much changed in the interval.

I will now give over jeering at my former inaccuracies, committed when I had been a student of logic for only about a quarter of a century, and was naturally not so well-versed in it as now, and will proceed to define probability. I must premiss that we, all of us, use this word with a degree of laxity which corrupts and rots our reasoning to a degree that very few of us are at all awake to. When I say our "reasoning," I mean not formal reasonings only but our thoughts in general, so far as they are concerned with any of those approaches toward knowledge which we confound with probability. The result is that we not only fall into the falsest ways of thinking, but, what is often still worse, we give up sundry problems as beyond our powers—problems of gravest concern, too —when, in fact, we should find they were not a bit so, if we only rightly discriminated between the different kinds of imperfection of certitude, and if we had only once acquainted ourselves with their different natures. I shall in these notes endeavor to mark the three ways of falling short of certainty by the three terms *probability, verisimilitude* or *likelihood,* and *plausibility.* Just at present I propose to deal only with Probability; but I will so far characterize *verisimilitude* and *plausibility* as to mark them off as being entirely different from Probability. Beginning with Plausibility, I will first endeavor to give an example of an idea which shall be strikingly marked by its very low degree of this quality. Suppose a particularly symmetrical larch tree near the house of a great lover of such trees had been struck by lightning and badly broken, and that as he was looking sorrowfully out of the window at it, he should have happened to say, "I wonder why that particular tree should have been struck, when there are so many about the place that seem more exposed!" Suppose, then, his wife should reply, "Perhaps there may be an eagle's eyrie on some of the hills in the neighborhood, and perhaps the male bird in building it may have used some stick that had a nail in it; and one of the eaglets may have scratched itself against the nail; so that the mother may have reproached the male for using such a dangerous stick; and he, being vexed with her teasing, may have determined to carry the piece to a great distance; it may have been while he was doing this that the explosion of lightning took place, and the electricity may have been deflected by the iron in such a way as to strike this tree. Mind, I do not say that this is what did happen; but if you want to find out why that tree was struck, I think you had better search for an eyrie, and see whether any of the eaglets have been scratched." This is an example of as unplausible a theory as I can think of. We should commonly say it was highly improbable; and I suppose it would be so. But were it ever so probable in all its elements, it would still deserve no attention, because it is perfectly gratuitous to suppose that the lightning was deflected at all; and this supposition does not help to explain the phenomenon.

Eusapia Palladino had been proved to be a very clever prestigiateuse and cheat, and was visited by a Mr. Carrington,[2] whom I suppose to be so clever in finding out how tricks are done, that it is highly improbable that any given trick should long baffle him. In point of fact he has often caught the Palla-

[2] See Carrington's *Eusapia Palladino*, B. W. Dodge & Co., New York (1909).

dino creature in acts of fraud. Some of her performances, however, he cannot explain; and thereupon he urges the theory that these are supernatural, or, as he prefers to phrase it, "supernormal." Well, I know how it is that when a man has been long intensely exercised and over-fatigued by an enigma, his common-sense will sometimes desert him; but it seems to me that the Palladino has simply been too clever for him, as no doubt she would be for me. The theory that there is anything "supernormal," or *super* anything but *superchérie* in the case, seems to me as needless as any theory I ever came across. That is to say, granted that it is not yet *proved* that women who deceive for gain receive aid from the spiritual world, I think it more plausible that there are tricks that can deceive Mr. Carrington than that the Palladino woman has received such aid. By Plausible, I mean that a theory that has not yet been subjected to any test, although more or less surprising phenomena have occurred which it would explain if it were true, is in itself of such character as to recommend it for further examination or, if it be *highly* plausible, justify us in seriously inclining toward belief in it, as long as the phenomena be inexplicable otherwise.

I will now give an idea of what I mean by *likely* or *verisimilar*. It is to be understood that I am only endeavouring so far to explain the meanings I attach to "plausible" and to "likely," as this may be an assistance to the reader in understanding the meaning I attach to *probable*. I call that theory *likely* which is not yet proved but is supported by such evidence that if the rest of the conceivably possible evidence should turn out upon examination to be of a *similar* character, the theory would be conclusively proved. Strictly speaking, matters of fact never can be demonstrably proved, since it will always remain conceivable that there should be some mistake about it. For instance, I regard it as *sufficiently* proved that my name is Charles Peirce and that I was born in Cambridge, Massachusetts, in a stone-colored wooden house in Mason Street. But even of the part of this of which I am most assured—of my name—there is a certain small probability that I am in an abnormal condition and have got it wrong. I am conscious myself of occasional lapses of memory about other things; and though I well remember—or think I do—living in that house at a tender age, I do not in the least remember being born there, impressive as such a first experience might be expected to be. Indeed, I cannot specify any date on which any certain person informed me I had been born there; and it certainly would have been easy to deceive me in the matter had there been any serious reason for doing so; and how can I be so sure as I surely am that no such reason did exist? It would be a theory without plausibility; that is all.

The history of science, particularly physical science, in contradistinction to natural science—or, as I usually, though inadequately, phrase the distinction, the history of nomological in contradistinction to classificatory sciences—this history, ever since I first seriously set myself, at the age of thirteen, in 1852, to the study of logic,[3] shows only too grievously how great a boon would be any way [of] determining and expressing by numbers the degree of likelihood that a theory had attained—any general recognition, even among leading men of science, of the true degree of significance of a given fact, and of the proper method of determining it. I hope my writings may, at any rate, awaken a few to the enormous waste of effort it would save. But any numerical determination of likelihood is more than I can expect.

The only kind of reasoning which can render our conclusions certain—and even this kind can do so only under the proviso that no blunder has been committed in the process—attains this certainty by limiting the conclusion (as Kant virtually said, and others before him) to facts already expressed and accepted in the premises. This is called necessary, or syllogistic reasoning. Syllogism, not confined to the kind that Aristotle and Theophrastus studied, is merely an artificial form in which it may be expressed, and it is not its best form, from any point of view. But the kind of reasoning which creates likelihoods by virtue of observations may render a likeli-

[3] [Peirce read Whately's *Logic* at this time.]

hood *practically* certain—as certain as that a stone let loose
from the clutch will, under circumstances not obviously ex-
ceptional, fall to the ground—and this conclusion may be that
under a certain general condition, easily verified, a certain
actuality will be *probable,* that is to say, will come to pass once
in so often in the long run. One such familiar conclusion, for
example, is that a die thrown from a dice box will with a
probability of one-third, that is, once in three times in the
long run, turn up a number (either *tray* or *size*) that is divisible by three. But this can be affirmed with practical certainty
only if by a "long run" be meant an endless series of trials,
and (as just said) infinity divided by infinity gives of itself an
entirely indefinite quotient. It is therefore necessary to define
the phrase. I might give the definition with reference to the
probability, *p,* where *p* is any vulgar fraction, and in reference
to a generic condition, *m,* and a specific kind of event *n.* But
I think the reader will follow me more readily, if in place of
the letter *m* (which in itself is but a certain letter, to which is
attached a peculiar meaning, that of the fulfillment of some
generic condition) I put instead the supposition that a die is
thrown from a dice box; and this special supposition will be as
readily understood by the reader to be replaceable by any
other general condition along with a simultaneous replacement of the *event,* that a number divisible by three is turned
up, and at the same time with the replacement of one third
by whatever other vulgar fraction may be called for when
some different example of a probability is before us. I am,
then, to define the meaning of the statement that the *probability,* that if a die be thrown from a dice box it will turn up a
number divisible by three, is one-third. The statement means
that the die has a certain "would-be"; and to say that a die has
a "would-be" is to say that it has a property, quite analogous
to any *habit* that a man might have. Only the "would-be" of
the die is presumably as much simpler and more definite than
the man's habit as the die's homogeneous composition and
cubical shape is simpler than the nature of the man's nervous
system and soul; and just as it would be necessary, in order to

define a man's habit, to describe how it would lead him to behave and upon what sort of occasion—albeit this statement would by no means imply that the habit *consists* in that action —so to define the die's "would-be" it is necessary to say how it would lead the die to behave on an occasion that would bring out the full consequence of the "would-be"; and this statement will not of itself imply that the "would-be" of the die *consists* in such behavior.

Now in order that the full effect of the die's "would-be" may find expression, it is necessary that the die should undergo an endless series of throws from the dice box, the result of no throw having the slightest influence upon the result of any other throw, or, as we express it, the throws must be *independent* each of every other.

It will be no objection to our considering the consequences of the supposition that the die is thrown an endless succession of times, and that with a finite pause after each throw, that such an endless series of events is impossible, for the reason that the impossibility is merely a physical, and not a logical, impossibility, as was well illustrated in that famous sporting event in which Achilles succeeded in overtaking the champion tortoise, in spite of his giving the latter the start of a whole *stadion*. For it having been ascertained, by delicate measurements between a mathematical point between the shoulder-blades of Achilles (marked [by] a limit between a red, a green, and a violet sector of a stained disk) and a similar point on the carapace of the tortoise, that when Achilles arrived where the tortoise started, the latter was just 60 feet 8 inches and $\frac{1}{10}$ inch further on, which is just one tenth of a stadion, and that when Achilles reached that point the tortoise was still 6 feet and 8 $\frac{1}{100}$ inch in advance of him, and finally that, both advancing at a perfectly uniform rate, the tortoise had run just 67 feet 5 inches when he was overtaken by Achilles, it follows that the tortoise progressed at just one tenth the speed of Achilles, the latter running a distance in *stadia* of 1.111111111, so that he had to traverse the sum of an infinite multitude of finite distances, each in a finite time, and yet covered the *stadion* and one ninth in a finite time. No contradiction, therefore, is involved in the idea of an endless series of finite times or spaces having but a finite sum, provided there is no *fixed* finite quality [4] which every member of an endless part of that series must each and every one *exceed*.

The reader must pardon me for occupying any of his time with such puerile stuff as that $0.1111 = \frac{1}{9}$; for astounding as it seems, it has more than once happened to me that men have come to me—every one of them not merely educated men, but highly accomplished—men who might well enough be famous over the civilized world, if fame were anything to the purpose, but men whose studies had been such that one would have expected to find each of them an adept in the accurate statement of arguments, and yet each has come and has undertaken to prove to me that the old catch of Achilles and the tortoise is a sound argument. If I tell you what after listening to them by the hour, I have always ended by saying—it may serve your turn on a similar occasion—I have said, "I suppose you do not mean to say that you really believe that a fast runner cannot, as a matter of fact, overtake a slow one. I therefore conclude that the argument which you have been unable to state, either syllogistically or in any other intelligible form, is intended to show that Zeno's reasoning about Achilles and the tortoise is sound according to some system of logic which admits that sound necessary reasoning may lead from true premises to a false conclusion. But in my system of logic what I mean by bad necessary reasoning is precisely an argument which might lead from true premises to a false conclusion—just that and nothing else. If you prefer to call such reasoning a sound necessary argument, I have no objection in the world to your doing so; and you will kindly allow me to employ my different nomenclature. For I am such a plain, uncultured soul that when I reason I aim at nothing else than just to find out the truth." To get back, then, to the die and its habit—its "would-be"—I really know no other way of defining a habit than by describing the kind of behavior in which the habit becomes

4 [Quantity?—Ed.]

actualized. So I am obliged to define the statement that there is a probability of one-third that the die when thrown will turn up either a three or a six by stating how the numbers will run when the die is thrown.

But my purpose in doing so is to explain what *probability*, as I use the word, consists in. Now it would be no explanation at all to say that it consists in something being *probable*. So I must avoid using that word or any synonym of it. If I were to use such an expression, you would very properly turn upon me and say, "I either know what it is to be *probable*, in your sense of the term, or I do not. If I don't, how can I be expected to understand you until you have explained yourself; and if I do, what is the use of the explanation?" But the fact [is] that the probability of the die turning up a three or a six is not *sure* to produce any determination [of] the run of the numbers thrown in any *finite* series of throws. It is only when the series is endless that we can be *sure* that it will have a particular character. Even when there is an endless series of throws, there is no syllogistic certainty, no "mathematical" certainty (if you are more familiar with this latter phrase)— that the die will not turn up a six obstinately at every single throw. It might be that if in the course of the endless series, some friends should borrow the die to make a pair for a game of backgammon, there might be nothing unusual in the behavior of the lent die, and yet when it was returned and our experimental series was resumed where it had been interrupted, the die might return to turning up nothing but six every time. I say it *might*, in the sense that it would not violate the principle of contradiction if it did. It sanely *would not*, however, unless a miracle were performed; and moreover if such miracle *were* worked, I should say (since it is my use of the term "probability" that we have supposed to be in question) that during this experimental series of throws, the die took on an abnormal, a miraculous, habit. For I should think that the performance of a certain line of behavior, throughout an endless succession of occasions, without exception, very decidedly *constituted* a habit. There may be some doubt about this, for owing to our not being accustomed to reason in this way about successions of events which are endless *in the sequence* and yet are completed *in time,* it is hard for me quite to satisfy myself what I ought to say in such a case. But I have reflected seriously on it, and though I am not perfectly sure of my ground (and I am a cautious reasoner), yet I am more that what you would understand by "pretty confident," that supposing one to be in a condition to assert what *would surely be* the behavior, *in any single determinate respect,* of any subject throughout an endless series of occasions of a stated kind, he *ipso facto* knows a "would-be," or habit, of that subject. It is very true, mind you, that *no* collection whatever of single acts, though it were ever so many grades greater than a simple endless series, can constitute a would-be, nor can the knowledge of single acts, whatever their multitude, tell us for *sure* of a would-be. But there are two remarks to be made; first, that in the case under consideration a person is supposed to be in a condition to assert what surely *would be* the behavior of the subject throughout the endless series of occasions—a knowledge which cannot have been derived from reasoning from its behavior on the single occasions; and second, that that which in our case renders it true, as stated, that the person supposed "*ipso facto* knows a would-be of that subject," is not the occurrence of the single acts, but the fact that the person supposed "was in condition to assert what *would surely be* the behavior of the subject throughout an endless series of occasions." [5]

I will now describe the behavior of the die during the endless series of throws, in respect to turning up numbers divisible by three. It would be perfectly possible to construct a machine that would automatically throw the die and pick it up, and continue doing so as long as it was supplied with energy. It would further be still easier to design the plan of

[5] Meantime it may be remarked that, though an endless series of acts is not a habit, nor a would-be, it does present the first of an endless series of steps toward the full nature of a would-be. Compare what I wrote nineteen [thirteen!] years ago, in an article on the logic of relatives.

an arrangement whereby a hand should after each throw move over an arc graduated so as to indicate the value of the quotient of the number of throws of three or six that had been known since the beginning of the experiment, divided by the total number of throws since the beginning. It is true that the mechanical difficulties would become quite insuperable before the die had been thrown many times; but fortunately a general description of the way the hand would move will answer our purpose much better than would the actual machine, were it ever so perfect.

After the first throw, the hand will go either to $0 = \%$ or $1 = \frac{1}{4}$; and there it may stay for several throws. But when it once moves, it will move after every throw, without exception, since the denominator of the fraction at whose value it points will always increase by 1, and consequently the value of the fraction will be diminished if the numerator remains unchanged, as it will be increased in case the numerator is increased by 1, these two being the only possible cases. The behavior of the hand may be described as an excessively irregular oscillation, back and forth, from one side of $\frac{1}{8}$ to the other. . . .

THE PROBABILITY OF INDUCTION [1]

I [RULES FOR THE ADDITION AND MULTIPLICATION OF PROBABILITIES]

We have found that every argument derives its force from the general truth of the class of inferences to which it belongs; and that probability is the proportion of arguments carrying truth with them among those of any *genus*. This is most conveniently expressed in the nomenclature of the medieval logicians. They called the fact expressed by a premiss an *antecedent,* and that which follows from it its *consequent;* while the leading principle, that every (or almost every) such antecedent is followed by such a consequent, they termed the *consequence.* Using this language, we may say that probability belongs exclusively to *consequences,* and the probability of any consequence is the number of times in which antecedent and consequent both occur divided by the number of all the times in which the antecedent occurs. From this definition are deduced the following rules for the addition and multiplication of probabilities:

Rule for the Addition of Probabilities.—Given the separate probabilities of two consequences having the same antecedent and incompatible consequents. Then the sum of these two numbers is the probability of the consequence, that from the same antecedent one or other of those consequents follows.

Rule for the Multiplication of Probabilities.—Given the separate probabilities of the two consequences, "If A then B," and "If both A and B, then C." Then the product of these two numbers is the probability of the consequence, "If A, then both B and C."

[1] [*Popular Science Monthly,* XII (1878), 705-18; intended as **Essay XI** of the "Search for a Method" (1893). (In *C.P.,* II, 415-432.)]

Special Rule for the Multiplication of Independent Probabilities.—Given the separate probabilities of two consequences having the same antecedents, "If A, then B," and "If A, then C." Suppose that these consequences are such that the probability of the second is equal to the probability of the consequence, "If both A and B, then C." Then the product of the two given numbers is equal to the probability of the consequence, "If A, then both B and C."

To show the working of these rules we may examine the probabilities in regard to throwing dice. What is the probability of throwing a six with one die? The antecedent here is the event of throwing a die; the consequent, its turning up a six. As the die has six sides, all of which are turned up with equal frequency, the probability of turning up any one is ⅙. Suppose two dice are thrown, what is the probability of throwing sixes? The probability of either coming up six is obviously the same when both are thrown as when one is thrown—namely, ⅙. The probability that either will come up six when the other does is also the same as that of its coming up six whether the other does or not. The probabilities are, therefore, independent; and, by our rule, the probability that both events will happen together is the product of their several probabilities, or ⅙ × ⅙. What is the probability of throwing deuce-ace? The probability that the first die will turn up ace and the second deuce is the same as the probability that both will turn up sixes—namely, ¹⁄₃₆; the probability that the *second* will turn up ace and the *first* deuce is likewise ¹⁄₃₆; these two events—first, ace; second, deuce; and, second, ace; first, deuce—are incompatible. Hence the rule for addition holds, and the probability that either will come up ace and the other deuce is ¹⁄₃₆ + ¹⁄₃₆, or ¹⁄₁₈.

In this way all problems about dice, etc., may be solved. When the number of dice thrown is supposed very large, mathematics (which may be defined as the art of making groups to facilitate numeration) comes to our aid with certain devices to reduce the difficulties.

II [MATERIALISTIC AND CONCEPTUALISTIC VIEWS OF PROBABILITY]

The conception of probability as a matter of *fact,* i.e., as the proportion of times in which an occurrence of one kind is accompanied by an occurrence of another kind, is termed by Mr. Venn the materialistic view of the subject. But probability has often been regarded as being simply the degree of belief which ought to attach to a proposition, and this mode of explaining the idea is termed by Venn the conceptualistic view. Most writers have mixed the two conceptions together. They, first, define the probability of an event as the reason we have to believe that it has taken place, which is conceptualistic; but shortly after they state that it is the ratio of the number of cases favorable to the event to the total number of cases favorable or contrary, and all equally possible. Except that this introduces the thoroughly unclear idea of cases equally possible in place of cases equally frequent, this is a tolerable statement of the materialistic view. The pure conceptualistic theory has been best expounded by Mr. De Morgan in his *Formal Logic: or, the Calculus of Inference, Necessary and Probable.*

The great difference between the two analyses is, that the conceptualists refer probability to an event, while the materialists make it the ratio of frequency of events of a *species* to those of a *genus* over that *species,* thus *giving it two terms instead of one.* The opposition may be made to appear as follows:

Suppose that we have two rules of inference, such that, of all the questions to the solution of which both can be applied, the first yields correct answers to $^{81}\!/_{100}$, and incorrect answers to the remaining $^{19}\!/_{100}$; while the second yields correct answers to $^{93}\!/_{100}$, and incorrect answers to the remaining $^{7}\!/_{100}$. Suppose, further, that the two rules are entirely independent as to their truth, so that the second answers correctly $^{93}\!/_{100}$ of the questions which the first answers correctly, and also $^{93}\!/_{100}$ of the questions which the first answers incorrectly, and answers incorrectly the remaining $\frac{7}{100}$ of the questions which the first answers correctly, and also the remaining $\frac{7}{100}$ of the questions which the first answers incorrectly. Then, of all the questions to the solution of which both rules can be applied—

both answer correctly $\frac{93}{100}$ of $\frac{81}{100}$, or $\frac{93 \times 81}{100 \times 100}$;

the second answers correctly and the first incorrectly

$$\frac{93}{100} \text{ of } \frac{19}{100}, \text{ or } \frac{93 \times 19}{100 \times 100};$$

the second answers incorrectly and the first correctly

$$\frac{7}{100} \text{ of } \frac{81}{100}, \text{ or } \frac{7 \times 81}{100 \times 100};$$

and both answer incorrectly

$$\frac{7}{100} \text{ of } \frac{19}{100}, \text{ or } \frac{7 \times 19}{100 \times 100}.$$

Suppose, now, that, in reference to any question, both give the same answer. Then (the questions being always such as are to be answered by *yes* or *no*), those in reference to which their answers agree are the same as those which both answer correctly together with those which both answer falsely, or $\frac{93 \times 81}{100 \times 100} + \frac{7 \times 19}{100 \times 100}$ of all. The proportion of those which both answer correctly out of those their answers to which agree is, therefore—

$$\frac{\dfrac{93 \times 81}{100 \times 100}}{\dfrac{93 \times 81}{100 \times 100} + \dfrac{7 \times 19}{100 \times 100}} \text{ or } \frac{93 \times 81}{(93 \times 81) + (7 \times 19)}.$$

This is, therefore, the probability that if both modes of inference yield the same result, that result is correct. We may here conveniently make use of another mode of expression. *Probability* is the ratio of the favorable cases to all the cases.

Instead of expressing our result in terms of this ratio, we may make use of another—the ratio of favorable to unfavorable cases. This last ratio may be called the *chance* of an event. Then the chance of a true answer by the first mode of inference is $81/19$ and by the second is $93/7$; and the chance of a correct answer from both, when they agree, is—

$$\frac{81 \times 93}{19 \times 7}, \text{ or } \frac{81}{19} \times \frac{93}{7},$$

or the product of the chances of each singly yielding a true answer.

It will be seen that a chance is a quantity which may have any magnitude, however great. An event in whose favor there is an even chance, or $1/1$, has a probability of $1/2$. An argument having an even chance can do nothing toward reinforcing others, since according to the rule its combination with another would only multiply the chance of the latter by 1.

Probability and chance undoubtedly belong primarily to consequences, and are relative to premises; but we may, nevertheless, speak of the chance of an event absolutely, meaning by that the chance of the combination of all arguments in reference to it which exist for us in the given state of our knowledge. Taken in this sense it is incontestable that the chance of an event has an intimate connection with the degree of our belief in it. Belief is certainly something more than a mere feeling; yet there is a feeling of believing, and this feeling does and ought to vary with the chance of the thing believed, as deduced from all the arguments. Any quantity which varies with the chance might, therefore, it would seem, serve as a thermometer for the proper intensity of belief. Among all such quantities there is one which is peculiarly appropriate. When there is a very great chance, the feeling of belief ought to be very intense. Absolute certainty, or an infinite chance, can never be attained by mortals, and this may be represented appropriately by an infinite belief. As the chance diminishes the feeling of believing should diminish, until an even chance is reached, where it should completely vanish and not incline either toward or away from the proposition. When the chance becomes less, then a contrary belief should spring up and should increase in intensity as the chance diminishes, and as the chance almost vanishes (which it can never quite do) the contrary belief should tend toward an infinite intensity. Now, there is one quantity which, more simply than any other, fulfills these conditions; it is the *logarithm* of the chance. But there is another consideration which must, if admitted, fix us to this choice for our thermometer. It is that our belief ought to be proportional to the weight of evidence, in this sense, that two arguments which are entirely independent, neither weakening nor strengthening each other, ought, when they concur, to produce a belief equal to the sum of the intensities of belief which either would produce separately. Now, we have seen that the chances of independent concurrent arguments are to be multiplied together to get the chance of their combination, and, therefore, the quantities which best express the intensities of belief should be such that they are to be *added* when the *chances* are multiplied in order to produce the quantity which corresponds to the combined chance. Now, the logarithm is the only quantity which fulfills this condition. There is a general law of sensibility, called Fechner's psychophysical law. It is that the intensity of any sensation is proportional to the logarithm of the external force which produces it. It is entirely in harmony with this law that the feeling of belief should be as the logarithm of the chance, this latter being the expression of the state of facts which produces the belief.

The rule for the combination of independent concurrent arguments takes a very simple form when expressed in terms of the intensity of belief, measured in the proposed way. It is this: Take the sum of all the feelings of belief which would be produced separately by all the arguments *pro,* subtract from that the similar sum for arguments *con,* and the remainder is the feeling of belief which we ought to have on the whole. This is a proceeding which men often resort to, under the name of *balancing reasons.*

These considerations constitute an argument in favor of the conceptualistic view. The kernel of it is that the conjoint probability of all the arguments in our possession, with reference to any fact, must be intimately connected with the just degree of our belief in that fact; and this point is supplemented by various others showing the consistency of the theory with itself and with the rest of our knowledge.

But probability, to have any value at all, must express a fact. It is, therefore, a thing to be inferred upon evidence. Let us, then, consider for a moment the formation of a belief of probability. Suppose we have a large bag of beans from which one has been secretly taken at random and hidden under a thimble. We are now to form a probable judgment of the color of that bean, by drawing others singly from the bag and looking at them, each one to be thrown back, and the whole well mixed up after each drawing. Suppose the first drawing is white and the next black. We conclude that there is not an immense preponderance of either color, and that there is something like an even chance that the bean under the thimble is black. But this judgment may be altered by the next few drawings. When we have drawn ten times, if 4, 5, or 6, are white, we have more confidence that the chance is even. When we have drawn a thousand times, if about half have been white, we have great confidence in this result. We now feel pretty sure that, if we were to make a large number of bets upon the color of single beans drawn from the bag, we could approximately insure ourselves in the long run by betting each time upon the white, a confidence which would be entirely wanting if, instead of sampling the bag by 1,000 drawings, we had done so by only two. Now, as the whole utility of probability is to insure us in the long run, and as that assurance depends, not merely on the value of the chance, but also on the accuracy of the evaluation, it follows that we ought not to have the same feeling of belief in reference to all events of which the chance is even. In short, to express the proper state of our belief, not *one* number but *two* are requisite, the first depending on the inferred probability, the second on the amount of knowledge on which that probability is based.[1] It is true that when our knowledge is very precise, when we have made many drawings from the bag, or, as in most of the examples in the books, when the total contents of the bag are absolutely known, the number which expresses the uncertainty of the assumed probability and its liability to be changed by further experience may become insignificant, or utterly vanish. But, when our knowledge is very slight, this number may be even more important than the probability itself; and when we have no knowledge at all this completely overwhelms the other, so that there is no sense in saying that the chance of the totally unknown event is even (for what expresses absolutely no fact has absolutely no meaning), and what ought to be said is that the chance is entirely indefinite. We thus perceive that the conceptualistic view, though answering well enough in some cases, is quite inadequate.

Suppose that the first bean which we drew from our bag was black. That would constitute an argument, no matter how slender, that the bean under the thimble was also black. If the second bean was also to turn out black, that would be a second independent argument reinforcing the first. If the whole of the first twenty beans drawn should prove black, our confidence that the hidden bean was black would justly attain considerable strength. But suppose the twenty-first bean was to be white and that we were to go on drawing until we found that we had drawn 1,010 black beans and 990 white ones. We should conclude that our first twenty beans being black was simply an extraordinary accident, and that in fact the proportion of white beans to black was sensibly equal, and that it was an even chance that the hidden bean was black. Yet according to the rule of *balancing reasons,* since all the drawings of black beans are so many independent arguments in favor of the one under the thimble being black, and all the white drawings so many against it, an excess of twenty black

[1] Strictly we should need an infinite series of numbers each depending on the probable error of the last.

beans ought to produce the same degree of belief that the hidden bean was black, whatever the total number drawn.

In the conceptualistic view of probability, complete ignorance, where the judgment ought not to swerve either toward or away from the hypothesis, is represented by the probability ½.[2]

But let us suppose that we are totally ignorant what colored hair the inhabitants of Saturn have. Let us, then, take a color-chart in which all possible colors are shown shading into one another by imperceptible degrees. In such a chart the relative areas occupied by different classes of colors are perfectly arbitrary. Let us inclose such an area with a closed line, and ask what is the chance on conceptualistic principles that the color of the hair of the inhabitants of Saturn falls within that area? The answer cannot be indeterminate because we must be in some state of belief; and, indeed, conceptualistic writers do not admit indeterminate probabilities. As there is no certainty in the matter, the answer lies between *zero* and *unity*. As no numerical value is afforded by the data, the number must be determined by the nature of the scale of probability itself, and not by calculation from the data. The answer can, therefore, only be one-half, since the judgment should neither favor nor oppose the hypothesis. What is true of this area is true of any other one; and it will equally be true of a third area which embraces the other two. But the probability for each of the smaller areas being one-half, that for the larger should be at least unity, which is absurd.

III [ON THE CHANCE OF UNKNOWN EVENTS]

All our reasonings are of two kinds: 1. *Explicative, analytic,* or *deductive;* 2. *Amplifiative, synthetic,* or (loosely speaking) *inductive.* In explicative reasoning, certain facts are first laid down in the premises. These facts are, in every case, an in-

2 "Perfect indecision, belief inclining neither way, an even chance."— De Morgan, p. 182.

exhaustible multitude, but they may often be summed up in one simple proposition by means of some regularity which runs through them all. Thus, take the proposition that Socrates was a man; this implies (to go no further) that during every fraction of a second of his whole life (or, if you please, during the greater part of them) he was a man. He did not at one instant appear as a tree and at another as a dog; he did not flow into water, or appear in two places at once; you could not put your finger through him as if he were an optical image, etc. Now, the facts being thus laid down, some order among some of them, not particularly made use of for the purpose of stating them, may perhaps be discovered; and this will enable us to throw part or all of them into a new statement, the possibility of which might have escaped attention. Such a statement will be the conclusion of an analytic inference. Of this sort are all mathematical demonstrations. But synthetic reasoning is of another kind. In this case the facts summed up in the conclusion are not among those stated in the premisses. They are different facts, as when one sees that the tide rises m times and concludes that it will rise the next time. These are the only inferences which increase our real knowledge, however useful the others may be.

In any problem in probabilities, we have given the relative frequency of certain events, and we perceive that in these facts the relative frequency of another event is given in a hidden way. This being stated makes the solution. This is, therefore, mere explicative reasoning, and is evidently entirely inadequate to the representation of synthetic reasoning, which goes out beyond the facts given in the premisses. There is, therefore, a manifest impossibility in so tracing out any probability for a synthetic conclusion.

Most treatises on probability contain a very different doctrine. They state, for example, that if one of the ancient denizens of the shores of the Mediterranean, who had never heard of tides, had gone to the bay of Biscay, and had there seen the tide rise, say m times, he could know that there was a probability equal to

$$\frac{m+1}{m+2}$$

that it would rise the next time. In a well-known work by Quetelet,[1] much stress is laid on this, and it is made the foundation of a theory of inductive reasoning.

But this solution betrays its origin if we apply it to the case in which the man has never seen the tide rise at all; that is, if we put $m = 0$. In this case, the probability that it will rise the next time comes out ½, or, in other words, the solution involves the conceptualistic principle that there is an even chance of a totally unknown event. The manner in which it has been reached has been by considering a number of urns all containing the same number of balls, part white and part black. One urn contains all white balls, another one black and the rest white, a third two black and the rest white, and so on, one urn for each proportion, until an urn is reached containing only black balls. But the only possible reason for drawing any analogy between such an arrangement and that of Nature is the principle that alternatives of which we know nothing must be considered as equally probable. But this principle is absurd. There is an indefinite variety of ways of enumerating the different possibilities, which, on the application of this principle, would give different results. If there be any way of enumerating the possibilities so as to make them all equal, it is not that from which this solution is derived, but is the following: Suppose we had an immense granary filled with black and white balls well mixed up; and suppose each urn were filled by taking a fixed number of balls from this granary quite at random. The relative number of white balls in the granary might be anything, say one in three. Then in one-third of the urns the first ball would be white, and in two-thirds black. In one-third of those urns of which the first ball was white, and also in one-third of those in which the first ball was black, the second ball would be white. In this way, we should have a distribution like that shown in the following table, where w

1 [*Théorie des probabilités,* deuxième partie, §1.]

stands for a white ball and *b* for a black one. The reader can, if he chooses, verify the table for himself.

wwww.

| wwwb. | wwbw. | wbww. | bwww. | | |
| wwwb. | wwbw. | wbww. | bwww. | | |

wwbb.	wbwb.	bwwb.	wbbw.	bwbw.	bbww.
wwbb.	wbwb.	bwwb.	wbbw.	bwbw.	bbww.
wwbb.	wbwb.	bwwb.	wbbw.	bwbw.	bbww.
wwbb.	wbwb.	bwwb.	wbbw.	bwbw.	bbww.

wbbb.	bwbb.	bbwb.	bbbw.
wbbb.	bwbb.	bbwb.	bbbw.
wbbb.	bwbb.	bbwb.	bbbw.
wbbb.	bwbb.	bbwb.	bbbw.
wbbb.	bwbb.	bbwb.	bbbw.
wbbb.	bwbb.	bbwb.	bbbw.
wbbb.	bwbb.	bbwb.	bbbw.
wbbb.	bwbb.	bbwb.	bbbw.

bbbb.
bbbb.
bbbb.
bbbb.
bbbb.
bbbb.
bbbb.
bbbb.
bbbb.
bbbb.
bbbb.
bbbb.
bbbb.
bbbb.
bbbb.
bbbb.

In the second group, where there is one b, there are two sets just alike; in the third there are 4, in the fourth 8, and in the fifth 16, doubling every time. This is because we have supposed twice as many black balls in the granary as white ones; had we supposed 10 times as many, instead of

$$1, \quad 2, \quad 4, \quad 8, \quad 16$$

sets we should have had

$$1, \quad 10, \quad 100, \quad 1000, \quad 10000$$

sets; on the other hand, had the numbers of black and white balls in the granary been even, there would have been but one set of each group. Now suppose two balls were drawn from one of these urns and were found to be both white, what would be the probability of the next one being white? If the two drawn out were the first two put into the urns, and the next to be drawn out were the third put in, then the probability of this third being white would be the same whatever the colors of the first two, for it has been supposed that just the same proportion of urns has the third ball white among those which have the first two *white-white, white-black, black-white,* and *black-black.* Thus, in the case, the chance of the third ball being white would be the same whatever the first two were. But, by inspecting the table, the reader can see that in each group all orders of the balls occur with equal frequency, so that it makes no difference whether they are drawn out in the order they were put in or not. Hence the colors of the balls already drawn have no influence on the probability of any other being white or black.

Now, if there be any way of enumerating the possibilities of Nature so as to make them equally probable, it is clearly one which should make one arrangement or combination of the elements of Nature as probable as another, that is, a distribution like that we have supposed, and it, therefore, appears that the assumption that any such thing can be done, leads simply to the conclusion that reasoning from past to future experience is absolutely worthless. In fact, the moment that you assume that the chances in favor of that of which we are totally ignorant are even, the problem about the tides does not differ, in any arithmetical particular, from the case in which a penny (known to be equally likely to come up heads or tails) should turn up heads m times successively. In short, it would be to assume that Nature is a pure chaos, or chance combination of independent elements, in which reasoning from one fact to another would be impossible; and since, as we shall hereafter see, there is no judgment of pure observation without reasoning, it would be to suppose all human cognition illusory and no real knowledge possible. It would be to suppose that if we have found the order of Nature more or less regular in the past, this has been by a pure run of luck which we may expect is now at an end. Now, it may be we have no scintilla of proof to the contrary, but reason is unnecessary in reference to that belief which is of all the most settled, which nobody doubts or can doubt, and which he who should deny would stultify himself in so doing.

The relative probability of this or that arrangement of Nature is something which we should have a right to talk about if universes were as plenty as blackberries, if we could put a quantity of them in a bag, shake them well up, draw out a sample, and examine them to see what proportion of them had one arrangement and what proportion another. But, even in that case, a higher universe would contain us, in regard to whose arrangements the conception of probability could have no applicability.

IV [ON THE PROBABILITY OF SYNTHETIC INFERENCES]

We have examined the problem proposed by the conceptualists, which, translated into clear language, is this: Given a synthetic conclusion; required to know out of all possible states of things how many will accord, to any assigned extent, with this conclusion; and we have found that it is only an absurd attempt to reduce synthetic to analytic reason, and that no definite solution is possible.

But there is another problem in connection with this subject. It is this: Given a certain state of things, required to know what proportion of all synthetic inferences relating to it will be true within a given degree of approximation. Now, there is no difficulty about this problem (except for its mathematical complication); it has been much studied, and the answer is perfectly well known. And is not this, after all, what we want to know much rather than the other? Why should we want to know the probability that the fact will accord with our conclusion? That implies that we are interested in all possible worlds, and not merely the one in which we find ourselves placed. Why is it not much more to the purpose to know the probability that our conclusion will accord with the fact? One of these questions is the first above stated and the other the second, and I ask the reader whether, if people, instead of using the word probability without any clear apprehension of their own meaning, had always spoken of relative frequency, they could have failed to see that what they wanted was not to follow along the synthetic procedure with an analytic one, in order to find the probability of the conclusion; but, on the contrary, to begin with the fact at which the synthetic inference aims, and follow back to the facts it uses for premises in order to see the probability of their being such as will yield the truth.

As we cannot have an urn with an infinite number of balls to represent the inexhaustibleness of Nature, let us suppose one with a finite number, each ball being thrown back into the urn after being drawn out, so that there is no exhaustion of them. Suppose one ball out of three is white and the rest black, and that four balls are drawn. Then the table in III represents the relative frequency of the different ways in which these balls might be drawn. It will be seen that if we should judge by these four balls of the proportion in the urn, 32 times out of 81 we should find it ¼, and 24 times out of 81 we should find it ½, the truth being ⅓. To extend this table to high numbers would be great labor, but the mathematicians have found some ingenious ways of reckoning what the numbers would be. It is found that, if the true proportion of white balls is p, and s balls are drawn, then the error of the proportion obtained by the induction will be—

half the time within $\qquad 0.477\sqrt{\dfrac{2p(1-p)}{s}}$

9 times out of 10 within $\qquad 1.163\sqrt{\dfrac{2p(1-p)}{s}}$

99 times out of 100 within $\qquad 1.821\sqrt{\dfrac{2p(1-p)}{s}}$

999 times out of 1,000 within $\qquad 2.328\sqrt{\dfrac{2p(1-p)}{s}}$

9,999 times out of 10,000 within $\qquad 2.751\sqrt{\dfrac{2p(1-p)}{s}}$

9,999,999,999 times out of 10,000,000,000 within $\qquad 4.77\sqrt{\dfrac{2p(1-p)}{s}}$

The use of this may be illustrated by an example. By the census of 1870, it appears that the proportion of males among native white children under one year old was 0.5082, while among colored children of the same age the proportion was only 0.4977. The difference between these is 0.0105, or about one in 100. Can this be attributed to chance, or would the difference always exist among a great number of white and colored children under like circumstances? Here p may be taken at ½; hence $2p(1-p)$ is also ½. The number of white children counted was near 1,000,000; hence the fraction whose square root is to be taken is about ½₀₀₀₀₀₀. The root is about ¼₄₀₀, and this multiplied by 0.477 gives about 0.0003 as the probable error in the ratio of males among the whites as obtained from the induction. The number of black children was about 150,000, which gives 0.0008 for the probable error. We see that the actual discrepancy is ten times the sum of these, and such a result would happen, according to our table, only once out of 10,000,000,000 censuses, in the long run.

It may be remarked that when the real value of the probability sought inductively is either very large or very small, the reasoning is more secure. Thus, suppose there were in reality one white ball in 100 in a certain urn, and we were to judge of the number by 100 drawings. The probability of drawing no white ball would be ³⁶⁶⁄₁₀₀₀; that of drawing one white ball would be ³⁷⁰⁄₁₀₀₀; that of drawing two would be ¹⁸⁵⁄₁₀₀₀; that of drawing three would be ⁶¹⁄₁₀₀₀; that of drawing four would be ¹⁵⁄₁₀₀₀; that of drawing five would be only ³⁄₁₀₀₀, etc. Thus we should be tolerably certain of not being in error by more than one ball in 100.

It appears, then, that in one sense we can, and in another we cannot, determine the probability of synthetic inference. When I reason in this way:

> Ninety-nine Cretans in a hundred are liars,
> But Epimenides is a Cretan;
> Therefore, Epimenides is a liar;

I know that reasoning similar to that would carry truth 99 times in 100. But when I reason in the opposite direction:

> Minos, Sarpedon, Rhadamanthus, Deucalion, and Epimenides, are all the Cretans I can think of,
> But these were all atrocious liars;
> Therefore, pretty much all Cretans must have been liars;

I do not in the least know how often such reasoning would carry me right. On the other hand, what I do know is that some definite proportion of Cretans must have been liars, and that this proportion can be probably approximated to by an induction from five or six instances. Even in the worst case for the probability of such an inference, that in which about half the Cretans are liars, the ratio so obtained would probably not be in error by more than ⅙. So much I know; but, then, in the present case the inference is that pretty much all Cretans are liars, and whether there may not be a special improbability in that I do not know.

V [THE RATIONALE OF SYNTHETIC INFERENCE]

Late in the last century, Immanuel Kant asked the question, "How are synthetical judgments *a priori* possible?" By synthetical judgments he meant such as assert positive fact and are not mere affairs of arrangement; in short, judgments of the kind which synthetical reasoning produces, and which analytic reasoning cannot yield. By *a priori* judgments he meant such as that all outward objects are in space, every event has a cause, etc., propositions which according to him can never be inferred from experience. Not so much by his answer to this question as by the mere asking of it, the current philosophy of that time was shattered and destroyed, and a new epoch in its history was begun. But before asking *that* question he ought to have asked the more general one, "How are any synthetical judgments at all possible?" How is it that a man can observe one fact and straightway pronounce judgment concerning another different fact not involved in the first? Such reasoning, as we have seen, has, at least in the usual sense of the phrase, no definite probability; how, then, can it add to our knowledge? This is a strange paradox; the Abbé Gratry says it is a miracle, and that every true induction is an immediate inspiration from on high.[1] I respect this explanation far more than many a pedantic attempt to solve the question by some juggle with probabilities, with the forms of syllogism, or what not. I respect it because it shows an appreciation of the depth of the problem, because it assigns an adequate cause, and because it is intimately connected—as the true account should be—with a general philosophy of the universe. At the same time, I do not accept this explanation, because an explanation should tell *how* a thing is done, and to assert a perpetual miracle seems to be an abandonment of all hope of doing that, without sufficient justification.

It will be interesting to see how the answer which Kant gave to his question about synthetical judgments *a priori* will appear if extended to the question of synthetical judgments in general. That answer is, that synthetical judgments *a priori* are possible because whatever is universally true is involved in the conditions of experience. Let us apply this to a general synthetical reasoning. I take from a bag a handful of beans; they are all purple, and I infer that all the beans in the bag are purple. How can I do that? Why, upon the principle that whatever is universally true of my experience (which is here the appearance of these different beans) is involved in the condition of experience. The condition of this special experience is that all these beans were taken from that bag. According to Kant's principle, then, whatever is found true of all the beans drawn from the bag must find its explanation in some

---

[1] *Logique.* The same is true, according to him, of every performance of a differentiation, but not of integration. He does not tell us whether it is the supernatural assistance which makes the former process so much the easier.

peculiarity of the contents of the bag. This is a satisfactory statement of the principle of induction.

When we draw a deductive or analytic conclusion, our rule of inference is that facts of a certain general character are either invariably or in a certain proportion of cases accompanied by facts of another general character. Then our premiss being a fact of the former class, we infer with certainty or with the appropriate degree of probability the existence of a fact of the second class. But the rule for synthetic inference is of a different kind. When we sample a bag of beans we do not in the least assume that the fact of some beans being purple involves the necessity or even the probability of other beans being so. On the contrary, the conceptualistic method of treating probabilities, which really amounts simply to the deductive treatment of them, when rightly carried out leads to the result that a synthetic inference has just an even chance in its favor, or in other words is absolutely worthless. The color of one bean is entirely independent of that of another. But synthetic inference is founded upon a classification of facts, not according to their characters, but according to the manner of obtaining them. Its rule is, that a number of facts obtained in a given way will in general more or less resemble other facts obtained in the same way; or, *experiences whose conditions are the same will have the same general characters.*

In the former case, we know that premisses precisely similar in form to those of the given ones will yield true conclusions, just once in a calculable number of times. In the latter case, we only know that premisses obtained under circumstances similar to the given ones (though perhaps themselves very different) will yield true conclusions, at least once in a calculable number of times. We may express this by saying that in the case of analytic inference we know the probability of our conclusion (if the premisses are true), but in the case of synthetic inferences we only know the degree of trustworthiness of our proceeding. As all knowledge comes from synthetic inference, we must equally infer that all human certainty consists merely in our knowing that the processes by which our knowledge has been derived are such as must generally have led to true conclusions.

Though a synthetic inference cannot by any means be reduced to deduction, yet that the rule of induction will hold good in the long run may be deduced from the principle that reality is only the object of the final opinion to which sufficient investigation would lead. That belief gradually tends to fix itself under the influence of inquiry is, indeed, one of the facts with which logic sets out.

THE ORDER OF NATURE [1]

I [THE SIGNIFICANCE OF ORDER]

Any proposition whatever concerning the order of Nature must touch more or less upon religion. In our day, belief, even in these matters, depends more and more upon the observation of facts. If a remarkable and universal orderliness be found in the universe, there must be some cause for this regularity, and science has to consider what hypotheses might account for the phenomenon. One way of accounting for it, certainly, would be to suppose that the world is ordered by a superior power. But if there is nothing in the universal subjection of phenomena to laws, nor in the character of those laws themselves (as being benevolent, beautiful, economical, etc.), which goes to prove the existence of a governor of the universe, it is hardly to be anticipated that any other sort of evidence will be found to weigh very much with minds emancipated from the tyranny of tradition.

Nevertheless, it cannot truly be said that even an absolutely negative decision of that question could altogether destroy religion, inasmuch as there are faiths in which, however much they differ from our own, we recognize those essential characters which make them worthy to be called religions, and which, nevertheless, do not postulate an actually existing Deity. That one, for instance, which has had the most numerous and by no means the least intelligent following of any on earth, teaches that the Divinity in his highest perfection is wrapped away from the world in a state of profound and eternal sleep, which really does not differ from non-existence, whether it be called by that name or not. No candid mind who has followed

[1] [*Popular Science Monthly*, XIII (1878), 203-217. (In *C.P.*, VI, 283-301.)]

the writings of M. Vacherot can well deny that his religion is as earnest as can be. He worships the Perfect, the Supreme Ideal; but he conceives that the very notion of the Ideal is repugnant to its real existence.[2] In fact, M. Vacherot finds it agreeable to his reason to assert that nonexistence is an essential character of the perfect, just as St. Anselm and Descartes found it agreeable to theirs to assert the extreme opposite. I confess that there is one respect in which either of these positions seems to me more congruous with the religious attitude than that of a theology which stands upon evidences; for as soon as the Deity presents himself to either Anselm or Vacherot, and manifests his glorious attributes, whether it be in a vision of the night or day, either of them recognizes his adorable God, and sinks upon his knees at once; whereas the theologian of evidences will first demand that the divine apparition shall identify himself, and only after having scrutinized his credentials and weighed the probabilities of his being found among the totality of existences will he finally render his circumspect homage, thinking that no characters can be adorable but those which belong to a real thing.

If we could find out any general characteristic of the universe, any mannerism in the ways of Nature, any law everywhere applicable and universally valid, such a discovery would be of such singular assistance to us in all our future reasoning that it would deserve a place almost at the head of the principles of logic. On the other hand, if it can be shown that there is nothing of the sort to find out, but that every discoverable regularity is of limited range, this again will be of logical importance. What sort of a conception we ought to have of the universe, how to think of the *ensemble* of things, is a fundamental problem in the theory of reasoning.

2 [Cf. *La Religion* (1869), Bk. II, Ch. 5.]

II [UNIFORMITIES]

It is the legitimate endeavor of scientific men now, as it was twenty-three hundred years ago, to account for the formation of the solar system and of the cluster of stars which forms the galaxy, by the fortuitous concourse of atoms. The greatest expounder of this theory, when asked how he could write an immense book on the system of the world without one mention of its author, replied, very logically, "Je n'avais pas besoin de cette hypothèse-là." But, in truth, there is nothing atheistical in the theory, any more than there was in this answer. Matter is supposed to be composed of molecules which obey the laws of mechanics and exert certain attractions upon one another; and it is to these regularities (which there is no attempt to account for) that general arrangement of the solar system would be due, and not to hazard.

If anyone has ever maintained that the universe is a pure throw of the dice, the theologians have abundantly refuted him. "How often," says Archbishop Tillotson, "might a man, after he had jumbled a set of letters in a bag, fling them out upon the ground before they would fall into an exact poem, yea, or so much as make a good discourse in prose! And may not a little book be as easily made by chance as this great volume of the world?" [1] The chance-world, here shown to be so different from that in which we live, would be one in which there were no laws, the characters of different things being entirely independent; so that, should a sample of any kind of objects ever show a prevalent character, it could only be by accident, and no general proposition could ever be established. Whatever further conclusions we may come to in regard to the order of the universe, this much may be regarded as solidly established, that the world is not a mere chance-medley.

But whether the world makes an exact poem or not, is another question. When we look up at the heavens at night,

[1] [*Works* (London, 1820), I, 346.]

we readily perceive that the stars are not simply splashed onto the celestial vault; but there does not seem to be any precise system in their arrangement either. It will be worth our while, then, to inquire into the degree of orderliness in the universe; and, to begin, let us ask whether the world we live in is any more orderly than a purely chance-world would be.

Any uniformity, or law of Nature, may be stated in the form, "Every A is B"; as, every ray of light is a noncurved line, every body is accelerated toward the earth's center, etc. This is the same as to say, "There does not exist any A which is not B"; there is no curved ray; there is no body not accelerated toward the earth; so that the uniformity consists in the non-occurrence in Nature of a certain combination of characters (in this case, the combination of being A with being non-B).[2] And, conversely, every case of the non-occurrence of a combination of characters would constitute a uniformity in Nature. Thus, suppose the quality A is never found in combination with the quality C: for example, suppose the quality of idiocy is never found in combination with that of having a well-developed brain. Then nothing of the sort A is of the sort C, or everything of the sort A is of the sort non-C (or say, every idiot has an ill-developed brain), which, being something universally true of the A's, is a uniformity in the world. Thus we see that, in a world where there were no uniformities, no logically possible combination of characters would be excluded, but every combination would exist in some object. But two objects not identical must differ in some of their characters, though it be only in the character of being in such and such a place. Hence, precisely the same combination of characters could not be found in two different objects; and, consequently, in a chance-world every combination involving either the positive or negative of every character would belong to just one thing. Thus, if there were but five

2 For the present purpose, the negative of a character is to be considered as much a character as the positive, for a uniformity may either be affirmative or negative. I do not say that no distinction can be drawn between positive and negative uniformities.

simple characters in such a world,[3] we might denote them by A, B, C, D, E, and their negatives by a, b, c, d, e; and then, as there would be 2^5 or 32 different combinations of these characters, completely determinate in reference to each of them, that world would have just 32 objects in it, their characters being as in the following table:

TABLE I

ABCDE	AbCDE	aBCDE	abCDE
ABCDe	AbCDe	aBCDe	abCDe
ABCdE	AbCdE	aBCdE	abCdE
ABCde	AbCde	aBCde	abCde
ABcDE	AbcDE	aBcDE	abcDE
ABcDe	AbcDe	aBcDe	abcDe
ABcdE	AbcdE	aBcdE	abcdE
ABcde	Abcde	aBcde	abcde

For example, if the five primary characters were *hard, sweet, fragrant, green, bright,* there would be one object which reunited all these qualities, one which was hard, sweet, fragrant, and green, but not bright; one which was hard, sweet, fragrant, and bright, but not green; one which was hard, sweet, and fragrant, but neither green nor bright; and so on through all the combinations.

This is what a thoroughly chance-world would be like, and certainly nothing could be imagined more systematic. When a quantity of letters are poured out of a bag, the appearance of disorder is due to the circumstance that the phenomena are only partly fortuitous. The laws of space are supposed, in that case, to be rigidly preserved, and there is also a certain amount of regularity in the formation of the letters. The result is that some elements are orderly and some are disorderly, which is precisely what we observe in the actual world. Tillotson, in the passage of which a part has been quoted, goes on to ask, "How long might 20,000 blind men which should be

---

[3] There being 5 simple characters, with their negatives, they could be compounded in various ways so as to make 241 characters in all, without counting the characters *existence* and *non-existence*, which make up 243 or 3^5.

sent out from the several remote parts of England, wander up
and down before they would all meet upon Salisbury Plains,
and fall into rank and file in the exact order of an army? And
yet this is much more easy to be imagined than how the innumerable blind parts of matter should rendezvous themselves into a world." [4] This is very true, but in the actual
world the *blind men* are, as far as we can see, *not* drawn up
in any particular order at all. And, in short, while a certain
amount of order exists in the world, it would seem that the
world is not so orderly as it might be, and, for instance, not
so much so as a world of pure chance would be.

But we can never get to the bottom of this question until
we take account of a highly-important logical principle [5] which
I now proceed to enounce. This principle is that any plural-
ity or lot of objects whatever have some character in common
(no matter how insignificant) which is peculiar to them and
not shared by anything else. The word "character" here is
taken in such a sense as to include negative characters, such
as incivility, inequality, etc., as well as their positives, civility,
equality, etc. To prove the theorem, I will show what character any two things, A and B, have in common, not shared
by anything else. The things, A and B, are each distinguished
from all other things by the possession of certain characters
which may be named A-ness and B-ness. Corresponding to
these positive characters are the negative characters un-A-
ness, which is possessed by everything except A, and un-B-ness,
which is possessed by everything except B. These two characters are united in everything except A and B; and this
union of the characters un-A-ness and un-B-ness makes a compound character which may be termed A-B-lessness. This is
not possessed by either A or B, but it is possessed by everything else. This character, like every other, has its corresponding negative un-A-B-lessness, and this last is the character pos-

4 [*Op. cit.*, p. 347.]

5 This principle was, I believe, first stated by Mr. De Morgan. [See his
"On the Syllogism," No. V, etc. *Transactions of the Cambridge Philosophical Society*, X (1864), 456, 467; *Formal Logic* (London, 1847), p. 39.]

sessed by both *A* and *B,* and by nothing else. It is obvious that what has thus been shown true of two things is *mutatis mutandis,* true of any number of things. Q. E. D.

In any world whatever, then, there must be a character peculiar to each possible group of objects. If, as a matter of nomenclature, characters peculiar to the same group be regarded as only different aspects of the same character, then we may say that there will be precisely one character for each possible group of objects. Thus, suppose a world to contain five things, a, β, γ, δ, ϵ. Then it will have a separate character for each of the 31 groups (with *non-existence* making up 32 or 2^5) shown in the following table:

TABLE II

	$a\beta$	$a\beta\gamma$	$a\beta\gamma\delta$	$a\beta\gamma\delta\epsilon$
a	$a\gamma$	$a\beta\delta$	$a\beta\gamma\epsilon$	
β	$a\delta$	$a\beta\epsilon$	$a\beta\delta\epsilon$	
γ	$a\epsilon$	$a\gamma\delta$	$a\gamma\delta\epsilon$	
δ	$\beta\gamma$	$a\gamma\epsilon$	$\beta\gamma\delta\epsilon$	
ϵ	$\beta\delta$	$a\delta\epsilon$		
	$\beta\epsilon$	$\beta\gamma\delta$		
	$\gamma\delta$	$\beta\gamma\epsilon$		
	$\gamma\epsilon$	$\beta\delta\epsilon$		
	$\delta\epsilon$	$\gamma\delta\epsilon$		

This shows that a contradiction is involved in the very idea of a chance-world, for in a world of 32 things, instead of there being only 3^5 or 243 characters, as we have seen that the notion of a chance-world requires, there would, in fact, be no less than 2^{32}, or 4,294,967,296 characters, which would not be all independent, but would have all possible relations with one another.

We further see that so long as we regard characters abstractly, without regard to their relative importance, etc., there is no possibility of a more or less degree of orderliness in the world, the whole system of relationship between the different characters being given by mere logic; that is, being implied in those facts which are tacitly admitted as soon as we admit that there is any such thing as reasoning.

In order to descend from this abstract point of view, it is requisite to consider the characters of things as relative to the perceptions and active powers of living beings. Instead, then, of attempting to imagine a world in which there should be no uniformities, let us suppose one in which none of the uniformities should have reference to characters interesting or important to us. In the first place, there would be nothing to puzzle us in such a world. The small number of qualities which would directly meet the senses would be the ones which would afford the key to everything which could possibly interest us. The whole universe would have such an air of system and perfect regularity that there would be nothing to ask. In the next place, no action of ours, and no event of Nature, would have important consequences in such a world. We should be perfectly free from all responsibility, and there would be nothing to do but to enjoy or suffer whatever happened to come along. Thus there would be nothing to stimulate or develop either the mind or the will, and we consequently should neither act nor think. We should have no memory, because that depends on a law of our organization. Even if we had any senses, we should be situated toward such a world precisely as inanimate objects are toward the present one, provided we suppose that these objects have an absolutely transitory and instantaneous consciousness without memory—a supposition which is a mere mode of speech, for that would be no consciousness at all. We may, therefore, say that a world of chance is simply our actual world viewed from the standpoint of an animal at the very vanishing-point of intelligence. The actual world is almost a chance-medley to the mind of a polyp. The interest which the uniformities of Nature have for an animal measures his place in the scale of intelligence.

Thus, nothing can be made out from the orderliness of Nature in regard to the existence of a God, unless it be maintained that the existence of a finite mind proves the existence of an infinite one.

III [INDUCTION]

In the last of these papers we examined the nature of inductive or synthetic reasoning. We found it to be a process of sampling. A number of specimens of a class are taken, not by selection within that class, but at random. These specimens will agree in a great number of respects. If, now, it were likely that a second lot would agree with the first in the majority of these respects, we might base on this consideration an inference in regard to any one of these characters. But such an inference would neither be of the nature of induction, nor would it (except in special cases) be valid, because the vast majority of points of agreement in the first sample drawn would generally be entirely accidental, as well as insignificant. To illustrate this, I take the ages at death of the first five poets given in Wheeler's *Biographical Dictionary*. They are:

> Aagard, 48.
> Abeille, 70.
> Abulola, 84.
> Abunowas, 48.
> Accords, 45.

These five ages have the following characters in common:

1. The difference of the two digits composing the number, divided by three, leaves a remainder of *one*.
2. The first digit raised to the power indicated by the second, and divided by three, leaves a remainder of *one*.
3. The sum of the prime factors of each age, including one, is divisible by three.

It is easy to see that the number of accidental agreements of this sort would be quite endless. But suppose that, instead of considering a character because of its prevalence in the sample, we designate a character before taking the sample, selecting it for its importance, obviousness, or other point of interest. Then two considerable samples drawn at random are extremely likely to agree approximately in regard to the proportion of occurrences of a character so chosen. *The inference that a previously designated character has nearly the same frequency of occurrence in the whole of a class that it has in a sample drawn at random out of that class is induction.* If the character be not previously designated, then a sample in which it is found to be prevalent can only serve to suggest that it *may be* prevalent in the whole class. We may consider this surmise as an inference if we please—an inference of possibility; but a second sample must be drawn to test the question of whether the character actually is prevalent. Instead of designating beforehand a single character in reference to which we will examine a sample, we may designate two, and use the same sample to determine the relative frequencies of both. This will be making two inductive inferences at once; and, of course, we are less certain that both will yield correct conclusions than we should be that either separately would do so. What is true of two characters is true of any limited number. Now, the number of characters which have any considerable interest for us in reference to any class of objects is more moderate than might be supposed. As we shall be sure to examine any sample with reference to these characters, they may be regarded not exactly as predesignated, but as predetermined (which amounts to the same thing); and we may infer that the sample represents the class in all these respects if we please, remembering only that this is not so secure an inference as if the particular quality to be looked for had been fixed upon beforehand.

The demonstration of this theory of induction rests upon principles and follows methods which are accepted by all those who display in other matters the particular knowledge and force of mind which qualify them to judge of this. The theory itself, however, quite unaccountably seems never to have occurred to any of the writers who have undertaken to explain synthetic reasoning. The most widely-spread opinion in the matter is one which was much promoted by Mr. John

Stuart Mill [1]—namely, that induction depends for its validity upon the uniformity of Nature—that is, on the principle that what happens once will, under a sufficient degree of similarity of circumstances, happen again as often as the same circumstances recur. The application is this: The fact that different things belong to the same class constitutes the similarity of circumstances, and the induction is good, provided this similarity is "sufficient." What happens once is, that a number of these things are found to have a certain character; what may be expected, then, to happen again as often as the circumstances recur consists in this, that all things belonging to the same class should have the same character.

This analysis of induction has, I venture to think, various imperfections, to some of which it may be useful to call attention. In the first place, when I put my hand in a bag and draw out a handful of beans, and, finding three-quarters of them black, infer that about three-quarters of all in the bag are black, my inference is obviously of the same kind as if I had found any larger proportion, or the whole, of the sample black, and had assumed that it represented in that respect the rest of the contents of the bag. But the analysis in question hardly seems adapted to the explanation of this *proportionate* induction, where the conclusion, instead of being that a certain event uniformly happens under certain circumstances, is precisely that it does not uniformly occur, but only happens in a certain proportion of cases. It is true that the whole sample may be regarded as a single object, and the inference may be brought under the formula proposed by considering the conclusion to be that any similar sample will show a similar proportion among its constituents. But this is to treat the induction as if it rested on a single instance, which gives a very false idea of its probability.

In the second place, if the uniformity of Nature were the sole warrant of induction, we should have no right to draw one in regard to a character whose constancy we knew noth-

1 [*A System of Logic*, Bk. III, Ch. 3, §1.]

ing about. Accordingly, Mr. Mill says [2] that, though none but white swans were known to Europeans for thousands of years, yet the inference that all swans were white was "not a good induction," because it was not known that color was a usual generic character (it, in fact, not being so by any means). But it is mathematically demonstrable that an inductive inference may have as high a degree of probability as you please independent of any antecedent knowledge of the constancy of the character inferred. Before it was known that color is not usually a character of genera, there was certainly a considerable probability that all swans were white. But the further study of the genera of animals led to the induction of their non-uniformity in regard to color. A deductive application of this general proposition would have gone far to overcome the probability of the universal whiteness of swans before the black species was discovered. When we do know anything in regard to the general constancy or inconstancy of a character, the application of that general knowledge to the particular class to which any induction relates, though it serves to increase or diminish the force of the induction, is, like every application of general knowledge to particular cases, deductive in its nature and not inductive.

In the third place, to say that inductions are true because similar events happen in similar circumstances—or, what is the same thing, because objects similar in some respects are likely to be similar in others—is to overlook those conditions which really are essential to the validity of inductions. When we take all the characters into account, any pair of objects resemble one another in just as many particulars as any other pair. If we limit ourselves to such characters as have for us any importance, interest, or obviousness, then a synthetic conclusion may be drawn, but only on condition that the specimens by which we judge have been taken at random from the class in regard to which we are to form a judgment, and not selected as belonging to any sub-class. The induction only has its full force when the character concerned has been desig-

2 [*Ibid.*, Bk. III, Ch. 3, §3.]

nated before examining the sample. These are the essentials of induction, and they are not recognized in attributing the validity of induction to the uniformity of Nature. The explanation of induction by the doctrine of probabilities, given in the last of these papers, is not a mere metaphysical formula, but is one from which all the rules of synthetic reasoning can be deduced systematically and with mathematical cogency. But the account of the matter by a principle of Nature, even if it were in other respects satisfactory, presents the fatal disadvantage of leaving us quite as much afloat as before in regard to the proper method of induction. It does not surprise me, therefore, that those who adopt this theory have given erroneous rules for the conduct of reasoning, nor that the greater number of examples put forward by Mr. Mill in his first edition, as models of what inductions should be, proved in the light of further scientific progress so particularly unfortunate that they had to be replaced by others in later editions. One would have supposed that Mr. Mill might have based an induction on *this* circumstance, especially as it is his avowed principle that, if the conclusion of an induction turns out false, it cannot have been a good induction. Nevertheless, neither he nor any of his scholars seem to have been led to suspect, in the least, the perfect solidity of the framework which he devised for securely supporting the mind in its passage from the known to the unknown, although at its first trial it did not answer quite so well as had been expected.

IV [MIND AND NATURE]

When we have drawn any statistical induction—such, for instance, as that one-half of all births are of male children—it is always possible to discover, by investigation sufficiently prolonged, a class of which the same predicate may be affirmed universally; to find out, for instance, *what sort of* births are of male children. The truth of this principle follows immediately from the theorem that there is a character peculiar to every possible group of objects. The form in which the principle is usually stated is, that *every event must have a cause.*

But, though there exists a cause for every event, and that of a kind which is capable of being discovered, yet if there be nothing to guide us to the discovery; if we have to hunt among all the events in the world without any scent; if, for instance, the sex of a child might equally be supposed to depend on the configuration of the planets, on what was going on at the antipodes, or on anything else—then the discovery would have no chance of ever getting made.

That we ever do discover the precise causes of things, that any induction whatever is absolutely without exception, is what we have no right to assume. On the contrary, it is an easy corollary, from the theorem just referred to, that every empirical rule has an exception. But there are certain of our inductions which present an approach to universality so extraordinary that, even if we are to suppose that they are not strictly universal truths, we cannot possibly think that they have been reached merely by accident. The most remarkable laws of this kind are those of *time* and *space.* With reference to space, Bishop Berkeley first showed, in a very conclusive manner, that it was not a thing *seen,* but a thing *inferred.*[1] Berkeley chiefly insists on the impossibility of directly seeing the third dimension of space, since the retina of the eye is a surface. But, in point of fact, the retina is not even a surface; it is a conglomeration of nerve-needles directed toward the light and having only their extreme points sensitive, these points lying at considerable distances from one another compared with their areas. Now, of these points, certainly the excitation of no one singly can produce the perception of a surface, and consequently not the aggregate of all the sensations can amount to this. But certain relations subsist between the excitations of different nerve-points, and these constitute the premises upon which the hypothesis of space is founded, and from which it is inferred. That space is not immediately perceived is now universally admitted; and a mediate cognition

[1] [*A New Theory of Vision*, Sections 2 and 3.]

is what is called an inference, and is subject to the criticism of logic. But what are we to say to the fact of every chicken as soon as it is hatched solving a problem whose data are of a complexity sufficient to try the greatest mathematical powers? It would be insane to deny that the tendency to light upon the conception of space is inborn in the mind of the chicken and of every animal. The same thing is equally true of time. That time is not directly perceived is evident, since no lapse of time is present, and we only perceive what is present. That, not having the idea of time, we should never be able to perceive the flow of our sensations without some particular aptitude for it, will probably also be admitted. The idea of force —at least, in its rudiments—is another conception so early arrived at, and found in animals so low in the scale of intelligence, that it must be supposed innate. But the innateness of an idea admits of degree, for it consists in the tendency of that idea to present itself to the mind. Some ideas, like that of space, do so present themselves irresistibly at the very dawn of intelligence, and take possession of the mind on small provocation, while of other conceptions we are prepossessed, indeed, but not so strongly, down a scale which is greatly extended. The tendency to personify every thing, and to attribute human characters to it, may be said to be innate; but it is a tendency which is very soon overcome by civilized man in regard to the greater part of the objects about him. Take such a conception as that of gravitation varying inversely as the square of the distance. It is a very simple law. But to say that it is simple is merely to say that it is one which the mind is particularly adapted to apprehend with facility. Suppose the idea of a quantity multiplied into another had been no more easy to the mind than that of a quantity raised to the power indicated by itself—should we ever have discovered the law of the solar system?

It seems incontestable, therefore, that the mind of man is strongly adapted to the comprehension of the world; at least, so far as this goes, that certain conceptions, highly important for such a comprehension, naturally arise in his mind; and, without such a tendency, the mind could never have had any development at all.

How are we to explain this adaptation? The great utility and indispensableness of the conceptions of time, space, and force, even to the lowest intelligence, are such as to suggest that they are the results of natural selection. Without something like geometrical, kinetical, and mechanical conceptions, no animal could seize his food or do anything which might be necessary for the preservation of the species. He might, it is true, be provided with an instinct which would generally have the same effect; that is to say, he might have conceptions different from those of time, space, and force, but which coincided with them in regard to the ordinary cases of the animal's experience. But, as that animal would have an immense advantage in the struggle for life whose mechanical conceptions did not break down in a novel situation (such as development must bring about), there would be a constant selection in favor of more and more correct ideas of these matters. Thus would be attained the knowledge of that fundamental law upon which all science rolls; namely, that forces depend upon relations of time, space, and mass. When this idea was once sufficiently clear, it would require no more than a comprehensible degree of genius to discover the exact nature of these relations. Such an hypothesis naturally suggests itself, but it must be admitted that it does not seem sufficient to account for the extraordinary accuracy with which these conceptions apply to the phenomena of Nature, and it is probable that there is some secret here which remains to be discovered.

V [DESIGN]

Some important questions of logic depend upon whether we are to consider the material universe as of limited extent and finite age, or quite boundless in space and in time. In the former case, it is conceivable that a general plan or design embracing the whole universe should be discovered, and it would be proper to be on the alert for some traces of such a unity. In the latter case, since the proportion of the world of which we can have any experience is less than the smallest assignable fraction, it follows that we never could discover any *pattern* in the universe except a repeating one; any design embracing the whole would be beyond our powers to discern, and beyond the united powers of all intellects during all time. Now, what is absolutely incapable of being known is, as we have seen in a former paper, not real at all. An absolutely incognizable existence is a nonsensical phrase. If, therefore, the universe is infinite, the attempt to find in it any design embracing it as a whole is futile, and involves a false way of looking at the subject. If the universe never had any beginning, and if in space world stretches beyond world without limit, there is no *whole* of material things, and consequently no general character to the universe, and no need or possibility of any governor for it. But if there was a time before which absolutely no matter existed, if there are certain absolute bounds to the region of things outside of which there is a mere void, then we naturally seek for an explanation of it, and, since we cannot look for it among material things, the hypothesis of a great disembodied animal, the creator and governor of the world, is natural enough.

The actual state of the evidence as to the limitation of the universe is as follows: As to time, we find on our earth a constant progress of development since the planet was a red-hot ball; the solar system seems to have resulted from the condensation of a nebula, and the process appears to be still going on. We sometimes see stars (presumably with systems of worlds) destroyed and apparently resolved back into the nebulous condition, but we have no evidence of any existence of the world previous to the nebulous stage from which it seems to have been evolved. All this rather favors the idea of a beginning than otherwise. As for limits in space, we cannot be sure that we see anything outside of the system of the Milky Way. Minds of theological predilections have therefore no need of distorting the facts to reconcile them with their views.

But the only scientific presumption is, that the unknown parts of space and time are like the known parts, occupied; that, as we see cycles of life and death in all development which we can trace out to the end, the same holds good in regard to solar systems; that as enormous distances lie between the different planets of our solar system, relatively to their diameters, and as still more enormous distances lie between our system relatively to its diameter and other systems, so it may be supposed that other galactic clusters exist so remote from ours as not to be recognized as such with certainty. I do not say that these are strong inductions; I only say that they are the presumptions which, in our ignorance of the facts, should be preferred to hypotheses which involve conceptions of things and occurrences totally different in their character from any of which we have had any experience, such as disembodied spirits, the creation of matter, infringements of the laws of mechanics, etc.

The universe ought to be presumed too vast to have any character. When it is claimed that the arrangements of Nature are benevolent, or just, or wise, or of any other peculiar kind, we ought to be prejudiced against such opinions, as being the offspring of an ill-founded notion of the finitude of the world. And examination has hitherto shown that such beneficences, justice, etc., are of a most limited kind—limited in degree and limited in range.

In like manner, if anyone claims to have discovered a plan in the structure of organized beings, or a scheme in their classification, or a regular arrangement among natural objects, or a system of proportionality in the human form, or an order of development, or a correspondence between conjunctions of the planets and human events, or a significance in numbers, or a key to dreams, the first thing we have to ask is whether such relations are susceptible of explanation on mechanical principles, and if not they should be looked upon with disfavor as having already a strong presumption against them; and examination has generally exploded all such theories.

There are minds to whom every prejudice, every presumption, seems unfair. It is easy to say what minds these are. They are those who never have known what it is to draw a well-grounded induction, and who imagine that other people's knowledge is as nebulous as their own. That all science rolls upon presumption (not of a formal but of a real kind) is no argument with them, because they cannot imagine that there is anything solid in human knowledge. These are the people who waste their time and money upon perpetual motions and other such rubbish.

But there are better minds who take up mystical theories (by which I mean all those which have no possibility of being mechanically explained). These are persons who are strongly prejudiced in favor of such theories. We all have natural tendencies to believe in such things; our education often strengthens this tendency; and the result is, that to many minds nothing seems so antecedently probable as a theory of this kind. Such persons find evidence enough in favor of their views, and in the absence of any recognized logic of induction they cannot be driven from their belief.

But to the mind of a physicist there ought to be a strong presumption against every mystical theory; and therefore it seems to me that those scientific men who have sought to make out that science was not hostile to theology have not been so clear-sighted as their opponents.

It would be extravagant to say that science can at present disprove religion; but it does seem to me that the spirit of science is hostile to any religion except such a one as that of M. Vacherot. Our appointed teachers inform us that Buddhism is a miserable and atheistical faith, shorn of the most glorious and needful attributes of a religion; that its priests can be of no use to agriculture by praying for rain, nor to war by commanding the sun to stand still. We also hear the remonstrances of those who warn us that to shake the general belief in the living God would be to shake the general morals, public and private. This, too, must be admitted; such a revolution of thought could no more be accomplished without waste and desolation than a plantation of trees could be transferred to new ground, however wholesome in itself, without all of them languishing for a time, and many of them dying. Nor is it, by the way, a thing to be presumed that a man would have taken part in a movement having a possible atheistical issue without having taken serious and adequate counsel in regard to that responsibility. But, let the consequences of such a belief be as dire as they may, one thing is certain: that the state of the facts, whatever it may be, will surely get found out, and no human prudence can long arrest the triumphal car of truth—no, not if the discovery were such as to drive every individual of our race to suicide!

But it would be folly to suppose that any metaphysical theory in regard to the mode of being of the perfect is to destroy that aspiration toward the perfect which constitutes the essence of religion. It is true that, if the priests of any particular form of religion succeed in making it generally believed that religion cannot exist without the acceptance of certain formulas, or if they succeed in so interweaving certain dogmas with the popular religion that the people can see no essential analogy between a religion which accepts these points of faith and one which rejects them, the result may very well be to render those who cannot believe these things irreligious. Nor can we ever hope that any body of priests should consider themselves more teachers of religion in general than of the particular system of theology advocated by their own party. But no man need be excluded from participation in the common feelings, nor from so much of the public expression of them as is open to all the laity, by the unphilosophical narrowness of those who guard the mysteries of worship. Am I to be prevented from joining in that common joy at the revelation of enlightened principles of religion which we celebrate at Easter and Christmas because I think that certain scientific, logical, and metaphysical ideas which have been mixed up with these principles are untenable? No; to do so would be to estimate those errors as of more consequence than the truth—an opinion which few would admit. People who do not believe what are really the fundamental principles of Christianity are rare to find, and all but these few ought to feel at home in the churches.

DEDUCTION, INDUCTION, AND HYPOTHESIS [1]

I [RULE, CASE, AND RESULT]

The chief business of the logician is to classify arguments; for all testing clearly depends on classification. The classes of the logicians are defined by certain typical forms called syllogisms. For example, the syllogism called *Barbara* is as follows:

S is M, M is P;
Hence, S is P.

Or, to put words for letters—

Enoch and Elijah were men, all men die;
Hence, Enoch and Elijah must have died.

The "is P" of the logicians stands for any verb, active or neuter. It is capable of strict proof (with which, however, I will not trouble the reader) that all arguments whatever can be put into this form; but only under the condition that the *is* shall mean "*is* for the purposes of the argument" or "is represented by." Thus, an induction will appear in this form something like this:

These beans are two-thirds white,
But, the beans in this bag are (represented by) these beans;
∴ The beans in the bag are two-thirds white.

But, because all inference may be reduced in some way to *Barbara,* it does not follow that this is the most appropriate form in which to represent every kind of inference. On the

[1] [*Popular Science Monthly*, XIII (1878), 470-82; intended as Essay XIII of the "Search for a Method" (1893). (In *C.P.*, II, 372-388.)]

contrary, to show the distinctive characters of different sorts of inference, they must clearly be exhibited in different forms peculiar to each. *Barbara* particularly typifies deductive reasoning; and so long as the *is* is taken literally, no inductive reasoning can be put into this form. *Barbara* is, in fact, nothing but the application of a rule. The so-called major premiss lays down this rule; as, for example, *All men are mortal.* The other or minor premiss states a case under the rule; as, *Enoch was a man.* The conclusion applies the rule to the case and states the result: *Enoch is mortal.* All deduction is of this character; it is merely the application of general rules to particular cases. Sometimes this is not very evident, as in the following:

> All quadrangles are figures,
> But no triangle is a quadrangle;
> Therefore, some figures are not triangles.

But here the reasoning is really this:

Rule.—Every quadrangle is other than a triangle.
Case.—Some figures are quadrangles.
Result.—Some figures are not triangles.

Inductive or synthetic reasoning, being something more than the mere application of a general rule to a particular case, can never be reduced to this form.

If, from a bag of beans of which we know that ⅔ are white, we take one at random, it is a deductive inference that this bean is probably white, the probability being ⅔. We have, in effect, the following syllogism:

Rule.—The beans in this bag are ⅔ white.
Case.—This bean has been drawn in such a way that in the long run the relative number of white beans so drawn would be equal to the relative number in the bag.
Result.—This bean has been drawn in such a way that in the long run it would turn out white ⅔ of the time.

If instead of drawing one bean we draw a handful at random and conclude that about ⅔ of the handful are probably white, the reasoning is of the same sort. If, however, not knowing what proportion of white beans there are in the bag, we draw a handful at random and, finding ⅔ of the beans in the handful white, conclude that about ⅔ of those in the bag are white, we are rowing up the current of deductive sequence, and are concluding a rule from the observation of a result in a certain case. This is particularly clear when all the handful turn out one color. The induction then is:

These beans were in this bag. ————————————

These beans are white. ——————————————

∴ All the beans in the bag were white. ——————

Which is but an inversion of the deductive
    syllogism:

    Rule.—All the beans in the bag were white. ——

    Case.—These beans were in the bag. ————

    Result.—These beans are white. ——————

So that induction is the inference of the *rule* from the *case* and *result*.

But this is not the only way of inverting a deductive syllogism so as to produce a synthetic inference. Suppose I enter a room and there find a number of bags, containing different kinds of beans. On the table there is a handful of white beans; and, after some searching, I find one of the bags contains white beans only. I at once infer as a probability, or as a fair guess, that this handful was taken out of that bag. This sort of inference is called *making an hypothesis*. It is the inference of a *case* from a *rule* and a *result*. We have, then—

DEDUCTION.

    Rule.—All the beans from this bag are white.

    Case.—These beans are from this bag.

∴ *Result.*—These beans are white.

INDUCTION.

Case.—These beans are from this bag.
Result.—These beans are white.
∴*Rule.*—All the beans from this bag are white.

HYPOTHESIS.

Rule.—All the beans from this bag are white.
Result.—These beans are white.
∴*Case.*—These beans are from this bag.

We, accordingly, classify all inference as follows:

Inference.

Deductive or Analytic.   Synthetic.

Induction.   Hypothesis.

Induction is where we generalize from a number of cases of which something is true, and infer that the same thing is true of a whole class. Or, where we find a certain thing to be true of a certain proportion of cases and infer that it is true of the same proportion of the whole class. Hypothesis is where we find some very curious circumstance, which would be explained by the supposition that it was a case of a certain general rule, and thereupon adopt that supposition. Or, where we find that in certain respects two objects have a strong resemblance, and infer that they resemble one another strongly in other respects.

I once landed at a seaport in a Turkish province; and, as I was walking up to the house which I was to visit, I met a man upon horseback, surrounded by four horsemen holding a canopy over his head. As the governor of the province was the only personage I could think of who would be so greatly honored, I inferred that this was he. This was an hypothesis.

Fossils are found; say, remains like those of fishes, but far in the interior of the country. To explain the phenomenon, we suppose the sea once washed over this land. This is another hypothesis.

Numberless documents and monuments refer to a conqueror called Napoleon Bonaparte. Though we have not seen the man, yet we cannot explain what we have seen, namely, all these documents and monuments, without supposing that he really existed. Hypothesis again.

As a general rule, hypothesis is a weak kind of argument. It often inclines our judgment so slightly toward its conclusion that we cannot say that we believe the latter to be true; we only surmise that it may be so. But there is no difference except one of degree between such an inference and that by which we are led to believe that we remember the occurrences of yesterday from our feeling as if we did so.

II [BAROCO AND BOCARDO; HYPOTHESIS AND INDUCTION]

Besides the way just pointed out of inverting a deductive syllogism to produce an induction or hypothesis, there is another. If from the truth of a certain premiss the truth of a certain conclusion would necessarily follow, then from the falsity of the conclusion the falsity of the premiss would follow. Thus, take the following syllogism in *Barbara:*

> *Rule.*—All men are mortal,
> *Case.*—Enoch and Elijah were men;
> ∴*Result.*—Enoch and Elijah were mortal.

Now, a person who denies this result may admit the rule, and, in that case, he must deny the case. Thus:

> *Denial of Result.*—Enoch and Elijah were not mortal,
> *Rule.*—All men are mortal;
> ∴*Denial of Case.*—Enoch and Elijah were not men.

This kind of syllogism is called *Baroco,* which is the typical mood of the second figure. On the other hand, the person who denies the result may admit the case, and in that case he must deny the rule. Thus:

Denial of the Result.—Enoch and Elijah were not
  mortal,
Case.—Enoch and Elijah were men;
∴*Denial of the Rule.*—Some men are not mortal.

This kind of syllogism is called *Bocardo,* which is the typical
mood of the third figure.

Baroco and *Bocardo* are, of course, deductive syllogisms;
but of a very peculiar kind. They are called by logicians indirect moods, because they need some transformation to appear as the application of a rule to a particular case. But if,
instead of setting out as we have here done with a necessary
deduction in *Barbara,* we take a probable deduction of similar
form, the indirect moods which we shall obtain will be—

Corresponding to *Baroco,* an hypothesis;
and, Corresponding to *Bocardo,* an induction.

For example, let us begin with this probable deduction in
Barbara:

Rule.—Most of the beans in this bag are white,
Case.—This handful of beans are from this bag;
∴*Result.*—Probably, most of this handful of beans are
  white.

Now, deny the result, but accept the rule:

Denial of Result.—Few beans of this handful are white,
Rule.—Most beans in this bag are white;
∴*Denial of Case.*—Probably, these beans were taken from
  another bag.

This is an hypothetical inference. Next, deny the result, but
accept the case:

Denial of Result.—Few beans of this handful are white.
Case.—These beans came from this bag.
∴*Denial of Rule.*—Probably, few beans in the bag are
  white.

This is an induction.

The relation thus exhibited between synthetic and deductive reasoning is not without its importance. When we adopt a certain hypothesis, it is not alone because it will explain the observed facts, but also because the contrary hypothesis would probably lead to results contrary to those observed. So, when we make an induction, it is drawn not only because it explains the distribution of characters in the sample, but also because a different rule would probably have led to the sample being other than it is.

But the advantage of this way of considering the subject might easily be overrated. An induction is really the inference of a rule, and to consider it as the denial of a rule is an artificial conception, only admissible because, when statistical or proportional propositions are considered as rules, the denial of a rule is itself a rule. So, an hypothesis is really a subsumption of a case under a class and not the denial of it, except for this, that to deny a subsumption under one class is to admit a subsumption under another.

Bocardo may be considered as an induction, so timid as to lose its amplifiative character entirely. Enoch and Elijah are specimens of a certain kind of men. All that kind of men are shown by these instances to be immortal. But instead of boldly concluding that all very pious men, or all men favorites of the Almighty, etc., are immortal, we refrain from specifying the description of men, and rest in the merely explicative inference that *some* men are immortal. So *Baroco* might be considered as a very timid hypothesis. Enoch and Elijah are not mortal. Now, we might boldly suppose them to be gods or something of that sort, but instead of that we limit ourselves to the inference that they are of *some* nature different from that of man.

But, after all, there is an immense difference between the relation of *Baroco* and *Bocardo* to *Barbara* and that of Induction and Hypothesis to Deduction. *Baroco* and *Bocardo* are based upon the fact that if the truth of a conclusion necessarily follows from the truth of a premiss, then the falsity of the premiss follows from the falsity of the conclusion. This is always true. It is different when the inference is only probable. It by no means follows that, because the truth of a certain premiss would render the truth of a conclusion probable, therefore the falsity of the conclusion renders the falsity of the premiss probable. At least, this is only true, as we have seen in a former paper, when the word "probable" is used in one sense in the antecedent and in another in the consequent.

III   [RULES FOR INDUCTION AND HYPOTHESES]

A certain anonymous writing is upon a torn piece of paper. It is suspected that the author is a certain person. His desk, to which only he has had access, is searched, and in it is found a piece of paper, the torn edge of which exactly fits, in all its irregularities, that of the paper in question. It is a fair hypothetic inference that the suspected man was actually the author. The ground of this inference evidently is that two torn pieces of paper are extremely unlikely to fit together by accident. Therefore, of a great number of inferences of this sort, but a very small proportion would be deceptive. The analogy of hypothesis with induction is so strong that some logicians have confounded them. Hypothesis has been called an induction of characters. A number of characters belonging to a certain class are found in a certain object; whence it is inferred that all the characters of that class belong to the object in question. This certainly involves the same principle as induction; yet in a modified form. In the first place, characters are not susceptible of simple enumeration like objects; in the next place, characters run in categories. When we make an hypothesis like that about the piece of paper, we only examine a single line of characters, or perhaps two or three, and we take no specimen at all of others. If the hypothesis were nothing but an induction, all that we should be justified in concluding, in the example above, would be that the two pieces of paper which matched in such irregularities as have been examined would be found to match in other, say slighter, irregularities. The inference from the shape of the paper to its ownership is precisely what distinguishes hypothesis from induction, and makes it a bolder and more perilous step.

The same warnings that have been given against imagining that induction rests upon the uniformity of Nature might be repeated in regard to hypothesis. Here, as there, such a theory not only utterly fails to account for the validity of the inference, but it also gives rise to methods of conducting it which are absolutely vicious. There are, no doubt, certain uniformities in Nature, the knowledge of which will fortify an hypothesis very much. For example, we suppose that iron, titanium, and other metals exist in the sun, because we find in the solar spectrum many lines coincident in position with those which these metals would produce; and this hypothesis is greatly strengthened by our knowledge of the remarkable distinctiveness of the particular line of characters observed. But such a fortification of hypothesis is of a deductive kind, and hypothesis may still be probable when such reinforcement is wanting.

There is no greater nor more frequent mistake in practical logic than to suppose that things which resemble one another strongly in some respects are any the more likely for that to be alike in others. That this is absolutely false, admits of rigid demonstration; but, inasmuch as the reasoning is somewhat severe and complicated (requiring, like all such reasoning, the use of A, B, C, etc., to set it forth), the reader would probably find it distasteful, and I omit it. An example, however, may illustrate the proposition: The comparative mythologists occupy themselves with finding points of resemblance between solar phenomena and the careers of the heroes of all sorts of traditional stories; and upon the basis of such resemblances they infer that these heroes are impersonations of the sun. If there be anything more in their reasonings, it has never been made clear to me. An ingenious logician, to show how futile all that is, wrote a little book, in which he pretended to prove, in the same manner, that Napoleon Bonaparte is only an impersonation of the sun. It was really wonderful to see how many points of resemblance he made out. The truth is, that any two things resemble one another just as strongly as any two others, if recondite resemblances are admitted. But, in order that the process of making an hypothesis should lead to a probable result, the following rules must be followed:

1. The hypothesis should be distinctly put as a question, before making the observations which are to test its truth. In other words, we must try to see what the result of predictions from the hypothesis will be.

2. The respect in regard to which the resemblances are noted must be taken at random. We must not take a particular kind of predictions for which the hypothesis is known to be good.

3. The failures as well as the successes of the predictions must be honestly noted. The whole proceeding must be fair and unbiased.

Some persons fancy that bias and counter-bias are favorable to the extraction of truth—that hot and partisan debate is the way to investigate. This is the theory of our atrocious legal procedure. But Logic puts its heel upon this suggestion. It irrefragably demonstrates that knowledge can only be furthered by the real desire for it, and that the methods of obstinacy, of authority, and every mode of trying to reach a foregone conclusion, are absolutely of no value. These things are proved. The reader is at liberty to think so or not as long as the proof is not set forth, or as long as he refrains from examining it. Just so, he can preserve, if he likes, his freedom of opinion in regard to the propositions of geometry; only, in that case, if he takes a fancy to read Euclid, he will do well to skip whatever he finds with A, B, C, etc., for, if he reads attentively that disagreeable matter, the freedom of his opinion about geometry may unhappily be lost forever.

How many people there are who are incapable of putting to their own consciences this question, "Do I want to know how the fact stands, or not?"

The rules which have thus far been laid down for induction and hypothesis are such as are absolutely essential. There are many other maxims expressing particular contrivances for making synthetic inferences strong, which are extremely valuable and should not be neglected. Such are, for example, Mr. Mill's four methods. Nevertheless, in the total neglect of these, inductions and hypotheses may and sometimes do attain the greatest force.

IV   [EMPIRICAL FORMULAE AND THEORIES]

Classifications in all cases perfectly satisfactory hardly exist. Even in regard to the great distinction between explicative and ampliative inferences, examples could be found which seem to lie upon the border between the two classes, and to partake in some respects of the characters of either. The same thing is true of the distinction between induction and hypothesis. In the main, it is broad and decided. By induction, we conclude that facts, similar to observed facts, are true in cases not examined. By hypothesis, we conclude the existence of a fact quite different from anything observed, from which, according to known laws, something observed would necessarily result. The former is reasoning from particulars to the general law; the latter, from effect to cause. The former classifies, the latter explains. It is only in some special cases that there can be more than a momentary doubt to which category a given inference belongs. One exception is where we observe, not facts similar under similar circumstances, but facts different under different circumstances—the difference of the former having, however, a definite relation to the difference of the latter. Such inferences, which are really inductions, sometimes present, nevertheless, some indubitable resemblances to hypotheses.

Knowing that water expands by heat, we make a number of observations of the volume of a constant mass of water at different temperatures. The scrutiny of a few of these suggests a form of algebraical formula which will approximately express

the relation of the volume to the temperature. It may be, for
instance, that v being the relative volume, and t the temperature, a few observations examined indicate a relation of the
form—

$$v = 1 + at + bt^2 + ct^3.$$

Upon examining observations at other temperatures taken at
random, this idea is confirmed; and we draw the inductive
conclusion that all observations within the limits of temperature from which we have drawn our observations could
equally be so satisfied. Having once ascertained that such a
formula is possible, it is a mere affair of arithmetic to find the
values of a, b, and c, which will make the formula satisfy the
observations best. This is what physicists call an *empirical
formula*, because it rests upon mere induction, and is not explained by any hypothesis.

Such formulae, though very useful as means of describing
in general terms the results of observations, do not take any
high rank among scientific discoveries. The induction which
they embody, that expansion by heat (or whatever other phenomenon is referred to) takes place in a perfectly gradual
manner without sudden leaps or innumerable fluctuations, although really important, attracts no attention, because it is
what we naturally anticipate. But the defects of such expressions are very serious. In the first place, as long as the observations are subject to error, as all observations are, the formula
cannot be expected to satisfy the observations exactly. But the
discrepancies cannot be due solely to the errors of the observations, but must be partly owing to the error of the formula
which has been deduced from erroneous observations. Moreover, we have no right to suppose that the real facts, if they
could be had free from error, could be expressed by such a
formula at all. They might, perhaps, be expressed by a similar formula with an infinite number of terms; but of what use
would that be to us, since it would require an infinite number of coefficients to be written down? When one quantity
varies with another, if the corresponding values are exactly

known, it is a mere matter of mathematical ingenuity to find some way of expressing their relation in a simple manner. If one quantity is of one kind—say, a specific gravity—and the other of another kind—say, a temperature—we do not desire to find an expression for their relation which is wholly free from numerical constants, since if it were free from them when, say, specific gravity as compared with water, and temperature as expressed by the Centigrade thermometer, were in question, numbers would have to be introduced when the scales of measurement were changed. We may, however, and do desire to find formulae expressing the relations of physical phenomena which shall contain no more arbitrary numbers than changes in the scales of measurement might require.

When a formula of this kind is discovered, it is no longer called an empirical formula, but a law of Nature; and is sooner or later made the basis of an hypothesis which is to explain it. These simple formulae are not usually, if ever, exactly true, but they are none the less important for that; and the great triumph of the hypothesis comes when it explains not only the formula, but also the deviations from the formula. In the current language of the physicists, an hypothesis of this importance is called a theory, while the term hypothesis is restricted to suggestions which have little evidence in their favor. There is some justice in the contempt which clings to the word hypothesis. To think that we can strike out of our own minds a true preconception of how Nature acts, is a vain fancy. As Lord Bacon well says: "The subtlety of Nature far exceeds the subtlety of sense and intellect: so that these fine meditations, and speculations, and reasonings of men are a sort of insanity, only there is no one at hand to remark it." [1] The successful theories are not pure guesses, but are guided by reasons.

The kinetical theory of gases is a good example of this. This theory is intended to explain certain simple formulae, the chief of which is called the law of Boyle. It is, that if air or any other gas be placed in a cylinder with a piston, and if

[1] [*Novum Organum*, Bk. I, Aphorism X.]

its volume be measured under the pressure of the atmosphere, say fifteen pounds on the square inch, and if then another fifteen pounds per square inch be placed on the piston, the gas will be compressed to one-half its bulk, and in similar inverse ratio for other pressures. The hypothesis which has been adopted to account for this law is that the molecules of a gas are small, solid particles at great distances from each other (relatively to their dimensions), and moving with great velocity, without sensible attractions or repulsions, until they happen to approach one another very closely. Admit this, and it follows that when a gas is under pressure what prevents it from collapsing is not the incompressibility of the separate molecules, which are under no pressure at all, since they do not touch, but the pounding of the molecules against the piston. The more the piston falls, and the more the gas is compressed, the nearer together the molecules will be; the greater number there will be at any moment within a given distance of the piston, the shorter the distance which any one will go before its course is changed by the influence of another, the greater number of new courses of each in a given time, and the oftener each, within a given distance of the piston, will strike it. This explains Boyle's law. The law is not exact; but the hypothesis does not lead us to it exactly. For, in the first place, if the molecules are large, they will strike each other oftener when their mean distances are diminished, and will consequently strike the piston oftener, and will produce more pressure upon it. On the other hand, if the molecules have an attraction for one another, they will remain for a sensible time within one another's influence, and consequently they will not strike the wall so often as they otherwise would, and the pressure will be less increased by compression.

When the kinetical theory of gases was first proposed by Daniel Bernoulli,[2] in 1738, it rested only on the law of Boyle, and was therefore pure hypothesis. It was accordingly quite naturally and deservedly neglected. But, at present, the theory presents quite another aspect; for, not to speak of the con-

[2] [In his *Hydrodynamica*.]

siderable number of observed facts of different kinds with which it has been brought into relation, it is supported by the mechanical theory of heat. That bringing together bodies which attract one another, or separating bodies which repel one another, when sensible motion is not produced or destroyed, is always accompanied by the evolution of heat, is little more than an induction. Now, it has been shown by experiment that, when a gas is allowed to expand without doing work, a very small amount of heat disappears. This proves that the particles of the gas attract one another slightly, and but very slightly. It follows that, when a gas is under pressure, what prevents it from collapsing is not any repulsion between the particles, since there is none. Now, there are only two modes of force known to us, force of position or attractions and repulsions, and force of motion. Since, therefore, it is not the force of position which gives a gas its expansive force, it must be the force of motion. In this point of view, the kinetical theory of gases appears as a deduction from the mechanical theory of heat. It is to be observed, however, that it supposes the same law of mechanics (that there are only those two modes of force) which holds in regard to bodies such as we can see and examine, to hold also for what are very different, the molecules of bodies. Such a supposition has but a slender support from induction. Our belief in it is greatly strengthened by its connection with the law of Boyle, and it is, therefore, to be considered as an hypothetical inference. Yet it must be admitted that the kinetical theory of gases would deserve little credence if it had not been connected with the principles of mechanics.

The great difference between induction and hypothesis is, that the former infers the existence of phenomena such as we have observed in cases which are similar, while hypothesis supposes something of a different kind from what we have directly observed, and frequently something which it would be impossible for us to observe directly. Accordingly, when we stretch an induction quite beyond the limits of our observation, the inference partakes of the nature of hypothesis. It

would be absurd to say that we have no inductive warrant for
a generalization extending a little beyond the limits of experience, and there is no line to be drawn beyond which we cannot push our inference; only it becomes weaker the further it
is pushed. Yet, if an induction be pushed very far, we cannot
give it much credence unless we find that such an extension
explains some fact which we can and do observe. Here, then,
we have a kind of mixture of induction and hypothesis supporting one another; and of this kind are most of the theories
of physics.

V [ON THE DIFFERENCE BETWEEN INDUCTION AND HYPOTHESIS]

That synthetic inferences may be divided into induction
and hypothesis in the manner here proposed,[1] admits of no
question. The utility and value of the distinction are to be
tested by their applications.

Induction is, plainly, a much stronger kind of inference
than hypothesis; and this is the first reason for distinguishing
between them. Hypotheses are sometimes regarded as provisional resorts, which in the progress of science are to be replaced by inductions. But this is a false view of the subject.
Hypothetic reasoning infers very frequently a fact not capable
of direct observation. It is an hypothesis that Napoleon Bonaparte once existed. How is that hypothesis ever to be replaced
by an induction? It may be said that from the premiss that
such facts as we have observed are as they would be if Napoleon existed, we are to infer by induction that *all* facts that
are hereafter to be observed will be of the same character.
There is no doubt that every hypothetic inference may be
distorted into the appearance of an induction in this way. But
the essence of an induction is that it infers from one set of

[1] This division was first made in a course of lectures by the author before the Lowell Institute, Boston, in 1866, and was printed in the *Pro-
ceedings of the American Academy of Arts and Sciences,* for April 9, 1867.

facts another set of similar facts, whereas hypothesis infers from facts of one kind to facts of another. Now, the facts which serve as grounds for our belief in the historic reality of Napoleon are not by any means necessarily the only kind of facts which are explained by his existence. It may be that, at the time of his career, events were being recorded in some way not now dreamed of, that some ingenious creature on a neighboring planet was photographing the earth, and that these pictures on a sufficiently large scale may some time come into our possession, or that some mirror upon a distant star will, when the light reaches it, reflect the whole story back to earth. Never mind how improbable these suppositions are; everything which happens is infinitely improbable. I am not saying that *these* things are likely to occur, but that *some* effect of Napoleon's existence which now seems impossible is certain nevertheless to be brought about. The hypothesis asserts that such facts, when they do occur, will be of a nature to confirm, and not to refute, the existence of the man. We have, in the impossibility of inductively inferring hypothetical conclusions, a second reason for distinguishing between the two kinds of inference.

A third merit of the distinction is, that it is associated with an important psychological or rather physiological difference in the mode of apprehending facts. Induction infers a rule. Now, the belief of a rule is a habit. That a habit is a rule active in us is evident. That every belief is of the nature of a habit, in so far as it is of a general character, has been shown in the earlier papers of this series. Induction, therefore, is the logical formula which expresses the physiological process of formation of a habit. Hypothesis substitutes, for a complicated tangle of predicates attached to one subject, a single conception. Now, there is a peculiar sensation belonging to the act of thinking that each of these predicates inheres in the subject. In hypothetic inference this complicated feeling so produced is replaced by a single feeling of greater intensity, that belonging to the act of thinking the hypothetic conclusion. Now, when our nervous system is excited in a compli-

cated way, there being a relation between the elements of the
excitation, the result is a single harmonious disturbance which
I call an emotion. Thus, the various sounds made by the instruments of an orchestra strike upon the ear, and the result
is a peculiar musical emotion, quite distinct from the sounds
themselves. This emotion is essentially the same thing as an
hypothetic inference, and every hypothetic inference involves
the formation of such an emotion. We may say, therefore,
that hypothesis produces the *sensuous* element of thought,
and induction the *habitual* element. As for deduction, which
adds nothing to the premises, but only out of the various
facts represented in the premises selects one and brings the
attention down to it, this may be considered as the logical formula for paying attention, which is the *volitional* element of
thought, and corresponds to nervous discharge in the sphere
of physiology.

Another merit of the distinction between induction and
hypothesis is, that it leads to a very natural classification of
the sciences and of the minds which prosecute them. What
must separate different kinds of scientific men more than anything else are the differences of their *techniques*. We cannot
expect men who work with books chiefly to have much in
common with men whose lives are passed in laboratories. But,
after differences of this kind, the next most important are differences in the modes of reasoning. Of the natural sciences,
we have, first, the classificatory sciences, which are purely inductive—systematic botany and zoölogy, mineralogy, and chemistry. Then, we have the sciences of theory, as above explained
—astronomy, pure physics, etc. Then, we have sciences of hypothesis—geology, biology, etc.

There are many other advantages of the distinction in question which I shall leave the reader to find out by experience.
If he will only take the custom of considering whether a given
inference belongs to one or other of the two forms of synthetic inference given [p. 129], I can promise him that he will
find his advantage in it, in various ways.

✺ VII ✺

[THE SOCIAL THEORY OF LOGIC] [1]

The difficulty of showing how the law of deductive reasoning is true depends upon our inability to conceive of its not being true. In the case of probable reasoning the difficulty is of quite another kind; here, where we see precisely what the procedure is, we wonder how such a process can have any validity at all. How magical it is that by examining a part of a class we can know what is true of the whole of the class, and by study of the past can know the future; in short, that we can know what we have not experienced!

Is not this an intellectual intuition! Is it not that besides ordinary experience which is dependent on there being a certain physical connection between our organs and the thing experienced, there is a second avenue of truth dependent only on there being a certain intellectual connection between our previous knowledge and what we learn in that way? Yes, this is true. Man has this faculty, just as opium has a somnific virtue; but some further questions may be asked, nevertheless. How is the existence of this faculty accounted for? In one sense, no doubt, by natural selection. Since it is absolutely essential to the preservation of so delicate an organism as man's, no race which had it not has been able to sustain itself. This accounts for the prevalence of this faculty, provided it was only a possible one. But how can it be possible? What could enable the mind to know physical things which do not physically influence it and which it does not influence? The question cannot be answered by any statement concerning the

---

[1] [The concluding portion (§3) of "Grounds of Validity of the Laws of Logic: Further Consequences of Four Incapacities," originally published in *Journal of Speculative Philosophy*, II (1868), 193-208; with corrections of 1893. (In *C.P.*, V, 212-222.)]

144

human mind, for it is equivalent to asking what makes the facts usually to be, as inductive and hypothetic conclusions from true premises represent them to be? Facts of a certain kind are usually true when facts having certain relations to them are true; what is the cause of this? That is the question.

The usual reply is that nature is everywhere regular; as things have been, so they will be; as one part of nature is, so is every other. But this explanation will not do. Nature is not regular. No disorder would be less orderly than the existing arrangement. It is true that the special laws and regularities are innumerable; but nobody thinks of the irregularities, which are infinitely more frequent. Every fact true of any one thing in the universe is related to every fact true of every other. But the immense majority of these relations are fortuitous and irregular. A man in China bought a cow three days and five minutes after a Greenlander had sneezed. Is that abstract circumstance connected with any regularity whatever? And are not such relations infinitely more frequent than those which are regular? But if a very large number of qualities were to be distributed among a very large number of things in almost any way, there would chance to be some few regularities. If, for example, upon a checker-board of an enormous number of squares, painted all sorts of colors, myriads of dice were to be thrown, it could hardly fail to happen, that upon some color, or shade of color, out of so many, some one of the six numbers should not be uppermost on any die. This would be a regularity; for, the universal proposition would be true that upon that color that number is never turned up. But suppose this regularity abolished, then a far more remarkable regularity would be created, namely, that on every color every number is turned up. Either way, therefore, a regularity must occur. Indeed, a little reflection will show that, although we have here only variations of color and of the numbers of the dice, many regularities must occur. And the greater the number of objects, the more respects in which they vary, and the greater the number of varieties in each respect, the greater will be the number of regularities. Now, in the universe, all these numbers are infinite. Therefore, however disorderly the chaos, the *number* of regularities must be infinite. The orderliness of the universe, therefore, if it exists, must consist in the large *proportion* of relations which present a regularity to those which are quite irregular. But this proportion in the actual universe is, as we have seen, as small as it can be; and, therefore, the orderliness of the universe is as little as that of any arrangement whatever.

But even if there were such an orderliness in things, it never could be discovered. For it would belong to things either collectively or distributively. If it belonged to things collectively, that is to say, if things formed a system, the difficulty would be that a system can only be known by seeing some considerable proportion of the whole. Now we never can know how great a part of the whole of nature we have discovered. If the order were distributive, that is, belonged to all things only by belonging to each thing, the difficulty would be that a character can only be known by comparing something which has it [2] with something which has it not. *Being, quality, relation,* and other universals are not known except as characters of words or other signs, attributed by a figure of speech to things. Thus, in neither case could the order of things be known. But the order of things would not help the validity of our reasoning—that is, would not help us to reason correctly—unless we knew what the order of things required the relation between the known reason [reasoned—Ed.] *from* to the unknown reasoned *to*, to be.

But even if this order both existed and were known, the knowledge would be of no use except as a general principle, from which things could be deduced. It would not explain how knowledge could be increased (in contradistinction to being rendered more distinct), and so it would not explain how it could itself have been acquired.

Finally, if the validity of induction and hypothesis were dependent on a particular constitution of the universe, we could imagine a universe in which these modes of inference should

2 ["With" and "it" were originally transposed.]

be valid, just as we can imagine a universe in which there
ld be no attraction, but things should merely drift about.
rdingly, J. S. Mill, who explains the validity of induc-
by the uniformity of nature,[3] maintains that he can imagine a universe without any regularity, so that no probable
inference would be valid in it.[4] In the universe as it is, probable arguments sometimes fail, nor can any definite proportion of cases be stated in which they hold good; all that can
be said is that in the long run they prove approximately correct. Can a universe be imagined in which this would not be
the case? It must be a universe where probable argument can
have some application, in order that it may fail half the time.
It must, therefore, be a universe experienced. Of the finite
number of propositions true of a finite amount of experience
of such a universe, no one would be universal in form, unless
the subject of it were an individual. For if there were a plural
universal proposition, inferences by analogy from one particular to another would hold good invariably in reference to
that subject. So that these arguments might be no better than
guesses in reference to other parts of the universe, but they
would invariably hold good in a finite proportion of it, and
so would on the whole be somewhat better than guesses.
There could, also, be no individuals in that universe, for
there must be some general class—that is, there must be some
things more or less alike—or probable argument would find
no premises there; therefore, there must be two mutually ex-

3 *Logic*, Book 3, Chap. 3, sec. 1.

4 *Ibid*. Book 3, Chap. 21, sec. 1. "I am convinced that any one accustomed to abstraction and analysis, who will fairly exert his faculties for
the purpose, will, when his imagination has once learnt to entertain the
notion, find no difficulty in conceiving that in some one, for instance, of
the many firmaments into which sidereal astronomy divides the universe,
events may succeed one another at random, without any fixed law; nor
can anything in our experience or mental nature constitute a sufficient, or
indeed any, reason for believing that this is nowhere the case.

"Were we to suppose (what it is perfectly possible to imagine) that the
present order of the universe were brought to an end, and that a chaos
succeeded, in which there was no fixed succession of events, and the past
gave no assurance of the future," etc.

clusive classes, since every class has a residue outside of it; hence, if there were any individual, that individual would be wholly excluded from one or other of these classes. Hence, the universal plural proposition would be true, that no one of a certain class was that individual. Hence, no universal proposition would be true. Accordingly, every combination of characters would occur in such a universe. But this would not be disorder, but the simplest order; it would not be unintelligible, but, on the contrary, everything conceivable would be found in it with equal frequency. The notion, therefore, of a universe in which probable arguments should fail as often as hold true, is absurd. We can suppose it in general terms, but we cannot specify how it should be other than self-contradictory.[5]

Since we cannot conceive of probable inferences as not generally holding good, and since no special supposition will serve to explain their validity, many logicians have sought to base this validity on that of deduction, and that in a variety of ways. The only attempt of this sort, however, which deserves to be noticed is that which seeks to determine the probability of a future event by the theory of probabilities, from the fact that a certain number of similar events have been observed. Whether this can be done or not depends on the meaning assigned to the word probability. But if this word is to be taken in such a sense that a form of conclusion which is probable is valid; since the validity of an inference (or its correspondence with facts) consists solely in this, that when such premisses are true, such a conclusion is generally true, then probability can mean nothing but the ratio of the frequency of occurrence of a specific event to a general one over

[5] Boole (*Laws of Thought*, p. 370) has shown, in a very simple and elegant manner, that an *infinite* number of balls may have characters distributed in such a way, that from the characters of the balls already drawn, we could infer nothing in regard to that of the characters of the next one. The same is true of some arrangements of a finite number of balls, provided the inference takes place after a fixed number of drawings. But this does not invalidate the reasoning above, although it is an important fact without doubt.

it. In this sense of the term, it is plain that the probability of an inductive conclusion cannot be *deduced* from the premisses; for from the inductive premisses

$$S', S'', S''' \text{ are } M,$$
$$S', S'', S''' \text{ are } P,$$

nothing follows deductively, except that any M, which is S', or S'', or S''' is P; or, less explicitly, that some M is P.

Thus, we seem to be driven to this point. On the one hand, no determination of things, no *fact*, can result in the validity of probable arguments; nor, on the other hand, is such argument reducible to that form which holds good, however the facts may be. This seems very much like a reduction to absurdity of the validity of such reasoning; and a paradox of the greatest difficulty is presented for solution.

There can be no doubt of the importance of this problem. According to Kant, the central question of philosophy is "How are synthetical judgments *a priori* possible?" But antecedently to this comes the question how synthetical judgments in general, and still more generally, how synthetical reasoning is possible at all. When the answer to the general problem has been obtained, the particular one will be comparatively simple. This is the lock upon the door of philosophy.

All probable inference, whether induction or hypothesis, is inference from the parts to the whole. It is essentially the same, therefore, as statistical inference. Out of a bag of black and white beans I take a few handfuls, and from this sample I can judge approximately the proportions of black and white in the whole. This is identical with induction. Now we know upon what the validity of this inference depends. It depends upon the fact that in the long run, any one bean would be taken out as often as any other. For were this not so, the mean of a large number of results of such testings of the contents of the bag would not be precisely the ratio of the numbers of the two colors of beans in the bag. Now we may divide the question of the validity of induction into two parts: first, why of all inductions premisses for which occur, the generality should hold good, and second, why men are not fated always to light upon the small proportion of worthless inductions. Then, the first of these two questions is readily answered. For since all the members of any class are the same as all that are to be known; and since from any part of those which are to be known an induction is competent to the rest, in the long run any one member of a class will occur as the subject of a premiss of a possible induction as often as any other, and, therefore, the validity of induction depends simply upon the fact that the parts make up and constitute the whole. This in its turn depends simply upon there being such a state of things that any general terms are possible. But it has been shown that being at all is being in general. And thus this part of the validity of induction depends merely on there being any reality.

From this it appears that we cannot say that the generality of inductions are true, but only that in the long run they approximate to the truth. This is the truth of the statement, that the universality of an inference from induction is only the analogue of true universality. Hence, also, it cannot be said that we know an inductive conclusion to be true, however loosely we state it; we only know that by accepting inductive conclusions, in the long run our errors balance one another. In fact, insurance companies proceed upon induction—they do not know what will happen to this or that policyholder; they only know that they are secure in the long run.

The other question relative to the validity of induction, is why men are not fated always to light upon those inductions which are highly deceptive. The explanation of the former branch of the problem we have seen to be that there is something real. Now, since if there is anything real, then (on account of this reality consisting in the ultimate agreement of all men, and on account of the fact that reasoning from parts to whole is the only kind of synthetic reasoning which men possess) it follows necessarily that a sufficiently long succession of inferences from parts to whole will lead men to a knowledge of it, so that in that case they cannot be fated on the whole to be thoroughly unlucky in their inductions. This second branch of the problem is in fact equivalent to asking why there is anything real, and thus its solution will carry the solution of the former branch one step further.

The answer to this question may be put into a general and abstract, or a special detailed form. If men were not to be able to learn from induction, it must be because as a general rule, when they had made an induction, the order of things (as they appear in experience), would then undergo a revolution. Just herein would the unreality of such a universe consist; namely, that the order of the universe should depend on how much men should know of it. But this general rule would be capable of being itself discovered by induction; and so it must be a law of such a universe, that when this was discovered it would cease to operate. But this second law would itself be capable of discovery. And so in such a universe there would be nothing which would not sooner or later be known; and it would have an order capable of discovery by a sufficiently long course of reasoning. But this is contrary to the hypothesis, and therefore that hypothesis is absurd. This is the particular answer. But we may also say, in general, that if nothing real exists, then, since every question supposes that something exists—for it maintains its own urgency—it supposes only illusions to exist. But the existence even of an illusion is a reality; for an illusion affects all men, or it does not. In the former case, it is a reality according to our theory of reality; in the latter case, it is independent of the state of mind of any individuals except those whom it happens to affect. So that the answer to the question, Why is anything real? is this: That question means, "supposing anything to exist, why is something real?" The answer is, that that very existence is reality by definition.

All that has here been said, particularly of induction, applies to all inference from parts to whole, and therefore to hypothesis, and so to all probable inference.

Thus, I claim to have shown, in the first place, that it is

possible to hold a consistent theory of the validity of the laws of ordinary logic.

But now let us suppose the idealistic theory of reality, which I have in this paper taken for granted to be false. In that case, inductions would not be true unless the world were so constituted that every object should be presented in experience as often as any other; and further, unless we were so constituted that we had no more tendency to make bad inductions than good ones. These facts might be explained by the benevolence of the Creator; but, as has already been argued, they could not explain, but are absolutely refuted by the fact that no state of things can be conceived in which probable arguments should not lead to the truth. This affords a most important argument in favor of that theory of reality, and thus of those denials of certain faculties from which it was deduced, as well as of the general style of philosophizing by which those denials were reached.

Upon our theory of reality and of logic, it can be shown that no inference of any individual can be thoroughly logical without certain determinations of his mind which do not concern any one inference immediately; for we have seen that that mode of inference which alone can teach us anything, or carry us at all beyond what was implied in our premisses—in fact, does not give us to know any more than we knew before; only, we know that, by faithfully adhering to that mode of inference, we shall, on the whole, approximate to the truth. Each of us is an insurance company, in short. But, now, suppose that an insurance company, among its risks, should take one exceeding in amount the sum of all the others. Plainly, it would then have no security whatever. Now, has not every single man such a risk? What shall it profit a man if he shall gain the whole world and lose his own soul? If a man has a transcendent personal interest infinitely outweighing all others, then, upon the theory of validity of inference just developed, he is devoid of all security, and can make no valid inference whatever. What follows? That logic rigidly requires, before all else, that no determinate fact, nothing which can happen to a man's self, should be of more consequence to him than everything else. He who would not sacrifice his own soul to save the whole world, is illogical in all his inferences, collectively. So the social principle is rooted intrinsically in logic.

That being the case, it becomes interesting to inquire how it is with men as a matter of fact. There is a psychological theory that man cannot act without a view to his own pleasure. This theory is based on a falsely assumed subjectivism. Upon our principles of the objectivity of knowledge, it could not be based; and if they are correct, it is reduced to an absurdity. It seems to me that the usual opinion of the selfishness of man is based in large measure upon this false theory. I do not think that the facts bear out the usual opinion. The immense self-sacrifices which the most wilful men often make, show that wilfulness is a very different thing from selfishness. The care that men have for what is to happen after they are dead, cannot be selfish. And finally and chiefly, the constant use of the word *"we"*—as when we speak of our possessions on the Pacific—our destiny as a republic—in cases in which no personal interests at all are involved, show conclusively that men do not make their personal interests their only ones, and therefore may, at least, subordinate them to the interests of the community.

But just the revelation of the possibility of this complete self-sacrifice in man, and the belief in its saving power, will serve to redeem the logicality of all men. For he who recognizes the logical necessity of complete self-identification of one's own interests with those of the community, and its potential existence in man, even if he has it not himself, will perceive that only the inferences of that man who has it are logical, and so views his own inferences as being valid only so far as they would be accepted by that man. But so far as he has this belief, he becomes identified with that man. And that ideal perfection of knowledge by which we have seen that reality is constituted must thus belong to a community in which this identification is complete.

This would serve as a complete establishment of private

logicality, were it not that the assumption, that man or the community (which may be wider than man) shall ever arrive at a state of information greater than some definite finite information, is entirely unsupported by reasons. There cannot be a scintilla of evidence to show that at some time all living things shall not be annihilated at once, and that forever after there shall be throughout the universe any intelligence whatever. Indeed, this very assumption involves itself a transcendent and supreme interest, and therefore from its very nature is unsusceptible of any support from reasons. This infinite hope which we all have (for even the atheist will constantly betray his calm expectation that what is Best will come about) is something so august and momentous, that all reasoning in reference to it is a trifling impertinence. We do not want to know what are the weights of reasons *pro* and *con*—that is, how much *odds* we should wish to receive on such a venture in the long run—because there is no long run in the case; the question is single and supreme, and ALL is at stake upon it. We are in the condition of a man in a life and death struggle; if he have not sufficient strength, it is wholly indifferent to him how he acts, so that the only assumption upon which he can act rationally is the hope of success. So this sentiment is rigidly demanded by logic. If its object were any determinate fact, any private interest, it might conflict with the results of knowledge and so with itself; but when its object is of a nature as wide as the community can turn out to be, it is always a hypothesis uncontradicted by facts and justified by its indispensableness for making any action rational.

❦ VIII ❧

UNIFORMITY [1]

(1) A fact consisting in this: that, of a certain genus of facts, a proportion approaching unity (the whole) belongs, in the course of experience, to a certain species; so that, though of itself the knowledge of this uniformity gives no information concerning a certain thing or character, yet it will strengthen any inductive conclusion of a certain kind.

It is, therefore, a high objective probability concerning an objective probability. There are, in particular, four classes of uniformities, the knowledge of any of which, or of its falsity, may deductively strengthen or weaken an inductive conclusion. These four kinds of uniformity are as follows:

i. The members of a class may present an extraordinary resemblance to one another in regard to a certain line of characters. Thus, the Icelanders are said to resemble one another most strikingly in their opinions about general subjects. Knowing this, we should not need to question many Icelanders, if we found that the first few whom we met all shared a common superstition, in order to conclude with considerable confidence that nearly all Icelanders were of the same way of thinking. Philodemus [2] insists strongly upon this kind of uniformity as a support of induction.

ii. A character may be such that, in whatever genus it occurs at all, it almost always belongs to all the species of that genus; or this uniformity may be lacking. Thus, when only white swans were known, it would have been hazardous to assert that all swans were white, because whiteness is not usu-

---

[1] [*Baldwin's Dictionary of Philosophy and Psychology* (New York, 1902), II, 727-731. (In *C.P.*, VI, 75-85.)]

[2] [See Theodor Gomperz, *Herculanische Studien*, Pt. I (1865).]

155

ally a generic character. It is considerably more safe to assert that all crows are black, because blackness is oftener a generic character. This kind of uniformity is especially emphasized by J. S. Mill as important in inductive inquiries.[3]

iii. A certain set of characters may be intimately connected so as to be usually all present or all absent from certain kinds of objects. Thus, the different chemical reactions of gold are so inseparable that a chemist need only to succeed in getting, say, the purple of Cassius to be confident that the body under examination will show every reaction of gold.

iv. Of a certain object it may be known that its characteristic is that when it possesses one of a set of characters within a certain group of such sets, it possesses the rest. Thus, it may be known of a certain man that to whatever party he belongs, he is apt to embrace without reserve the entire creed of that party. We shall not, then, need to know many of his opinions, say in regard to politics, in order to infer with great confidence his position upon other political questions.

(2) The word "uniformity" plays such a singular and prominent rôle in the logic of J. S. Mill that it is proper to note it. He was apt to be greatly influenced by Ockham's razor in forming theories which he defended with great logical acumen; but he differed from other men of that way of thinking in that his natural candour led to his making many admissions without perceiving how fatal they were to his negative theories. In addition to that, perhaps more than other philosophers, in endeavouring to embrace several ideas under a common term, he often leaves us at a loss to find any other character common and peculiar to those notions except that of their having received from him that common designation. In one passage [4] of his *System of Logic* (1842), he declares, in reference to the difference in strength between two inductive conclusions, that whoever shall discover the cause of that difference will have discovered the secret of inductive reasoning.

3 [*System of Logic*, Bk. III, Ch. 4, §2.]
4 [*Op. cit.*, Bk. III, Ch. 3, §3.]

When, therefore, he shortly afterwards [5] points out that the distinction between those two inductions is that one of them is supported by a uniformity of the second of the above four classes, while the other is met by a distinct diversity of the same kind, and when he himself gives to that uniformity this designation when he afterwards declares that the validity of induction depends upon uniformity, his reader naturally supposes he means uniformity in that sense. But we find that he employs the word for quite another purpose. Namely, he does not like the word *law,* as applied to an inductive generalization of natural facts—such as the "law" of gravitation—because it implies an element in nature, the reality of a general, which no nominalist can admit. He, therefore, desires to call the reality to which a true universal proposition about natural phenomena corresponds a "uniformity." [6]

The implication of the word, thus used, is that the facts are, in themselves, entirely disconnected, and that it is the mind alone which unites them. One stone dropping to the earth has no real connection with another stone dropping to the earth. It is, surely, not difficult to see that this theory of uniformities, far from helping to establish the validity of induction, would be, if consistently admitted, an insuperable objection to such validity. For if two facts, *A* and *B,* are entirely independent in their real nature, then the truth of *B* cannot follow, either necessarily or probably, from the truth of *A.* If I have tried the experiment with a million stones and have found that every one of them fell when allowed to drop, it may be very natural for me to believe that almost any stone will act in the same way. But if it can be proved that there is no real connection between the behaviour of different stones, then there is nothing for it but to say that it was a chance coincidence that those million stones all behaved in the same way; for if there was any *reason* for it, and they *really* dropped, there was a *real reason,* that is, a real general. Now,

5 [*Ibid.*, Bk. III, Ch. 4, §2.]
6 [*Ibid.*, Bk. III, Ch. 4, §1.]

if it is mere chance that they all dropped, that affords no more reason for supposing that the next will drop than my throwing three double sixes successively with a pair of dice is a reason for thinking that the next throw will be double sixes.

(3) But now we find that Mill's good sense and candour will not allow him to take the course which a Hobbes would have taken, and utterly deny the validity of induction; and this leads to a new use of the word *uniformity,* in which he speaks of the "uniformity of nature." Before asking exactly what this phrase means, it may be noted that, whatever it means, the assertion of it is an assent to scholastic realism, except for a difference of emphasis. For to say that throughout the whole course of experience, events always, or even only usually, happen alike under the same conditions (what is usually called the "invariability" of nature) is to assert an agreement (complete or partial) which could not be ascribed to chance without self-contradiction. For chance is merely the possible discrepancy between the character of the limited experience to which it belongs and the whole course of experience. Hence, to say that of the *real,* objective facts some *general* character can be predicated, is to assert the reality of a general. It only differs from scholastic realism in that Mill and his followers treat this aspect of the matter lightly—that is to say, the objective reality of the general—while the Scholastics regarded it as a great and vital feature of the universe. Instead of "uniformity" now importing that what others call "laws" are fabrications of the human mind, this "uniformity of nature" is erected by Mill into the greatest of laws and absolutely objective and real.

Let us now inquire what the "uniformity of nature," with its synonymous expressions that "the future resembles the past," and so forth, can mean. Mill [7] says that it means that if all the circumstances attending two phenomena are the same, they will be alike. But taken strictly this means absolutely nothing, since no two phenomena ever can happen in circumstances precisely alike, nor are two phenomena pre-

[7] [*Ibid.,* Bk. III, Ch. 3, §1.]

cisely alike. It is, therefore, necessary to modify the statement in order to give it any meaning at all; and it will be found that, however it may be so modified, the moment it begins to carry a definite meaning, one of three things results: it becomes either, first, grossly false, or, second, an assertion which there is really no good reason to believe even approximately true, or, thirdly, it becomes a quasi-subjective truth, not lending any colour of validity to induction proper. If, for example, we were to say that, under any given species of circumstances presenting any similarity, phenomena of any given genus would be found to have a specific general resemblance in contrast with the specific character of phenomena of the same genus occurring under a different species of circumstances of the same genus, this would be monstrously false, whether intended as an absolutely universal proposition or merely as one approximately true. Let, for example, the genus of phenomena be the values of the throws of a pair of dice in a given series of successive throws indefinitely continued. Let the first species of circumstances be that the ordinal number of a throw in the series is *prime*. It is pretty certain that there would be no general character in the corresponding values of throws to distinguish them from those which would result when the ordinal number is divisible by 2, or by 3, or by any other prime. It thus appears that when we take *any* genus of circumstances, the law turns out false. Suppose, then, that we modify it by saying that, taking any genus of phenomena and separating this into two species, there will be found in the discoverable circumstances *some* general resemblance for all those attending phenomena of the same species in contrast to those attending phenomena of the other species. This is a proposition which there is not the slightest reason to believe. Take, for example, as the genus of phenomena, the many thousands of Latin descriptions of American species of plants by Asa Gray and his scholars. Now consider the species of this genus of phenomena which agree in this respect, that the two first words of the description have their first vowels the same. There is no reason to suppose that there was any general respect in which the circumstances of that species of the genus of phenomena agree with one another and differ from others, either universally or usually. It is a mere chance result. It is true that some persons will not be inclined to assent to this judgment; but they cannot prove it otherwise. It can afford no adequate basis for induction. We see, then, that when we consider *all* phenomena, there is no way of making the statement sufficiently definite and certain. Suppose, then, that we attempt still another modification of the law, that, of *interesting* resemblances and differences between phenomena, some considerable proportion are accompanied by corresponding resemblances and differences between those of the circumstances which appear to us to be *pertinent*. The proposition is now rather psychological than metaphysical. It would be impossible, with any evidentiary basis, to strengthen the expression "some considerable proportion"; and in other respects the statement is vague enough. Still, there is sufficient truth in it, perhaps, to warrant the presumptive adoption of hypotheses, provided this adoption merely means that they are taken as sufficiently reasonable to justify some expense in experimentation to test their truth by induction; but it gives no warrant at all to induction itself. For, in the first place, induction needs no such dubious support, since it is mathematically certain that the general character of a limited experience will, as that experience is prolonged, approximate to the character of what will be true in the long run, if anything is true in the long run. Now all that induction infers is what would be found true in the usual course of experience, if it were indefinitely prolonged. Since the method of induction must generally approximate to that truth, that is a sufficient justification for the use of that method, although no definite probability attaches to the inductive conclusion. In the second place, the law, as now formulated, neither helps nor hinders the validity of induction proper, for induction proper consists in judging of the relative frequency of a character among all the individuals of a class by the relative frequency of that character among the individuals of a random sample of that class. Now the law, as thus formulated, may tend to make our hypothesis approximately true; but that advantage has been gained before the operation of induction, which merely tests the hypothesis, begins. This inductive operation is just as valid when the hypothesis is bad as when it is good, when the character dealt with is trivial as when it is interesting. The ratio which induction ascertains may be nearer ½, and more remote from 1 or 0, when the characters are uninteresting; and in that case a larger number of instances will usually be requisite for obtaining the ratio with any given degree of precision (for if the ratio is really 1 or 0, it will be almost a miracle if in the sample it is far from that ratio, although this will not be impossible, if the whole class is infinite), but the essential validity of the process of induction remains unaffected by that circumstance.

What is usually meant by the uniformity of nature probably is that in proportion as the circumstances are alike or unlike, so are any phenomena connected with them alike or unlike. It may be asked to what degree nature is uniform in that sense. The only tenable answer is that it is as little uniform as it possibly could be imagined to be; for were any considerable proportion of existing uniformities, or laws, of nature destroyed, others would necessarily thereby result.

In fact, the great characteristic of nature is its diversity. For every uniformity known, there would be no difficulty in pointing out thousands of non-uniformities; but the diversities are usually of small use to us, and attract the attention of poets mainly, while the uniformities are the very staff of life. Hence, the higher and wider are our desires the greater will be the general impression of uniformity produced upon us by the contemplation of nature as it interests us.

(4) There are senses in which nature may not irrationally be held to be uniform; but opinions differ very widely as to the extent and nature of this uniformity. The chief of these are as follows:

(a) The majority of physicists, at least of the older generation, hold, with regard to the physical universe, that its elements are masses, their positions, and the variations of these positions with time. It is believed that every motion exactly obeys certain laws of attraction and repulsion; and there is no other kind of law, except that each atom or corpuscle is a centre of energy arranged in equipotential surfaces about it, which follow a regular law; and that this is a permanency. But the equations of motion are differential equations of the second order, involving, therefore, two arbitrary constants for each moving atom or corpuscle, and there is no uniformity connected with these constants. At least, no such uniformity is, with the least probability, discoverable. As for the distribution of potential about an atom or corpuscle, it is regular; but there is no ulterior reason for that regularity, or, at least, none is probably discoverable. What is absolutely beyond discovery, whether direct and specific or indirect and general, may be considered to be non-existent.

From this usual and in some sense standard opinion there are many divergences in both directions. First, in the direction of greater uniformity.

(b) Some hold that there is some exact uniformity in the arbitrary constants of the motion of the atoms, so that, for example, perhaps at some initial instant they all had some symmetrical or regular arrangement, like a pack of cards unshuffled; and that the velocities at that instant were regular also. But this regularity being of a purely aesthetic or formal kind, and the laws of motion equally formal and unrelated to any purpose, it follows that all kinds of arrangements will be produced, ungoverned by any uniformity, but mere effects of chance. Three stars may, for example, at some instant form an equilateral triangle; but there would be no particular reason for this: it would be merely a casual coincidence.

(c) Others go farther and maintain that the constants of position and velocity are subject to a law not merely formal, but are governed by final causes in such a way that there is no arrangement or coincidence whatever which was not specially intended by the Creator. To this theory, such words as *pro*-vidence and *fore*-knowledge are ill adapted; because the two constants which each atom or corpuscle has remain constant throughout all time, and ought not to be considered as having been fixed at any particular epoch. The very idea is that the arrangement is determined by what would be the result of different arrangements at each period of time. If, for example, a given prayer effects rain, it must be supposed that, in view of that prayer, and as its consequence, the different atoms had the appropriate constants; but that these were not given to the atoms at any particular epoch, being permanent values. Any intentional action on the part of a free agent is to be explained in the same way. If an agent is to be supposed really free, it is difficult to see what other physical explanation is compatible with the exactitude of law. This seems to be substantially the notion of most of those who have supported free will.

On the other hand, many philosophers suppose a less degree of uniformity in nature than is supposed in opinion (a). Of these the following have come to the present writer's notice as being actually defended.

(d) Some suppose that while law is absolute, yet there are constantly arising cases analogous to unstable equilibrium in which, owing to a passage of a velocity through infinity or otherwise, the law does not determine what the motion shall be. Thus if one Boscovichian point attracts another inversely as the square of the distance, and they move in one straight line, then when they come together they may move through one another, or move backwards on the same line, or may separate along any other line, without violating the differential equation. Such "singularities," as the mathematicians say, are theoretically possible; and may be supposed to occur very often. But to suppose that free action becomes possible in such a way is very illogical. In the first place, it supposes a direct interaction between "mind" and matter; infinitesimal, no doubt, but none the less real. Why not better suppose a slight but finite action of this kind, and so avoid the following objections? Namely, in the second place, this is to put faith, not scientific credence, in the inductive laws of matter infinitely beyond what induction can ever warrant. We know very well that mind, in some sense, acts on matter, and matter on mind: the question is *how*. It is not in speculations of this fanciful kind that the true answer is likely to be found. In the third place, although this speculation wanders so far beyond all present knowledge, it nevertheless comes into conflict with a legitimate induction, namely, the supposition of any real "singularity" or breach of continuity in nature is in as distinct conflict with all our knowledge as is a miracle.

(*e*) Sundry far less tenable hypotheses of lacunae between inviolable laws have often been proposed. One opinion frequently met with is that the law of energy does not prescribe the direction of velocity, but only its amount; so that the mind may cause atoms to "swerve," in regular Lucretian fashion.[8] This singular notion has even been embraced by mathematicians, who are thinking of a projectile shot into a curved tube, or other case of an equation of condition. Of course, if mind can construct absolute constraints, it can much easier exert force that is finite. Other writers suppose lacunae, without telling us of what particular description they are; they seem to think law is absolute as far as it goes, but that its jurisdiction is limited.

(*f*) Much more philosophical and less logically objectionable is the notion of St. Augustine and others (it is near to the opinion of Aristotle) that the only fundamental kind of causation is the action of final causes, and that efficient causation is, in all cases, secondary. Accordingly, when a miracle occurs there is no violation of the real *cursus naturae,* but only of the apparent course of things.

(*g*) The hypothesis suggested by the present writer is that all laws are results of evolution; that underlying all other laws is the only tendency which can grow by its own virtue, the tendency of all things to take habits. Now since this same tendency is the one sole fundamental law of mind, it follows that the physical evolution works towards ends in the same way that mental action works towards ends, and thus in one aspect of the matter it would be perfectly true to say that

8 [See *De rerum natura,* Bk. II, ll. 284-293.]

final causation is alone primary. Yet, on the other hand, the law of habit is a simple formal law, a law of efficient causation; so that either way of regarding the matter is equally true, although the former is more fully intelligent. Meantime, if law is a result of evolution, which is a process lasting through all time, it follows that no law is absolute. That is, we must suppose that the phenomena themselves involve departures from law analogous to errors of observation. But the writer has not supposed that this phenomenon had any connection with free will. In so far as evolution follows a law, the law of habit, instead of being a movement from homogeneity to heterogeneity, is growth from difformity to uniformity. But the chance divergences from law are perpetually acting to increase the variety of the world, and are checked by a sort of natural selection and otherwise (for the writer does not think the selective principle sufficient), so that the general result may be described as "organized heterogeneity," or, better, rationalized variety. In view of the principle of continuity, the supreme guide in framing philosophical hypotheses, we must, under this theory, regard matter as mind whose habits have become fixed so as to lose the powers of forming them and losing them, while mind is to be regarded as a chemical genus of extreme complexity and instability. It has acquired in a remarkable degree a habit of taking and laying aside habits. The fundamental divergences from law must here be most extraordinarily high, although probably very far indeed from attaining any directly observable magnitude. But their effect is to cause the laws of mind to be themselves of so fluid a character as to simulate divergences from law. All this, according to the writer, constitutes a hypothesis capable of being tested by experiment.

Literature: Besides most treatises on LOGIC (q.v., especially inductive) see Renouvier and Prat, *La nouvelle Monadologie* (1899).

THE REALITY OF THIRDNESS [1]

I proceed to argue that *Thirdness* is operative in Nature. Suppose we attack the question experimentally. Here is a stone. Now I place that stone where there will be no obstacle between it and the floor, and I will predict with confidence that as soon as I let go my hold upon the stone it will fall to the floor. I will prove that I can make a correct prediction by actual trial if you like. But I see by your faces that you all think it will be a very silly experiment. Why so? Because you all know very well that I can predict what will happen, and that the fact will verify my prediction.

But *how can* I know what is going to happen? You certainly do not think that it is by clairvoyance, as if the future event by its existential reactiveness could affect me directly, as in an *experience* of it, as an event scarcely past might affect me. You know very well that there is nothing of the sort in this case. Still, it remains true that I *do know* that that stone will drop, as a *fact,* as soon as I let go my hold. If I *truly know* anything, that which I know must be *real*. It would be quite absurd to say that I could be enabled to know how events are going to be determined over which I can exercise no more control than I shall be able to exercise over this stone after it shall have left my hand, that I can so peer in the future merely on the strength of any acquaintance with any pure fiction.

I know that this stone will fall if it is let go, because experience has convinced me that objects of this kind always do fall; and if anyone present has any doubt on the subject, I should be happy to try the experiment, and I will bet him a hundred to one on the result.

[1] [Originally published in *C.P.,* V, 64-67.—Ed.]

But the general proposition that all solid bodies fall in the absence of any upward forces or pressure, this formula I say, is of the nature of a representation. Our nominalistic friends would be the last to dispute that. They will go so far as to say that it is a *mere* representation—the word *mere* meaning that to be represented and really to be are two very different things; and that this formula has no being except a being represented. It certainly is of the nature of a representation. That is undeniable, I grant. And it is equally undeniable that that which is of the nature of a representation is not *ipso facto* real. In that respect there is a great contrast between an object of reaction and an object of representation. Whatever reacts is *ipso facto* real. But an object of representation is not *ipso facto* real. If I were to predict that on my letting go of the stone it would fly up in the air, that would be mere fiction; and the proof that it was so would be obtained by simply trying the experiment. That is clear. On the other hand, and by the same token, the fact that I *know* that this stone will fall to the floor when I let it go, as you all must confess, if you are not blinded by theory, that I *do* know—and you none of you care to take up my bet, I notice—is the proof that the formula, or uniformity, as furnishing a safe basis for prediction, is, or if you like it better, *corresponds to,* a reality.

Possibly at this point somebody may raise an objection and say: You admit, that [it] is one thing really to be and another to be represented; and you further admit that it is of the nature of the law of nature to be represented. Then it follows that it has not the mode of being of a reality. My answer to this would be that it rests upon an ambiguity. When I say that the general proposition as to what will happen, whenever a certain condition may be fulfilled, is of the nature of a representation, I mean that it refers to experiences *in futuro,* which I do not know are all of them experienced and never can know have been all experienced. But when I say that really to be is different from being represented, I mean that what really is, ultimately consists in what shall be forced upon us in experience, that there is an element of brute compulsion in fact and that fact is not a mere question of reasonableness. Thus, if I say, "I shall wind up my watch every day as long as I live," I never can have a positive experience which *certainly* covers all that is here promised, because I never shall know for certain that my last day has come. But what the real fact will be does not depend upon what I represent, but upon what the experiential reactions shall be. My assertion that I shall wind up my watch every day of my life may turn out to accord with facts, even though I be the most irregular of persons, by my dying before nightfall.

If we call that being true by chance, here is a case of a *general proposition* being entirely true in all its generality by chance.

Every general proposition is limited to a finite number of occasions in which it might conceivably be falsified, supposing that it is an assertion confined to what human beings may experience; and consequently it is conceivable that, although it should be true without exception, it should still only be by chance that it turns out true.

But if I see a man who is very regular in his habits and am led to offer to wager that that man will not miss winding his watch for the next month, you have your choice between two alternative hypotheses only:

1. You may suppose that some *principle* or *cause* is *really* operative to *make* him wind his watch daily, which *active principle* may have more or less strength; or

2. You may suppose that it is mere chance that his actions have hitherto been regular; and in that case, that regularity in the past affords you not the slightest reason for expecting its continuance in the future, any more than, if he had thrown sixes three times running, *that* event would render it either more or less likely that his next throw would show sixes.

It is the same with the operations of nature. With overwhelming uniformity, in our past experience, direct and in-

direct, stones left free to fall have fallen. Thereupon two
hypotheses only are open to us. Either—

1. the uniformity with which those stones have fallen has
been due to mere chance and affords no ground whatever,
not the slightest, for any expectation that the next stone
that shall be let go will fall; or
2. the uniformity with which stones have fallen has been
due to some *active general principle,* in which case it would
be a strange coincidence that it should cease to act at the
moment my prediction was based upon it.

That position, gentlemen, will sustain criticism. It is irre-
fragable.

Of course, every sane man will adopt the latter hypothesis.
If he could doubt it in the case of the stone—which he can't—
and I may as well drop the stone once for all—I told you so!—
if anybody doubts this still, a thousand other such inductive
predictions are getting verified every day, and he will have to
suppose every one of them to be merely fortuitous in order
reasonably to escape the conclusion that *general principles
are really operative in nature.* That is the doctrine of scholastic realism.

✒ X ✒

THE DOCTRINE OF NECESSITY EXAMINED [1]

I [THE MECHANICAL PHILOSOPHY]

In *The Monist* for January, 1891, I endeavored to show what elementary ideas ought to enter into our view of the universe. I may mention that on those considerations I had already grounded a cosmical theory, and from it had deduced a considerable number of consequences capable of being compared with experience. This comparison is now in progress, but under existing circumstances must occupy many years.

I propose here to examine the common belief that every single fact in the universe is precisely determined by law. It must not be supposed that this is a doctrine accepted everywhere and at all times by all rational men. Its first advocate appears to have been Democritus, the atomist, who was led to it, as we are informed, by reflecting upon the "impenetrability, translation, and impact of matter (ἀντιτυπία καὶ φορὰ καὶ πληγὴ τῆς ὕλης)." [2] That is to say, having restricted his attention to a field where no influence other than mechanical constraint could possibly come before his notice, he straightway jumped to the conclusion that throughout the universe that was the sole principle of action—a style of reasoning so usual in our day with men not unreflecting as to be more than excusable in the infancy of thought. But Epicurus, in revising the atomic doctrine and repairing its defenses, found himself obliged to suppose that atoms swerve from their courses by spontaneous chance; and thereby he conferred upon the theory life and entelechy.[3] For we now see clearly that the peculiar function of the molecular hypothesis in physics is to open an entry for

---

[1] [*The Monist,* II (1892), 321-337. (In *C.P.,* VI, 28-45.)]

[2] [See H. Diels, *Die Fragmente der Vorsokratiker,* c. 55, A66.]

[3] [See Aetius, *Placita,* I. 12. 15.]

the calculus of probabilities. Already, the prince of philosophers had repeatedly and emphatically condemned the dictum of Democritus (especially in the *Physics,* Book II, chapters 4, 5, 6), holding that events come to pass in three ways, namely, (1) by external compulsion, or the action of efficient causes, (2) by virtue of an inward nature, or the influence of final causes, and (3) irregularly without definite cause, but just by absolute chance; and this doctrine is of the inmost essence of Aristotelianism. It affords, at any rate, a valuable enumeration of the possible ways in which anything can be supposed to have come about. The freedom of the will, too, was admitted both by Aristotle [4] and by Epicurus.[5] But the Stoa,[6] which in every department seized upon the most tangible, hard, and lifeless element, and blindly denied the existence of every other, which, for example, impugned the validity of the inductive method and wished to fill its place with the *reductio ad absurdum,* very naturally became the one school of ancient philosophy to stand by a strict necessitarianism, thus returning to a single principle of Democritus that Epicurus had been unable to swallow. Necessitarianism and materialism with the Stoics went hand in hand, as by affinity they should. At the revival of learning, Stoicism met with considerable favor, partly because it departed just enough from Aristotle to give it the spice of novelty, and partly because its superficialities well adapted it for acceptance by students of literature and art who wanted their philosophy drawn mild. Afterwards, the great discoveries in mechanics inspired the hope that mechanical principles might suffice to explain the universe; and, though without logical justification, this hope has since been continually stimulated by subsequent advances in physics. Nevertheless, the doctrine was in too evident conflict with the freedom of the will and with miracles

---

[4] [See Aristotle, *De Interpretatione,* 18b, 31: 19a, 7. *Ethica Nicomachea,* 1112a, 7-10.]

[5] [Epicurus, *Epistle,* III. 133-134.]

[6] [See Cleanthes, in Epictetus, *Enchiridion,* 51; Seneca, *De Providentia,* V, 8.]

to be generally acceptable, at first. But meantime there arose that most widely spread of philosophical blunders, the notion that associationalism belongs intrinsically to the materialistic family of doctrines; and thus was evolved the theory of motives; and libertarianism became weakened. At present, historical criticism has almost exploded the miracles, great and small; so that the doctrine of necessity has never been in so great vogue as now.

The proposition in question is that the state of things existing at any time, together with certain immutable laws, completely determine the state of things at every other time (for a limitation to *future* time is indefensible). Thus, given the state of the universe in the original nebula, and given the laws of mechanics, a sufficiently powerful mind could deduce from these data the precise form of every curlicue of every letter I am now writing.

Whoever holds that every act of the will as well as every idea of the mind is under the rigid governance of a necessity [7] coördinated with that of the physical world will logically be carried to the proposition that minds are part of the physical world in such a sense that the laws of mechanics determine anything that happens according to immutable attractions and repulsions. In that case, that instantaneous state of things, from which every other state of things is calculable, consists in the positions and velocities of all the particles at any instant. This, the usual and most logical form of necessitarianism, is called the mechanical philosophy.

II [NECESSITY CONSIDERED AS A POSTULATE]

When I have asked thinking men what reason they had to believe that every fact in the universe is precisely determined by law, the first answer has usually been that the proposition is a "presupposition" or postulate of scientific reasoning. Well,

---

[7] [Peirce gives a list of various uses of the term "necessity" in the *Century Dictionary* (1889) and in *Baldwin's Dictionary*.]

if that is the best that can be said for it, the belief is doomed. Suppose it be "postulated": that does not make it true, nor so much as afford the slightest rational motive for yielding it any credence. It is as if a man should come to borrow money and, when asked for his security, should reply he "postulated" the loan. To "postulate" a proposition is no more than to hope it is true. There are, indeed, practical emergencies in which we act upon assumptions of certain propositions as true, because if they are not so, it can make no difference how we act. But all such propositions I take to be hypotheses of individual facts. For it is manifest that no universal principle can in its universality be comprised [1] in a special case or can be requisite for the validity of any ordinary inference. To say, for instance, that the demonstration by Archimedes of the property of the lever would fall to the ground if men were endowed with free will is extravagant; yet this is implied by those who make a proposition incompatible with the freedom of the will the postulate of all inference. Considering, too, that the conclusions of science make no pretense to being more than probable, and considering that a probable inference can at most only suppose something to be most frequently, or otherwise approximately, true, but never that anything is precisely true without exception throughout the universe, we see how far this proposition in truth is from being so postulated.

But the whole notion of a postulate being involved in reasoning appertains to a by-gone and false conception of logic. Non-deductive or ampliative inference is of three kinds: induction, hypothesis, and analogy. If there be any other modes, they must be extremely unusual and highly complicated, and may be assumed with little doubt to be of the same nature as those enumerated. For induction, hypothesis, and analogy, as far as their ampliative character goes, that is, so far as they conclude something not implied in the premises, depend upon one principle and involve the same procedure. All are essentially inferences from sampling. Suppose a ship arrives at Liverpool laden with wheat in bulk. Suppose that

[1] [The published paper has "compromised."]

by some machinery the whole cargo be stirred up with great thoroughness. Suppose that twenty-seven thimblefuls be taken equally from the forward, midships, and aft parts, from the starboard, center, and larboard parts, and from the top, half depth, and lower parts of her hold, and that these being mixed and the grains counted, four-fifths of the latter are found to be of quality A. Then we infer, experientially and provisionally, that approximately four-fifths of all the grain in the cargo is of the same quality. I say we infer this *experientially* and *provisionally*. By saying that we infer it *experientially,* I mean that our conclusion makes no pretension to knowledge of wheat-in-itself, our ἀλήθεια, as the derivation of that word implies, has nothing to do with *latent* wheat. We are dealing only with the matter of possible experience—experience in the full acceptation of the term as something not merely affecting the senses but also as the subject of thought. If there be any wheat hidden on the ship, so that it can neither turn up in the sample nor be heard of subsequently from purchasers—or if it be half-hidden, so that it may, indeed, turn up, but is less likely to do so than the rest—or if it can affect our senses and our pockets, but from some strange cause or causelessness cannot be reasoned about—all such wheat is to be excluded (or have only its proportional weight) in calculating that true proportion of quality A, to which our inference seeks to approximate. By saying that we draw the inference *provisionally,* I mean that we do not hold that we have reached any assigned degree of approximation as yet, but only hold that if our experience be indefinitely extended, and if every fact of whatever nature, as fast as it presents itself, be duly applied, according to the inductive method, in correcting the inferred ratio, then our approximation will become indefinitely close in the long run; that is to say, close to the experience *to come* (not merely close by the exhaustion of a finite collection) so that if experience in general is to fluctuate irregularly to and fro, in a manner to deprive the ratio sought of all definite value, we shall be able to find out approximately within what limits it fluctuates, and if, after having one definite value, it changes and assumes another, we shall be able to find that out, and in short, whatever may be the variations of this ratio in experience, experience indefinitely extended will enable us to detect them, so as to predict rightly, at last, what its ultimate value may be, if it have any ultimate value, or what the ultimate law of succession of values may be, if there be any such ultimate law, or that it ultimately fluctuates irregularly within certain limits, if it do so ultimately fluctuate. Now our inference, claiming to be no more than thus experiential and provisional, manifestly involves no postulate whatever.

For what is a postulate? It is the formulation of a material fact which we are not entitled to assume as a premiss, but the truth of which is requisite to the validity of an inference. Any fact, then, which might be supposed postulated, must either be such that it would ultimately present itself in experience, or not. If it will present itself, we need not postulate it now in our provisional inference, since we shall ultimately be entitled to use it as a premiss. But if it never would present itself in experience, our conclusion is valid but for the possibility of this fact being otherwise than assumed, that is, it is valid as far as possible experience goes, and that is all that we claim. Thus, every postulate is cut off, either by the provisionality or by the experientiality of our inference. For instance, it has been said that induction postulates that, if an indefinite succession of samples be drawn, examined, and thrown back each before the next is drawn, then in the long run every grain will be drawn as often as any other, that is to say, postulates that the ratio of the numbers of times in which any two are drawn will indefinitely approximate to unity. But no such postulate is made; for if, on the one hand, we are to have no other experience of the wheat than from such drawings, it is the ratio that presents itself in those drawings and not the ratio which belongs to the wheat in its latent existence that we are endeavoring to determine; while if, on the other hand, there is some other mode by which the wheat is to come under our knowledge, equivalent to another kind of sampling, so that after all our care in stirring up the wheat some experiential grains will present themselves in the first sampling operation more often than others in the long run, this very singular fact will be sure to get discovered by the inductive method, which must avail itself of every sort of experience; and our inference, which was only provisional, corrects itself at last. Again, it has been said, that induction postulates that under like circumstances like events will happen, and that this postulate is at bottom the same as the principle of universal causation. But this is a blunder, or *bévue,* due to thinking exclusively of inductions where the concluded ratio is either 1 or 0. If any such proposition were postulated, it would be that under like circumstances (the circumstances of drawing the different samples) different events occur in the same proportions in all the different sets—a proposition which is false and even absurd. But in truth no such thing is postulated, the experiential character of the inference reducing the condition of validity to this, that if a certain result does not occur, the opposite result will be manifested, a condition assured by the provisionality of the inference. But it may be asked whether it is not conceivable that every instance of a certain class destined to be ever employed as a datum of induction should have one character, while every instance destined not to be so employed should have the opposite character. The answer is that, in that case, the instances excluded from being subjects of reasoning would not be experienced in the full sense of the word, but would be among these *latent* individuals of which our conclusion does not pretend to speak.

To this account of the rationale of induction I know of but one objection worth mention: it is that I thus fail to deduce the full degree of force which this mode of inference in fact possesses; that according to my view, no matter how thorough and elaborate the stirring and mixing process had been, the examination of a single handful of grain would not give me any assurance, sufficient to risk money upon, that the next handful would not greatly modify the concluded value of the ratio under inquiry, while, in fact, the assurance would be very high that this ratio was not greatly in error. If the true ratio of grains of quality *A* were 0.80 and the handful contained a thousand grains, nine such handfuls out of every ten would contain from 780 to 820 grains of quality *A*. The answer to this is that the calculation given is correct when we know that the units of this handful and the quality inquired into have the normal independence of one another, if for instance the stirring has been complete and the character sampled for has been settled upon in advance of the examination of the sample. But in so far as these conditions are not known to be complied with, the above figures cease to be applicable. Random sampling and predesignation of the character sampled for should always be striven after in inductive reasoning, but when they cannot be attained, so long as it is conducted honestly, the inference retains some value. When we cannot ascertain how the sampling has been done or the sample-character selected, induction still has the essential validity which my present account of it shows it to have.

III [THE OBSERVATIONAL EVIDENCE FOR NECESSITARIANISM]

I do not think a man who combines a willingness to be convinced with a power of appreciating an argument upon a difficult subject can resist the reasons which have been given to show that the principle of universal necessity cannot be defended as being a postulate of reasoning. But then the question immediately arises whether it is not proved to be true, or at least rendered highly probable, by observation of nature.

Still, this question ought not long to arrest a person accustomed to reflect upon the force of scientific reasoning. For the essence of the necessitarian position is that certain continuous quantities have certain exact values. Now, how can observation determine the value of such a quantity with a probable error absolutely *nil?* To one who is behind the scenes, and knows that the most refined comparisons of masses, lengths, and angles, far surpassing in precision all other measurements, yet fall behind the accuracy of bank accounts, and that the ordinary determinations of physical constants, such as appear from month to month in the journals, are about on a par with an upholsterer's measurements of carpets and curtains, the idea of mathematical exactitude being demonstrated in the laboratory will appear simply ridiculous. There is a recognized method of estimating the probable magnitudes of errors in physics—the method of least squares. It is universally admitted that this method makes the errors smaller than they really are; yet even according to that theory an error indefinitely small is indefinitely improbable; so that any statement to the effect that a certain continuous quantity has a certain exact value, if well founded at all, must be founded on something other than observation.

Still, I am obliged to admit that this rule is subject to a certain qualification. Namely, it only applies to continuous [1] quantity. Now, certain kinds of continuous quantity are discontinuous at one or at two limits, and for such limits the rule must be modified. Thus, the length of a line cannot be less than zero. Suppose, then, the question arises how long a line a certain person had drawn from a marked point on a piece of paper. If no line at all can be seen, the observed length is zero; and the only conclusion this observation warrants is that the length of the line is less than the smallest length visible with the optical power employed. But indirect observations—for example, that the person supposed to have drawn the line was never within fifty feet of the paper—may make it probable that no line at all was made, so that the concluded length will be strictly zero. In like manner, experience no doubt would warrant the conclusion that there is absolutely *no* indigo in a given ear of wheat, and absolutely *no* attar in a given lichen. But such inferences can only be rendered valid by positive experiential evidence, direct or remote, and cannot rest upon a mere inability to detect the quantity in question. We have reason to think there is no indigo in the wheat, because we

---

[1] *Continuous* is not exactly the right word, but I let it go to avoid a long and irrelevant discussion.

have remarked that wherever indigo is produced it is produced in considerable quantities, to mention only one argument. We have reason to think there is no attar in the lichen,
because essential oils seem to be in general peculiar to single
species. If the question had been whether there was iron in
the wheat or the lichen, though chemical analysis should fail
to detect its presence, we should think some of it probably was
there, since iron is almost everywhere. Without any such information, one way or the other, we could only abstain from
any opinion as to the presence of the substance in question.
It cannot, I conceive, be maintained that we are in any *better*
position than this in regard to the presence of the element of
chance or spontaneous departures from law in nature.

Those observations which are generally adduced in favor of
mechanical causation simply prove that there is an element of
regularity in nature, and have no bearing whatever upon the
question of whether such regularity is exact and universal or
not. Nay, in regard to this *exactitude,* all observation is
directly *opposed* to it; and the most that can be said is that a
good deal of this observation can be explained away. Try to
verify any law of nature, and you will find that the more precise your observations, the more certain they will be to show
irregular departures from the law. We are accustomed to
ascribe these, and I do not say wrongly, to errors of observation; yet we cannot usually account for such errors in any
antecedently probable way. Trace their causes back far enough
and you will be forced to admit they are always due to arbitrary determination, or chance.

IV [ABSOLUTE CHANCE]

But it may be asked whether if there were an element of
real chance in the universe it must not occasionally be pro-
ductive of signal effects such as could not pass unobserved. In
answer to this question, without stopping to point out that
there is an abundance of great events which one might be

tempted to suppose were of that nature, it will be simplest to
remark that physicists hold that the particles of gases are moving about irregularly, substantially as if by real chance, and
that by the principles of probabilities there must occasionally
happen to be concentrations of heat in the gases contrary to
the second law of thermodynamics, and these concentrations,
occurring in explosive mixtures, must sometimes have tre-
mendous effects. Here, then, is in substance the very situation
supposed; yet no phenomena ever have resulted which we are
forced to attribute to such chance concentration of heat, or
which anybody, wise or foolish, has ever dreamed of accounting for in that manner.

In view of all these considerations, I do not believe that
anybody, not in a state of case-hardened ignorance respecting
the logic of science, can maintain that the precise and universal conformity of facts to law is clearly proved, or even rendered particularly probable, by any observations hitherto
made. In this way, the determined advocate of exact regularity
will soon find himself driven to *a priori* reasons to support his
thesis. These received such a socdolager from Stuart Mill [1] in
his examination of Hamilton, that holding to them now seems
to me to denote a high degree of imperviousness to reason, so
that I shall pass them by with little notice.

To say that we cannot help believing a given proposition is
no argument, but it is a conclusive fact if it be true; and with
the substitution of "I" for "we," it is true in the mouths of
several classes of minds: the blindly passionate, the unreflecting and ignorant, and the person who has overwhelming
evidence before his eyes. But that which has been inconceivable today has often turned out indisputable on the morrow.
Inability to conceive is only a stage through which every man
must pass in regard to a number of beliefs—unless endowed
with extraordinary obstinacy and obtuseness. His understanding is enslaved to some blind compulsion which a vigorous
mind is pretty sure soon to cast off.

[1] [See his *Examination of Sir William Hamilton's Philosophy*, Ch. XVI.]

Some seek to back up the *a priori* position with empirical arguments. They say that the exact regularity of the world is a natural belief, and that natural beliefs have generally been confirmed by experience. There is some reason in this. Natural beliefs, however, if they generally have a foundation of truth, also require correction and purification from natural illusions. The principles of mechanics are undoubtedly natural beliefs; but, for all that, the early formulations of them were exceedingly erroneous. The general approximation to truth in natural beliefs is, in fact, a case of the general adaptation of genetic products to recognizable utilities or ends. Now, the adaptations of nature, beautiful and often marvelous as they verily are, are never found to be quite perfect; so that the argument is quite *against* the absolute exactitude of any natural belief, including that of the principle of causation.

Another argument, or convenient commonplace, is that absolute chance is *inconceivable*. This word has eight current significations. The *Century Dictionary* [2] enumerates six. Those who talk like this will hardly be persuaded to say in what sense they mean that chance is inconceivable. Should they do so, it would easily be shown either that they have no sufficient reason for the statement or that the inconceivability is of a kind which does not prove that chance is non-existent.

Another *a priori* argument is that chance is unintelligible; that is to say, while it may perhaps be conceivable, it does not disclose to the eye of reason the how or why of things; and since a hypothesis can only be justified so far as it renders some phenomenon intelligible, we never can have any right to suppose absolute chance to enter into the production of anything in nature. This argument may be considered in connection with two others. Namely, instead of going so far as to say that the supposition of chance can *never* properly be used to explain any observed fact, it may be alleged merely that no facts are known which such a supposition could in any way help in explaining. Or again, the allegation being still further

2 [See page 3042, edition of 1889, for Peirce's definitions.]

weakened, it may be said that since departures from law are not unmistakably observed, chance is not a *vera causa,* and ought not unnecessarily to be introduced into a hypothesis.

These are no mean arguments, and require us to examine the matter a little more closely. Come, my superior opponent, let me learn from your wisdom. It seems to me that every throw of sixes with a pair of dice is a manifest instance of chance.

"While you would hold a throw of deuce-ace to be brought about by necessity?" (The opponent's supposed remarks are placed in quotation marks.)

Clearly one throw is as much chance as another.

"Do you think throws of dice are of a different nature from other events?"

I see that I must say that *all* the diversity and specificalness of events is attributable to chance.

"Would you, then, deny that there is any regularity in the world?"

That is clearly undeniable. I must acknowledge there is an approximate regularity, and that every event is influenced by it. But the diversification, specificalness, and irregularity of things I suppose is chance. A throw of sixes appears to me a case in which this element is particularly obtrusive.

"If you reflect more deeply, you will come to see that *chance* is only a name for a cause that is unknown to us."

Do you mean that we have no idea whatever what kind of causes could bring about a throw of sixes?

"On the contrary, each die moves under the influence of precise mechanical laws."

But it appears to me that it is not these *laws* which made the die turn up sixes; for these laws act just the same when other throws come up. The chance lies in the diversity of throws; and this diversity cannot be due to laws which are immutable.

"The diversity is due to the diverse circumstances under which the laws act. The dice lie differently in the box, and the motion given to the box is different. These are the unknown causes which produce the throws, and to which we give the name of chance; not the mechanical law which regulates the operation of these causes. You see you are already beginning to think more clearly about this subject."

Does the operation of mechanical law not increase the diversity?

"Properly not. You must know that the instantaneous state of a system of particles is defined by six times as many numbers as there are particles, three for the coördinates of each particle's position, and three more for the components of its velocity. This number of numbers, which expresses the amount of diversity in the system, remains the same at all times. There may be, to be sure, some kind of relation between the coordinates and component velocities of the different particles, by means of which the state of the system might be expressed by a smaller number of numbers. But, if this is the case, a precisely corresponding relationship must exist between the coördinates and component velocities at any other time, though it may doubtless be a relation less obvious to us. Thus, the intrinsic complexity of the system is the same at all times."

Very well, my obliging opponent, we have now reached an issue. You think all the arbitrary specifications of the universe were introduced in one dose, in the beginning, if there was a beginning, and that the variety and complication of nature has always been just as much as it is now. But I, for my part, think that the diversification, the specification, has been continually taking place. Should you condescend to ask me why I so think, I should give my reason as follows:

(1) Question any science which deals with the course of time. Consider the life of an individual animal or plant, or of a mind. Glance at the history of states, of institutions, of language, of ideas. Examine the successions of forms shown by paleontology, the history of the globe as set forth in geology, of what the astronomer is able to make out concerning the changes of stellar systems. Everywhere the main fact is growth and increasing complexity. Death and corruption are mere accidents or secondary phenomena. Among some of the lower

organisms, it is a moot point with biologists whether there be anything which ought to be called death. Races, at any rate, do not die out except under unfavorable circumstances. From these broad and ubiquitous facts we may fairly infer, by the most unexceptionable logic, that there is probably in nature some agency by which the complexity and diversity of things can be increased; and that consequently the rule of mechanical necessity meets in some way with interference.

(2) By thus admitting pure spontaneity or life as a character of the universe, acting always and everywhere though restrained within narrow bounds by law, producing infinitesimal departures from law continually, and great ones with infinite infrequency, I account for all the variety and diversity of the universe, in the only sense in which the really *sui generis* and new can be said to be accounted for. The ordinary view has to admit the inexhaustible multitudinous variety of the world, has to admit that its mechanical law cannot account for this in the least, that variety can spring only from spontaneity, and yet denies without any evidence or reason the existence of this spontaneity, or else shoves it back to the beginning of time and supposes it dead ever since. The superior logic of my view appears to me not easily controverted.

(3) When I ask the necessitarian how he would explain the diversity and irregularity of the universe, he replies to me out of the treasury of his wisdom that irregularity is something which from the nature of things we must not seek to explain. Abashed at this, I seek to cover my confusion by asking how he would explain the uniformity and regularity of the universe, whereupon he tells me that the laws of nature are immutable and ultimate facts, and no account is to be given of them. But my hypothesis of spontaneity does explain irregularity, in a certain sense; that is, it explains the general fact of irregularity, though not, of course, what each lawless event is to be. At the same time, by thus loosening the bond of necessity, it gives room for the influence of another kind of causation, such as seems to be operative in the mind in the formation of associations, and enables us to understand how the

uniformity of nature could have been brought about. That single events should be hard and unintelligible, logic will permit without difficulty: we do not expect to make the shock of a personally experienced earthquake appear natural and reasonable by any amount of cogitation. But logic does expect things *general* to be understandable. To say that there is a universal law, and that it is a hard, ultimate, unintelligible fact, the why and wherefore of which can never be inquired into, at this a sound logic will revolt, and will pass over at once to a method of philosophizing which does not thus barricade the road of discovery.

(4) Necessitarianism cannot logically stop short of making the whole action of the mind a part of the physical universe. Our notion that we decide what we are going to do, if, as the necessitarian says, it has been calculable since the earliest times, is reduced to illusion. Indeed, consciousness in general thus becomes a mere illusory aspect of a material system. What we call red, green, and violet are in reality only different rates of vibration. The sole reality is the distribution of qualities of matter in space and time. Brain-matter is protoplasm in a certain degree and kind of complication—a certain arrangement of mechanical particles. Its feeling is but an inward aspect, a phantom. For, from the positions and velocities of the particles at any one instant, and the knowledge of the immutable forces, the positions at all other times are calculable; so that the universe of space, time, and matter is a rounded system uninterfered with from elsewhere. But, from the state of feeling at any instant, there is no reason to suppose the states of feeling at all other instants are thus exactly calculable; so that feeling is, as I said, a mere fragmentary and illusive aspect of the universe. This is the way, then, that necessitarianism has to make up its accounts. It enters consciousness under the head of sundries, as a forgotten trifle; its scheme of the universe would be more satisfactory if this little fact could be dropped out of sight. On the other hand, by supposing the rigid exactitude of causation to yield, I care not how little—be it but by a strictly infinitesimal amount—we gain

room to insert mind into our scheme, and to put it into the place where it is needed, into the position which, as the sole self-intelligible thing, it is entitled to occupy, that of the fountain of existence; and in so doing we resolve the problem of the connection of soul and body.

(5) But I must leave undeveloped the chief of my reasons, and can only adumbrate it. The hypothesis of chance-spontaneity is one whose inevitable consequences are capable of being traced out with mathematical precision into considerable detail. Much of this I have done and find the consequences to agree with observed facts to an extent which seems to me remarkable.[3] But the matter and methods of reasoning are novel, and I have no right to promise that other mathematicians shall find my deductions as satisfactory as I myself do, so that the strongest reason for my belief must for the present remain a private reason of my own, and cannot influence others. I mention it to explain my own position; and partly to indicate to future mathematical speculators a veritable gold mine, should time and circumstances and the abridger of all joys prevent my opening it to the world.

If now I, in my turn, inquire of the necessitarian why he prefers to suppose that all specification goes back to the beginning of things, he will answer me with one of those last three arguments which I left unanswered.

First, he may say that chance is a thing absolutely unintelligible, and therefore that we never can be entitled to make such a supposition. But does not this objection smack of naïve impudence? It is not mine, it is his own conception of the universe which leads abruptly up to hard, ultimate, inexplicable, immutable law, on the one hand, and to inexplicable specification and diversification of circumstances on the other. My view, on the contrary, hypothetizes nothing at all, unless it be hypothesis to say that all specification came about in some sense, and is not to be accepted as unaccountable. To undertake to account for anything by saying baldly

[3] [The editors (Hartshorne and Weiss) have been unable to discover any manuscript whose contents clearly answer to the foregoing description.]

that it is due to chance would, indeed, be futile. But this I do not do. I make use of chance chiefly to make room for a principle of generalization, or tendency to form habits, which I hold has produced all regularities. The mechanical philosopher leaves the whole specification of the world utterly unaccounted for, which is pretty nearly as bad as to baldly attribute it to chance. I attribute it altogether to chance, it is true, but to chance in the form of a spontaneity which is to some degree regular. It seems to me clear at any rate that one of these two positions must be taken, or else specification must be supposed due to a spontaneity which develops itself in a certain and not in a chance way, by an objective logic like that of Hegel. This last way I leave as an open possibility, for the present; for it is as much opposed to the necessitarian scheme of existence as my own theory is.

Secondly, the necessitarian may say there are, at any rate, no observed phenomena which the hypothesis of chance could aid in explaining. In reply, I point first to the phenomenon of growth and developing complexity, which appears to be universal, and which, though it may possibly be an affair of mechanism perhaps, certainly presents all the appearance of increasing diversification. Then, there is variety itself, beyond comparison the most obtrusive character of the universe: no mechanism can account for this. Then, there is the very fact the necessitarian most insists upon, the regularity of the universe which for him serves only to block the road of inquiry. Then, there are the regular relationships between the laws of nature—similarities and comparative characters, which appeal to our intelligence as its cousins, and call upon us for a reason. Finally, there is consciousness, feeling, a patent fact enough, but a very inconvenient one to the mechanical philosopher.

Thirdly, the necessitarian may say that chance is not a *vera causa*, that we cannot know positively there is any such element in the universe. But the doctrine of the *vera causa* has nothing to do with elementary conceptions. Pushed to that extreme, it at once cuts off belief in the existence of a material universe; and without that necessitarianism could hardly maintain its ground. Besides, variety is a fact which must be admitted; and the theory of chance merely consists in supposing this diversification does not antedate all time. Moreover, the avoidance of hypotheses involving causes nowhere positively known to act is only a recommendation of logic, not a positive command. It cannot be formulated in any precise terms without at once betraying its untenable character—I mean as rigid rule, for as a recommendation it is wholesome enough.

I believe I have thus subjected to fair examination all the important reasons for adhering to the theory of universal necessity, and have shown their nullity. I earnestly beg that whoever may detect any flaw in my reasoning will point it out to me, either privately or publicly; for, if I am wrong, it much concerns me to be set right speedily. If my argument remains unrefuted, it will be time, I think, to doubt the absolute truth of the principle of universal law; and when once such a doubt has obtained a living root in any man's mind, my cause with him, I am persuaded, is gained.

[WHAT IS SCIENCE?]

I [THE ESSENCE OF SCIENCE] [1]

. . . Let us remember that science is a pursuit of living men, and that its most marked characteristic is that when it is genuine, it is in an inccssant state of metabolism and growth. If we resort to a dictionary, we shall be told that it is systematized knowledge. Most of the classifications of the sciences have been classifications of systematized and established knowledge—which is nothing but the exudation of living science—as if plants were to be classified according to the characters of their gums. . . .

Let us look upon science—the science of today—as a living thing. What characterizes it generally, from this point of view, is that the thoroughly established truths are labelled and put upon the shelves of each scientist's mind, where they can be at hand when there is occasion to use things—arranged, therefore, to suit his special convenience—while science itself, the living process, is busied mainly with conjectures, which are either getting framed or getting tested. When that systematized knowledge on the shelves is used, it is used almost exactly as a manufacturer or practising physician might use it; that is to say, it is merely applied. If it ever becomes the object of science, it is because in the advance of science, the moment has come when it must undergo a process of purification or of transformation.

A scientific man is likely in the course of a long life to pick up a pretty extensive acquaintance with the results of science; but in many branches, this is so little necessary that one will meet with men of the most deserved renown in science who

1 [From Ch. 2 of the "Minute Logic," 1902. Originally published in *C.P.*, I, 104-107. The heading "What Is Science?" has been supplied for this edition.—Ed.]

will tell you that, beyond their own little nooks, they hardly know anything of what others have done. Sylvester always used to say that he knew very little mathematics: true, he seemed to know more than he thought he did. In various branches of science, some of the most eminent men first took up those subjects as mere pastimes, knowing little or nothing of the accumulations of knowledge. So it was with the astronomer Lockyer: so it has been with many naturalists. Now, did those men gradually become men of science as their stores of knowledge increased, or was there an epoch in their lives, before which they were amateurs and after which they were scientists? I believe that the answer is that, like any other regeneration, the metamorphosis is commonly sudden, though sometimes slow. When it is sudden, what is it that constitutes the transformation? It is their being seized with a great desire to learn the truth, and their going to work with all their might by a well-considered method to gratify that desire. The man who is working in the right way to learn something not already known is recognized by all men of science as one of themselves, no matter how little he is informed. It would be monstrous to say that Ptolemy, Archimedes, Eratosthenes and Posidonius were not scientific men because their knowledge was comparatively small. The life of science is in the desire to learn. If this desire is not pure, but is mingled with a desire to prove the truth of a definite opinion, or of a general mode of conceiving of things, it will almost inevitably lead to the adoption of a faulty method; and *in so far* such men, among whom many have been looked upon in their day as great lights, are not genuine men of science; though it would be foul injustice to exclude them absolutely from that class. So if a man pursues a futile method through neglect to inform himself of effective methods, he is no scientific man; he has not been moved by an intelligently sincere and effective desire to learn. But if a man simply fails to inform himself of previous work which would have facilitated his own, although he is to blame, it would be too harsh to say that he has violated the essential principles of science. If a man pursues a method which, though very bad, is the best that the state of intellectual development of his time, or the state of the particular science he pursues, would enable a man to take—I mean, for example, such men as Lavater, Paracelsus and the earlier alchemists, the author of the first chapter of Genesis, and the old metaphysicians—we perhaps cannot call them scientific men, while perhaps we ought to do so. Opinions would differ about this. They are, at any rate, entitled to an honorable place in the vestibule of science. A pretty wild play of the imagination is, it cannot be doubted, an inevitable and probably even a useful prelude to science proper. For my part, if these men really had an effective rage to learn the very truth, and did what they did as the best way they knew, or could know, to find it out, I could not bring myself to deny them the title. The difficulty is that one of the things that coheres to that undeveloped state of intelligence is precisely a very imperfect and impure thirst for truth. Paracelsus and the alchemists were rank charlatans seeking for gold more than for truth. The metaphysicians were not only pedants and pretenders, but they were trying to establish foregone conclusions. Those are the traits which deprive those men of the title scientist, although we ought to entertain a high respect for them as mortals go; because they could no more escape the corruptness of their aims than they could the deficiencies of their knowledge. Science consists in actually drawing the bow upon truth with intentness in the eye, with energy in the arm. . . .

II THE MARRIAGE OF RELIGION AND SCIENCE [1]

What is science? The dictionary will say that it is systematized knowledge. Dictionary definitions, however, are too apt to repose upon derivations; which is as much as to say that they neglect too much the later steps in the evolution of

[1] [*The Open Court*, VII (1893), 3559-60. (In *C.P.*, VI, 302-304.)]

meanings. Mere knowledge, though it be systematized, may be a dead memory; while by science we all habitually mean a living and growing body of truth. We might even say that knowledge is not necessary to science. The astronomical researches of Ptolemy, though they are in great measure false, must be acknowledged by every modern mathematician who reads them to be truly and genuinely scientific. That which constitutes science, then, is not so much correct conclusions, as it is a correct method. But the method of science is itself a scientific result. It did not spring out of the brain of a beginner: it was a historic attainment and a scientific achievement. So that not even this method ought to be regarded as essential to the beginnings of science. That which is essential, however, is the scientific spirit, which is determined not to rest satisfied with existing opinions, but to press on to the real truth of nature. To science once enthroned in this sense, among any people, science in every other sense is heir apparent.

And what is religion? In each individual it is a sort of sentiment, or obscure perception, a deep recognition of a something in the circumambient All, which, if he strives to express it, will clothe itself in forms more or less extravagant, more or less accidental, but ever acknowledging the first and last, the A and Ω, as well as a relation to that Absolute of the individual's self, as a relative being. But religion cannot reside in its totality in a single individual. Like every species of reality, it is essentially a social, a public affair. It is the idea of a whole church, welding all its members together in one organic, systemic perception of the Glory of the Highest—an idea having a growth from generation to generation and claiming a supremacy in the determination of all conduct, private and public.

Now, as science grows, it becomes more and more perfect, considered as science; and no religionist can easily so narrow himself as to deny this. But as religion goes through the different stages of its history, it has, I fear we must confess, seldom been seen so vitalized as to become more and more perfect, even as judged from its own standpoint. Like a plucked flower, its destiny is to wilt and fade. The vital sentiment that gave it birth loses gradually its pristine purity and strength, till some new creed treads it down. Thus it happens quite naturally that those who are animated with the spirit of science are for hurrying forward, while those who have the interests of religion at heart are apt to press back.

While this double change has been taking place, religion has found herself compelled to define her position; and, in doing so, has inevitably committed herself to sundry propositions, which, one by one, have been, first questioned, then assailed, and finally overthrown by advancing science. Seeing such a chasm open before her feet, religion has at first violently recoiled, and at last has leapt it; satisfying herself as best she might with an altered creed. In most cases the leap has not seemed to hurt her; yet internal injuries may have been sustained. Who can doubt that the church really did suffer from the discovery of the Copernican system, although infallibility, by a narrow loophole, managed to escape? In this way, science and religion become forced into hostile attitudes. Science, to specialists, may seem to have little or nothing to say that directly concerns religion; but it certainly encourages a philosophy which, if in no other respect, is at any rate opposed to the prevalent tendency of religion, in being animated by a progressive spirit. There arises, too, a tendency to pooh-pooh at things unseen.

It would be ridiculous to ask to whose fault this situation is chargeable. You cannot lay blame upon elemental forces. Religion, from the nature of things, refuses to go through her successive transformations with sufficient celerity to keep always in accord with the convictions of scientific philosophy. The day has come, however, when the man whom religious experience most devoutly moves can recognize the state of the case. While adhering to the essence of religion, and so far as possible to the church, which is all but essential, say, penessential to it, he will cast aside that religious timidity that is forever prompting the church to recoil from the paths into which the Governor of history is leading the minds of men, a cowardice that has stood through the ages as the landmark and limit of her little faith, and will gladly go forward, sure that truth is not split into two warring doctrines, and that any change that knowledge can work in his faith can only affect its expression, but not the deep mystery expressed.

Such a state of mind may properly be called a religion of science. Not that it is a religion to which science or the scientific spirit has itself given birth; for religion, in the proper sense of the term, can arise from nothing but the religious sensibility. But it is a religion, so true to itself, that it becomes animated by the scientific spirit, confident that all the conquests of science will be triumphs of its own, and accepting all the results of science, as scientific men themselves accept them, as steps toward the truth, which may appear for a time to be in conflict with other truths, but which in such cases merely await adjustments which time is sure to effect. This attitude, be it observed, is one which religion will assume not at the dictate of science, still less by way of a compromise, but simply and solely out of a bolder confidence in herself and in her own destiny.

Meantime, science goes unswervingly its own gait. What is to be its goal is precisely what it must not seek to determine for itself, but let itself be guided by nature's strong hand. Teleological considerations, that is to say ideals, must be left to religion; science can allow itself to be swayed only by efficient causes; and philosophy, in her character of queen of the sciences, must not care, or must not seem to care, whether her conclusions be wholesome or dangerous.

✒ XII ✒

LESSONS FROM THE HISTORY OF SCIENCE [1]

I [THE SCIENTIFIC ATTITUDE]

If we endeavor to form our conceptions upon history and life, we remark three classes of men. The first consists of those for whom the chief thing is the qualities of feelings. These men create art. The second consists of the practical men, who carry on the business of the world. They respect nothing but power, and respect power only so far as it [is] exercised. The third class consists of men to whom nothing seems great but reason. If force interests them, it is not in its exertion, but in that it has a reason and a law. For men of the first class, nature is a picture; for men of the second class, it is an opportunity; for men of the third class, it is a cosmos, so admirable, that to penetrate to its ways seems to them the only thing that makes life worth living. These are the men whom we see possessed by a passion to learn, just as other men have a passion to teach and to disseminate their influence. If they do not give themselves over completely to their passion to learn, it is because they exercise self-control. Those are the natural scientific men; and they are the only men that have any real success in scientific research.

If we are to define science, not in the sense of stuffing it into an artificial pigeonhole where it may be found again by some insignificant mark, but in the sense of characterizing it as a living historic entity, we must conceive it as that about which such men as I have described busy themselves. As such, it does not consist so much in *knowing,* nor even in "organized knowledge," as it does in diligent inquiry into truth for

[1] [Notes for a projected, but never completed, *History of Science, c.* 1896. (Originally published in *C.P.,* I, 19-49.)]

truth's sake, without any sort of axe to grind, nor for the sake of the delight of contemplating it, but from an impulse to penetrate into the reason of things. This is the sense in which this book is entitled a History of *Science*. Science and philosophy seem to have been changed in their cradles. For it is not knowing, but the love of learning, that characterizes the scientific man; while the "philosopher" is a man with a system which he thinks embodies all that is best worth knowing. If a man burns to learn and sets himself to comparing his ideas with experimental results in order that he may correct those ideas, every scientific man will recognize him as a brother, no matter how small his knowledge may be.

But if a man occupies himself with investigating the truth of some question for some ulterior purpose, such as to make money, or to amend his life, or to benefit his fellows, he may be ever so much better than a scientific man, if you will—to discuss that would be aside from the question—but he is not a scientific man. For example, there are numbers of chemists who occupy themselves exclusively with the study of dyestuffs. They discover facts that are useful to scientific chemistry; but they do not rank as genuine scientific men. The genuine scientific chemist cares just as much to learn about erbium—the extreme rarity of which renders it commercially unimportant —as he does about iron. He is more eager to learn about erbium if the knowledge of it would do more to complete his conception of the Periodic Law, which expresses the mutual relations of the elements.

II [THE SCIENTIFIC IMAGINATION]

When a man desires ardently to know the truth, his first effort will be to imagine what that truth can be. He cannot prosecute his pursuit long without finding that imagination unbridled is sure to carry him off the track. Yet nevertheless, it remains true that there is, after all, nothing but imagination that can ever supply him an inkling of the truth. He can stare stupidly at phenomena; but in the absence of imagination they will not connect themselves together in any rational way. Just as for Peter Bell a cowslip was nothing but a cowslip, so for thousands of men a falling apple was nothing but a falling apple; and to compare it to the moon would by them be deemed "fanciful."

It is not too much to say that next after the passion to learn there is no quality so indispensable to the successful prosecution of science as imagination. Find me a people whose early medicine is not mixed up with magic and incantations, and I will find you a people devoid of all scientific ability. There is no magic in the medical Papyrus Ebers. The stolid Egyptian saw nothing in disease but derangement of the affected organ. There never was any true Egyptian science.

There are, no doubt, kinds of imagination of no value in science, mere artistic imagination, mere dreaming of opportunities for gain. The scientific imagination dreams of explanations and laws.

III   [SCIENCE AND MORALITY]

A scientific man must be single-minded and sincere with himself. Otherwise, his love of truth will melt away, at once. He can, therefore, hardly be otherwise than an honest, fair-minded man. True, a few naturalists have been accused of purloining specimens; and some men have been far from judicial in advocating their theories. Both of these faults must be exceedingly deleterious to their scientific ability. But on the whole, scientific men have been the best of men. It is quite natural, therefore, that a young man who might develop into a scientific man should be a well-conducted person.

Yet in more ways than one an exaggerated regard for morality is unfavorable to scientific progress. I shall present only one of those ways. It will no doubt shock some persons that I speak of morality as involving an element which can become bad. To them good conduct and moral conduct are one and the same—and they will accuse me of hostility to morality. I regard morality as highly necessary; but it is a means to good life, not necessarily coextensive with good conduct. Morality consists in the folklore of right conduct. A man is brought up to think he ought to behave in certain ways. If he behaves otherwise, he is uncomfortable. His conscience pricks him. That system of morals is the traditional wisdom of ages of experience. If a man cuts loose from it, he will become the victim of his passions. It is not safe for him even to reason about it, except in a purely speculative way. Hence, morality is essentially conservative. Good morals and good manners are identical, except that tradition attaches less importance to the latter. The gentleman is imbued with conservatism. This conservatism is a habit, and it is the law of habit that it tends to spread and extend itself over more and more of the life. In this way, conservatism about morals leads to conservatism about manners and finally conservatism about opinions of a speculative kind. Besides, to distinguish between speculative and practical opinions is the mark of the most cultivated intellects. Go down below this level and you come across reformers and rationalists at every turn—people who propose to remodel the ten commandments on modern science. Hence it is that morality leads to a conservatism which any new view, or even any free inquiry, no matter how purely speculative, shocks. The whole moral weight of such a community will be cast against science. To inquire into nature is for a Turk very unbecoming to a good Moslem; just as the family of Tycho Brahe regarded his pursuit of astronomy as unbecoming to a nobleman. (See Thomas Nash in *Pierce Pennilesse* for the character of a Danish nobleman.)

This tendency is necessarily greatly exaggerated in a country when the "gentleman," or recognized exponent of good manners, is appointed to that place as the most learned man. For then the inquiring spirit cannot say the gentlemen are a lot of ignorant fools. To the moral weight cast against progress in science is added the weight of superior learning. Wherever there is a large class of academic professors who are pro-

vided with good incomes and looked up to as gentlemen, scientific inquiry must languish. Wherever the bureaucrats are
the more learned class, the case will be still worse.

IV [MATHEMATICS]

The first questions which men ask about the universe are
naturally the most general and abstract ones. Nor is it true, as
has so often been asserted, that these are the most difficult
questions to answer. Francis Bacon is largely responsible for
this error, he having represented—having nothing but his imagination and no acquaintance with actual science to draw
upon—that the most general inductions must be reached by
successive steps. History does not at all bear out that theory.
The errors about very general questions have been due to a
circumstance which I proceed to set forth.

The most abstract of all the sciences is mathematics. That
this is so, has been made manifest in our day; because all
mathematicians now see clearly that mathematics is only
busied about *purely hypothetical questions*. As for what the
truth of existence may be the mathematician does not (*qua*
mathematician) care a straw. It is true that early mathematicians could not clearly see that this was so. But for all their
not seeing it, it was just as true of the mathematics of early
days as of our own. The early mathematician might perhaps
be more inclined to assert roundly that two straight lines in a
plane cut by a third so as to make the sum of the internal
angles on one side less than two right angles would meet at
some finite distance on that side if sufficiently produced; although, as a matter of fact, we observe no such tendency in
Euclid. But however that may have been, the early mathematician had certainly no more tendency than the modern to *inquire into the truth of that postulate*; but quite the reverse.
What he really did, therefore, was merely to deduce consequences of unsupported assumptions, whether he recognized
that this was the nature of his business or not. Mathematics,

then, really was, for him as for us, the most abstract of the sciences, cut off from all inquiry into existential truth. Consequently, the tendency to attack the most abstract problems first, not because they were *recognized* as such, but because such they *were,* led to mathematics being the earliest field of inquiry.

We find some peoples drawn more toward arithmetic; others more toward geometry. But in either case, a correct method of reasoning was sure to be reached before many centuries of real inquiry had elapsed. The reasoning would be at first awkward, and one case would be needlessly split up into several. But still all influences were pressing the reasoner to make use of a diagram, and as soon as he did that he was pursuing the correct method. For mathematical reasoning consists in constructing a diagram according to a general precept, in observing certain relations between parts of that diagram not explicitly required by the precept, showing that these relations will hold for all such diagrams, and in formulating this conclusion in general terms. All valid necessary reasoning is in fact thus diagrammatic. This, however, is far from being obviously true. There was nothing to draw the attention of the early reasoners to the need of a diagram in such reasoning. Finding that by their inward meditations they could deduce the truth concerning, for example, the height of an inaccessible pillar, they naturally concluded the same method could be applied to positive inquiries.

In this way, early success in mathematics would naturally lead to bad methods in the positive sciences, and especially in metaphysics.

V [SCIENCE AS A GUIDE TO CONDUCT]

We have seen how success in mathematics would necessarily create a confidence altogether unfounded in man's power of eliciting truth by inward meditation without any aid from ex-

perience. Both its confidence in what is within and the absolute certainty of its conclusions lead to the confusion of *a
priori* reason with conscience. For conscience, also, refuses to
submit its dicta to experiment, and makes an absolute dual
distinction between right and wrong. One result of this is that
men begin to rationalize about questions of purity and integrity, which in the long run, through moral decay, is unfavorable to science. But what is worse, from our point of view,
they begin to look upon science as a guide to conduct, that is,
no longer as pure science but as an instrument for a practical
end. One result of this is that all probable reasoning is de-
spised. If a proposition is to be applied to action, it has to be
embraced, or believed without reservation. There is no room
for doubt, which can only paralyze action. But the scientific
spirit requires a man to be at all times ready to dump his
whole cartload of beliefs, the moment experience is against
them. The desire to learn forbids him to be perfectly cocksure that he knows already. Besides positive science can only
rest on experience; and experience can never result in absolute certainty, exactitude, necessity, or universality. But it is
precisely with the universal and necessary, that is, with Law,
that [con]science concerns itself. Thus the real character of
science is destroyed as soon as it is made an adjunct to conduct; and especially all progress in the inductive sciences is
brought to a standstill.

VI [MORALITY AND SHAM REASONING]

The effect of mixing speculative inquiry with questions of
conduct results finally in a sort of half make-believe reasoning which deceives itself in regard to its real character. Conscience really belongs to the subconscious man, to that part
of the soul which is hardly distinct in different individuals, a
sort of community-consciousness, or public spirit, not absolutely one and the same in different citizens, and yet not by

any means independent in them. Conscience has been created by experience just as any knowledge is; but it is modified by further experience only with secular slowness.

When men begin to rationalize about their conduct, the first effect is to deliver them over to their passions and produce the most frightful demoralization, especially in sexual matters. Thus, among the Greeks, it brought about paederasty and a precedence of public women over private wives. But ultimately the subconscious part of the soul, being stronger, regains its predominance and insists on setting matters right. Men, then, continue to tell themselves they regulate their conduct by reason; but they learn to look forward and see what conclusions a given method will lead to before they give their adhesion to it. In short, it is no longer the reasoning which determines what the conclusion shall be, but it is the conclusion which determines what the reasoning shall be. This is sham reasoning. In short, as morality supposes self-control, men learn that they must not surrender themselves unreservedly to any method, without considering to what conclusions it will lead them. But this is utterly contrary to the single-mindedness that is requisite in science. In order that science may be successful, its votaries must hasten to surrender themselves at discretion to experimental inquiry, in advance of knowing what its decisions may be. There must be no reservations.

The effect of this shamming is that men come to look upon reasoning as mainly decorative, or at most, as a secondary aid in minor matters—a view not altogether unjust, if questions of conduct are alone to interest us. They, therefore, demand that it shall be plain and facile. If, in special cases, complicated reasoning is indispensable, they hire a specialist to perform it. The result of this state of things is, of course, a rapid deterioration of intellectual vigor, very perceptible from one generation to the next. This is just what is taking place among us before our eyes; and to judge from the history of Constantinople, it is likely to go on until the race comes to a despicable end.

VII [THE METHOD OF AUTHORITY]

When society is broken into bands, now warring, now allied, now for a time subordinated one to another, man loses his conceptions of truth and of reason. If he sees one man assert what another denies, he will, if he is concerned, choose his side and set to work by all means in his power to silence his adversaries. The truth for him is that for which he fights.

The next step which is to be expected in a logical development not interrupted by accidental occurrences will consist in the recognition that a central authority ought to determine the beliefs of the entire community. As far as morals and religion go, this plan admirably fulfills its purpose of producing uniformity. But in order that it may do this, it is desirable that there should be another less absolute authority which shall declare, not infallibly but yet with a weight of collective learning, the propositions which science from time to time puts out of reasonable doubt, and which shall aid the researches of competent investigators. The value of such services in the development of science is immense; though they are accompanied by very serious disadvantages in not allowing to unofficial studies the weight which ought to be accorded to them. The history of science is full of examples of this sort.

VIII [SCIENCE AND CONTINUITY]

One of the worst effects of the influence of moral and religious reasonings upon science lies in this, that the distinctions upon which both insist as fundamental are dual distinctions, and that their tendency is toward an ignoring of all distinctions that are not dual and especially of the conception of continuity. Religion recognizes the saints and the damned. It will not readily admit any third fate. Morality insists that a motive is either good or bad. That the gulf between them is bridged over and that most motives are somewhere near the middle of the bridge, is quite contrary to the teachings of any moral system which ever lived in the hearts and consciences of a people.

It is not necessary to read far in almost any work of philosophy written by a man whose training is that of a theologian, in order to see how helpless such minds are in attempting to deal with continuity. Now continuity, it is not too much to say, is the leading conception of science. The complexity of the conception of continuity is so great as to render it important wherever it occurs. Now it enters into every fundamental and exact law of physics or of psychics that is known. The few laws of chemistry which do not involve continuity seem for the most part to be very roughly true. It seems not unlikely that if the veritable laws were known continuity would be found to be involved in them. . . .

IX [THE ANALYTIC METHOD]

The first problems to suggest themselves to the inquirer into nature are far too complex and difficult for any early solution, even if any satisfactorily secure conclusion can ever be drawn concerning them. What ought to be done, therefore, and what in fact is done, is at first to substitute for those problems others much simpler, much more abstract, of which there is a good prospect of finding probable solutions. Then, the reasonably certain solutions of these last problems will throw a light more or less clear upon more concrete problems which are in certain respects more interesting.

This method of procedure is that Analytic Method to which modern physics owes all its triumphs. It has been applied with great success in psychical sciences also. (Thus, the classical political economists, especially Ricardo, pursued this method.) It is reprobated by the whole Hegelian army, who think it ought to be replaced by the "Historic Method," which studies complex problems in all their complexity, but which cannot boast any distinguished successes.

X [KINDS OF REASONING]

There are in science three fundamentally different kinds of reasoning. Deduction (called by Aristotle συναγωγή or ἀναγωγή), Induction (Aristotle's and Plato's ἐπαγωγή) and Retroduction (Aristotle's ἀπαγωγή, but misunderstood because of corrupt text, and as misunderstood usually translated *abduction*).[1] Besides these three, Analogy (Aristotle's παράδειγμα) combines the characters of Induction and Retroduction.

Deduction is that mode of reasoning which examines the state of things asserted in the premisses, forms a diagram of that state of things, perceives in the parts of that diagram relations not explicitly mentioned in the premisses, satisfies itself by mental experiments upon the diagram that these relations would always subsist, or at least would do so in a certain proportion of cases, and concludes their necessary, or probable, truth. For example, let the premiss be that there are four marked points upon a line which has neither extremity nor furcation. Then by means of a diagram,

we may conclude that there are two pairs of points such that in passing along the line in any way from one to the other point of either pair, one point of the second pair will be passed an odd number of times and the other point an even (or zero) number of times. This is *deduction*.

---

[1] [Peirce usually calls it "abduction"; sometimes "hypothesis."]

Induction is that mode of reasoning which adopts a conclusion as approximate, because it results from a method of inference which must generally lead to the truth in the long run. For example, a ship enters port laden with coffee. I go aboard and sample the coffee. Perhaps I do not examine over a hundred beans, but they have been taken from the middle, top, bottom of bags in every part of the hold. I conclude by *induction* that the whole cargo has approximately the same value per bean as the hundred beans of my sample. All that induction can do is to ascertain the value of a ratio.

Retroduction is the provisional adoption of a hypothesis, because every possible consequence of it is capable of experimental verification, so that the persevering application of the same method may be expected to reveal its disagreement with facts, if it does so disagree. For example, all the operations of chemistry fail to decompose hydrogen, lithium, glucinum, boron, carbon, nitrogen, oxygen, fluorine, sodium, . . . gold, mercury, thallium, lead, bismuth, thorium, and uranium. We provisionally suppose these bodies to be simple; for if not, similar experimentation will detect their compound nature, if it can be detected at all. That I term *retroduction*.

Analogy is the inference that a not very large collection of objects which agree in various respects may very likely agree in another respect. For instance, the earth and Mars agree in so many respects that it seems not unlikely they may agree in being inhabited.

The methods of reasoning of science have been studied in various ways and with results which disagree in important particulars. The followers of Laplace treat the subject from the point of view of the theory of probabilities. After corrections due to Boole [2] and others, that method yields substantially the results stated above. Whewell [3] described the reasoning just as it appeared to a man deeply conversant with several branches of science as only a genuine researcher can know them, and adding to that knowledge a full acquaint-

[2] [*Laws of Thought*, Chs. 16-21.]
[3] [*The Philosophy of the Inductive Sciences* (1840).]

ance with the history of science. These results, as might be expected, are of the highest value, although there are important distinctions and reasons which he overlooked. John Stuart Mill endeavored to explain the reasonings of science by the nominalistic metaphysics of his father. The superficial perspicuity of that kind of metaphysics rendered his logic extremely popular with those who think, but do not think profoundly; who know something of science, but more from the outside than the inside, and who for one reason or another delight in the simplest theories even if they fail to cover the facts.

Mill denies that there was any reasoning in Kepler's procedure. He says it is merely a description of the facts.[4] He seems to imagine that Kepler had all the places of Mars in space given him by Tycho's observations; and that all he did was to generalize and so obtain a general expression for them. Even had that been all, it would certainly have been inference. Had Mill had even so much practical acquaintance with astronomy as to have practised discussions of the motions of double stars, he would have seen that. But so to characterize Kepler's work is to betray total ignorance of it. Mill certainly never read the *De Motu* [*Motibus*] *Stellae Martis,* which is not easy reading. The reason it is not easy is that it calls for the most vigorous exercise of all the powers of reasoning from beginning to end.

What Kepler had given was a large collection of observations of the apparent places of Mars at different times. He also knew that, in a general way, the Ptolemaic theory agrees with the appearances, although there were various difficulties in making it fit exactly. He was furthermore convinced that the hypothesis of Copernicus ought to be accepted. Now this hypothesis, as Copernicus himself understood its first outline, merely modifies the theory of Ptolemy so far as [to] impart to all the bodies of the solar system one common motion, just what is required to annul the mean motion of the sun. It would seem, therefore, at first sight, that it ought not to affect the appearances at all. If Mill had called the work of

4 [*System of Logic,* Bk. III, Ch. 2, §3.]

Copernicus mere description he would not have been *so very far* from the truth as he was. But Kepler did not understand the matter quite as Copernicus did. Because the sun was so near the centre of the system, and was of vast size (even Kepler knew its diameter must be at least fifteen times that of the earth), Kepler, looking at the matter dynamically, thought it must have something to do with causing the planets to move in their orbits. This retroduction, vague as it was, cost great intellectual labor, and was most important in its bearings upon all Kepler's work. Now Kepler remarked that the lines of apsides of the orbits of Mars and of the earth are not parallel; and he utilized various observations most ingeniously to infer that they probably intersected in the sun. Consequently, it must be supposed that a general description of the motion would be simpler when referred to the sun as a fixed point of reference than when referred to any other point. Thence it followed that the proper times at which to take the observations of Mars for determining its orbit were when it appeared just opposite the sun—the true sun—instead of when it was opposite the *mean* sun, as had been the practice. Carrying out this idea, he obtained a theory of Mars which satisfied the longitudes at all the oppositions observed by Tycho and himself, thirteen in number, to perfection. But unfortunately, it did not satisfy the latitudes at all and was totally irreconcilable with observations of Mars when far from opposition.

At each stage of his long investigation, Kepler has a theory which is approximately true, since it approximately satisfied the observations (that is, within 8″, which is less than any but Tycho's observations could decisively pronounce an error), and he proceeds to modify this theory, after the most careful and judicious reflection, in such a way as to render it more rational or closer to the observed fact. Thus, having found that the centre of the orbit bisects the eccentricity, he finds in this an indication of the falsity of the theory of the equant and substitutes, for this artificial device, the principle of the equable description of areas. Subsequently, finding that the planet moves faster at ninety degrees from its apsides than it ought to do, the question is whether this is owing to an error in the law of areas or to a compression of the orbit. He ingeniously proves that the latter is the case.

Thus, never modifying his theory capriciously, but always with a sound and rational motive for just the modification he makes, it follows that when he finally reaches a modification—of most striking simplicity and rationality—which exactly satisfies the observations, it stands upon a totally different logical footing from what it would if it had been struck out at random, or the reader knows not how, and had been found to satisfy the observation. Kepler shows his keen logical sense in detailing the whole process by which he finally arrived at the true orbit. This is the greatest piece of Retroductive reasoning ever performed.

XI [THE STUDY OF THE USELESS]

. . . The old-fashioned political economist adored, as alone capable of redeeming the human race, the glorious principle of individual greed, although, as this principle requires for its action hypocrisy and fraud, he generally threw in some dash of inconsistent concessions to virtue, as a sop to the vulgar Cerberus. But it is easy to see that the only kind of science this principle would favor would be such as is immediately remunerative with a great preference for such as can be kept secret, like the modern sciences of dyeing and perfumery. Kepler's discovery rendered Newton possible, and Newton rendered modern physics possible, with the steam engine, electricity, and all the other sources of the stupendous fortunes of our age. But Kepler's discovery would not have been possible without the doctrine of conics. Now contemporaries of Kepler—such penetrating minds as Descartes and Pascal—were abandoning the study of geometry (in which they included what we now call the differential calculus, so far as that had at that time any existence) because they said it was so UTTERLY USELESS. There was the future of the human race almost trembling in the balance; for had not the geometry of conic sections already been worked out in large measure, and had their opinion that only sciences apparently useful ought to be pursued [prevailed], the nineteenth century would have had none of those characters which distinguish it from the *ancien régime*.

True science is distinctively the study of useless things. For the useful things will get studied without the aid of scientific men. To employ these rare minds on such work is like running a steam engine by burning diamonds.

The University of Paris encouraged useless studies in the most effective way possible, by training so many men as to be almost sure of getting a large proportion of all the minds that could be very serviceable in such studies. At the same time, it provided a sure living not only for such as were really successful, but even for those whose talents were of a somewhat inferior kind. On the other hand, like all universities, it set up an official standard of truth, and frowned on all who questioned it. Just so, the German universities for a whole generation turned the cold shoulder to every man who did not extol their stale Hegelianism, until it became a stench in the nostrils of every man of common sense. Then the official fashion shifted, and a Hegelian is today treated in Germany with the same arrogant stupidity with which an anti-Hegelian formerly was. Of course, so-called "universities," whose purpose is not the solution of great problems, but merely the fitting of a selection of young men to earn more money than their fellow citizens not so favored, have for the interests of science none of the value of the medieval and German universities, although they exercise the same baleful influence to about the same degree.

The small academies of continental Europe are reasonably free from the gravest fault of the universities. Their defect is that while they indirectly do much for their few members they extend little aid to the younger men, except that of giving a general tone of respectability to pure science.

The larger bodies give much less aid to individuals; but

they begin to aid them sooner. They have a distinct though limited use when they are specialized, like the Union of German chemists. But whether the Royal Society has been as serviceable to science as the French Académie des Sciences may be doubted.

XII [IL LUME NATURALE]

In examining the reasonings of those physicists who gave to modern science the initial propulsion which has insured its healthful life ever since, we are struck with the great, though not absolutely decisive, weight they allowed to instinctive judgments. Galileo appeals to *il lume naturale* at the most critical stages of his reasoning. Kepler, Gilbert, and Harvey— not to speak of Copernicus—substantially rely upon an inward power, not sufficient to reach the truth by itself, but yet supplying an essential factor to the influences carrying their minds to the truth.

It is certain that the only hope of retroductive reasoning ever reaching the truth is that there may be some natural tendency toward an agreement between the ideas which suggest themselves to the human mind and those which are concerned in the laws of nature.

XIII [GENERALIZATION AND ABSTRACTION]

The most important operation of the mind is that of generalization. There are some exceedingly difficult questions of theoretical logic connected with generalization. On the other hand, there are some valuable lessons which evade those puzzles. If we look at any earlier work upon mathematics as compared with a later one upon the same subject, that which most astonishes us is to see the difficulty men had in first seizing upon general conceptions which after we become a little familiarized to them are quite matters of course. That an Egyptian should have been able to think of adding one-fifth and one-fifth, and yet should not have been content to call the sum two-fifths, but must call it one-third plus one-fifteenth, as if he could not conceive of a sum of fractions unless their denominators were different, seems perverse stupidity. That decimals should have been so slow in coming in, and that, when they did come, the so-called decimal point should be written as if the relation of units to tenths were somehow peculiar, while what was logically called for was simply some mark attached to the units place, so that instead of 3.14159 [what] should have been written [was] $\hat{3}14159$, seems very surprising. That Descartes should have thought it necessary to work problems in analytical geometry four times over, according to the different quadrants between the axes of co-ordinates in which the point to be determined might occur, is astonishing. That which the early mathematicians failed to see in all these cases was that some feature which they were accustomed to insert into their theorems was quite irrelevant and could perfectly well be omitted without affecting in the slightest degree the cogency of any step of the demonstrations.

Another operation closely allied to generalization is abstraction; and the use of it is perhaps even more characteristic of mathematical reasoning than is generalization. This consists of seizing upon something which has been conceived as a ἔπος πτερόεν, a meaning not dwelt upon but through which something else is discerned, and converting it into an ἔπος ἀπτερόεν, a meaning upon which we rest as the principal subject of discourse. Thus, the mathematician conceives an operation as something itself to be operated upon. He conceives the collection of places of a moving particle as itself a place which can at one instant be totally occupied by a filament, which can again move, and the aggregate of all its places, considered as possibly occupied in one instant, is a surface, and so forth.

The intimate connection between generalization and continuity is to be pointed out.

XIV [THE EVALUATION OF EXACTITUDE]

For every line of scientific research there is in any given stage of its development, an appropriate standard of certitude and exactitude, such that it is useless to require more, and unsatisfactory to have less. This is a part of the doctrine of the Economy of Research. When Phoenix [1] made his celebrated survey of the route from San Francisco to the Mission of Dolores, the distance required was the sum of two parts, one of them resting on the guess of a driver, while the other was determined at great expense to a transcendental precision. As long as one part of the distance was extremely uncertain, there was no use in spending much money in ascertaining the other part precisely. For there is a relation between the value of an increased certainty of an item of knowledge and the cost of such increase of certainty, which enables us to determine whether it is better to expend our genius, energy, time, and money upon one investigation or upon another.

If a result is to be used merely to confirm the result of an independent investigation, it may have a high value even though its probability is not very high. But if it is only to be used in combination with other results, very little will be gained by increasing its probability far beyond the probabilities of those others. Of course, knowledge that is to be put to special purposes may need to be more precise than other knowledge. Thus, it pays to determine the places of a thousand stars with the utmost accuracy, leaving hundreds of thousands only roughly located, and others only recorded upon photographs. But where a high degree of exactitude and probability is unattainable, that is no reason for refusing to accept such knowledge as we can attain. Because we cannot reach great certainty about the life and teachings of Pythagoras is no reason for sulkily dismissing the subject as one we know nothing about, as Dr. Ed. Zeller [2] would have us do.

[1] [In his *Phoenixiana*, "Official Report."]
[2] [*A History of Greek Philosophy* (1881), I, 279.—Ed.]

XV [SCIENCE AND EXTRAORDINARY PHENOMENA]

Science is from the nature of its procedure confined to the investigation of the ordinary course of nature. I do not mean that it cannot investigate individual objects, such as the earth. But all its explanations of such objects must be limited to the supposition that they have come about in the ordinary course of nature. A statistical result may be obtained.

We may find that such and such a proportion of calves have five legs. But we never can conclude with any probability that the ratio is strictly zero; and even if we knew that the proportion of men with golden thighs is exactly zero, that would be no argument at all against Pythagoras having had a golden thigh. For something might be true of one man, or any number of men, and yet might occur in the long run in a finite number of cases out of an infinite series. Now a finite number divided by infinity is exactly zero. That Pythagoras had a golden thigh is the testimony of history. It is asserted by Aristotle, of all possible authorities the highest, by both Porphyry and Jamblichus after Nicomachus, by Herodotus, by Plutarch, Diogenes Laertius, Aelian, Apollonius,[1] etc. This is far stronger testimony than we have for the resurrection of Jesus. Are we then to admit as a part of the science of history that Pythagoras had a golden thigh?

To do so would be to make a retroductive inference. Now a retroductive conclusion is only justified by its *explaining* an observed fact. An explanation is a syllogism of which the major premiss, or rule, is a known law or rule of nature, or other general truth; the minor premiss, or case, is the hypothesis or retroductive conclusion, and the conclusion, or

---

[1] [Peirce seems to have secured his authorities from Zeller's *A History of Greek Philosophy* (1881), I, 328, n. 4. Zeller's references are not all accurate, and the authorities quoted are not independent. Peirce's annotated copy of this book is now, through the gift of his wife, the property of the Harvard College Library.]

result, is the observed (or otherwise established) fact. Such an explanation, in this case, would be like this:

Every fact about Pythagoras (unless kept secret or insignificant) would be reported by his ancient biographers.

That Pythagoras had a golden thigh was a fact about Pythagoras neither secret nor insignificant.

∴That Pythagoras had a golden thigh would be reported by all his ancient biographers.

But this syllogism may be condemned at once on the ground that it supposes we have statistical knowledge about such kinds of facts as are quite contrary to the usual course of nature. If the reply be made that it could make in regard to the reporting of the fact no difference whether it were a natural one or not, I rejoin, that granting that, it is not to the purpose. It only goes to show that there is no difference between natural and supernatural facts in this respect; from which the only just inference is that no such proposition can be known even in respect to natural facts. This, indeed, is the case. We cannot say that every remarkable public fact about Pythagoras would be reported, but only that every phenomenon would be told as it appeared to people in an almost primitive state of civilization. Nobody can think that the golden thigh was treated as a modern assayer would treat a gold brick. It was probably flexible and therefore its golden appearance was superficial. One of these days, we may find out something about the ancient Persians, Chorasmians, or Brahmins which may make this story significant. At present, it only illustrates the impossibility of science making any assertion about a fact out of the course of nature. Pythagoras was certainly a wonderful man. We have no right, at all, to say that supernal powers had not put a physical mark upon him as extraordinary as his personality. Science can no more deny a miracle than it can assert one.

But although science cannot infer any particular violation of the ordinary course of nature, it may very well be that it should find evidence that such violations are so frequent and usual that this fact is itself a part of the ordinary course of nature. For that reason, it is perfectly proper that science should inquire, for example, into the evidences of the fulfillment of prayers, etc. That is something open to experimental inquiry; and until such inquiry has been instituted nobody is entitled to any opinion whatever, or any bias, as to its result.

XVI [REASONING FROM SAMPLES]

Many persons seem to suppose that the state of things asserted in the premises of an induction renders the state of things asserted in the conclusion probable. The fact that Macaulay's essay on Bacon was admired in its day shows how little the absurdity of such a position was perceived. Even John Stuart Mill holds that the uniformity of nature makes the one state of things follow from the other. He overlooks the circumstance that if so it ought to follow necessarily, while in truth no definite probability can be assigned to it without absurd consequences. He also overlooks the fact that inductive reasoning does not invariably infer a uniformity; it may infer a diversity. I watch the throws of a die, I notice that about half are odd and half are even, and that they follow one another with the utmost irregularity. I conclude that about half of all the throws of that die are odd and that the odd and even follow one another with great irregularity. How can any principle of uniformity account for the truth of such an induction? Mill never made up his mind in what sense he took the phrase "uniformity of nature" when he spoke of it as the basis of induction. In some passages he clearly means any special uniformity by which a given character is likely to belong to the whole of a species, a genus, a family, or a class if it belongs to any members of that group. In this sense, as well as in others, overlooked by Mill, there is no doubt the knowledge of a uniformity strengthens an inductive conclusion; but it is equally free from doubt that such knowledge is not essential to induction. But in other passages Mill holds that it is not the knowledge of the uniformity, but the uniformity itself that supports induction, and furthermore that it is no special uniformity but a general uniformity in nature. Mill's mind was certainly acute and vigorous, but it was not mathematically accurate; and it is by that trait that I am forced to explain his not seeing that this general uniformity could not be so defined as not on the one hand to appear manifestly false or on the other hand to render no support to induction, or both. He says it means that under similar circumstances similar events will occur. But this is vague. Does he mean that objects alike in all respects but one are alike in that one? But plainly no two different real objects are alike in all respects but one. Does he mean that objects *sufficiently* alike in other respects are alike in any given respect? But that would be but another way of saying that no two different objects are alike in all respects but one. It is obviously true; but it has no bearing on induction, where we deal with objects which we well know are, like all existing things, alike in numberless respects and unlike in numberless other respects.

The truth is that induction is reasoning from a sample taken at random to the whole lot sampled. A sample is a *random* one, provided it is drawn by such machinery, artificial or physiological, that in the long run any one individual of the whole lot would get taken as often as any other. Therefore, judging of the statistical composition of a whole lot from a sample is judging by a method which will be right on the average in the long run, and, by the reasoning of the doctrine of chances, will be nearly right oftener than it will be far from right.

That this does justify induction is a mathematical proposition beyond dispute. It has been objected that the sampling cannot be random in this sense. But this is an idea which flies far away from the plain facts. Thirty throws of a die constitute an approximately random sample of all the throws of that die; and that the randomness should be approximate is all that is required.

This account of the rationale of induction is distinguished from others in that it has as its consequences two rules of inductive inference which are very frequently violated, although they have sometimes been insisted upon. The first of these is that the sample must be a random one. Upon that I shall not dwell here. The other rule is that the character, toward the ascertainment of the proportionate frequency of which in the lot sampled [the sampling is done], must not be determined by the character of the particular sample taken. For example, we must not take a sample of eminent men, and studying over them, find that they have certain characters and conclude that all eminent men will have those characters. We must first decide for what character we propose to examine the sample, and only after that decision examine the sample. The reason is that any sample will be peculiar and unlike the average of the lot sampled in innumerable respects. At the same time it will be approximately like the average of the whole lot in the great majority of respects.

In order to illustrate the necessity of this rule I take a random sample of eminent persons. It is quite a random one, for it consists of the first names on pages 100, 300, 500, 700, 900, of Phillips's *Great Index of Biography* [*Biographical Reference,* second edition, 1881]. The names are as follows:

	Born	Died	
Francis Baring	1740	1810	Sept. 12
Vicomte de Custine	1760	1794	Jan. 3
Hippostrates (of uncertain age)			
Marquis d' O.	1535	1594	Oct. 24
Theocrenes	1480	1536	Oct. 18

Now I might, in violation of the above rule of predesignation, draw the following inductions:

1. Three-fourths of these men were born in a year whose date ends in a cipher. Hence about three-fourths of all eminent men are probably so born. But, in fact, only one in ten is so born.

2. Three eminent men out of four die in autumn. In fact, only one out of four.

3. All eminent men die on a day of the month divisible by three. In fact, one out of three.

4. All eminent men die in years whose date doubled and increased by one gives a number whose last figure is the same as that in the tens' place of the date itself. In fact, only one in ten.

5. All eminent men who were living in any year ending in forty-four died at an age which after subtracting four becomes divisible by eleven. All others die at an age which increased by ten is divisible by eleven.

This rule is recognized in the requirement of physicists that a theory shall furnish predictions which shall be verified before any particular weight is accorded to it. The medical men, too, who deserve special mention for the reason that they have had since Galen a logical tradition of their own, recognize this rule, however dimly, in their working against reasoning *"post hoc, ergo propter hoc."* . . .

XVII [THE METHOD OF RESIDUAL PHENOMENA]

The so-called "method of residual phenomena" is so simple that it hardly calls for any remark. At any early stage of science when there are few observations of a given matter, and those rough ones, a law is made out which, when the observations come to be increased in number and made more accurate, is found not to hold exactly. The departures from this law are found themselves to follow a law which may now be shown to be true. But at a still later date it is found that this law again is interfered with, that there are still more minute departures from it, and these departures are again found to follow a law. All the successive laws so found may be real, or they may be merely empirical formulae . . . .

XVIII [OBSERVATION]

I have already remarked that a definition of science in general which shall express a really intelligent conception of it as a living historic entity must regard it as the occupation of that peculiar class of men, the scientific men. The same remark may be extended to definitions of the different branches of science. The men who pursue a given branch herd together. They understand one another; they live in the same world, while those who pursue another branch are for them foreigners.

It will be found upon close examination that that which renders the modes of thought of the students of a special branch of science peculiar is that their experience lies in a peculiar region. And the cause of this is that they are trained and equipped to make a peculiar kind of observations. The man who is continually making chemical analyses lives in a different region of nature from other men. The same thing is even more true of men who are constantly using a microscope.

It comes to this, that sciences must be classified according to the peculiar means of observation they employ.

So too the great landmarks in the history of science are to be placed at the points where new instruments, or other means of observation, are introduced. Astronomy before the telescope and astronomy after the telescope. Prephotographic astronomy and photographic astronomy. Chemistry before the exact analytic balance, and after.

XIX [EVOLUTION]

The evolutionary theory in general throws great light upon history and especially upon the history of science—both its public history and the account of its development in an individual intellect. As great a light is thrown upon the theory of evolution in general by the evolution of history, especially that of science—whether public or private.

The main theories of the evolution of organic species are three. First, the theory of Darwin, according to which the entire interval from Moner to Man has been traversed by successive purely fortuitous and insensible variations *in reproduction*. The changes on the whole follow a determinate course simply because a certain amount of change in certain directions destroys the species altogether, as the final result of successive weakenings of its reproductive power. Second, the theory of Lamarck, according to which the whole interval has been traversed by a succession of very minute changes. But these have not taken place in reproduction, which has absolutely nothing to do with the business, except to keep the average individuals plastic by their youth. The changes have not been fortuitous but wholly the result of strivings of the individuals. Third, the theory of cataclysmal evolution, according to which the changes have not been small and have not been fortuitous; but they have taken place chiefly in reproduction. According to this view, sudden changes of environment have taken place from time to time. These changes have put certain organs at a disadvantage, and there has been an effort to use them in new ways. Such organs are particularly apt to sport in reproduction and to change in the way which adapts them better to their recent mode of exercise.

Notwithstanding the teachings of Weismann, it seems altogether probable that all three of these modes of evolution have acted. It is probable that the last has been the most efficient. These three modes of organic evolution have their parallels in other departments of evolution.

Let us consider, for example, the evolution of standards of weights and measures. In order to define the word "pound" in the *Century Dictionary*,[1] I made a list of about four hundred

---

[1] [Peirce wrote the definitions of terms in mechanics, mathematics, astronomy, astrology, weights and measures, logic, metaphysics, all those relating to universities, and many on psychology for the *Century Dictionary*, edition of 1889.]

pounds which had been in use in different parts of Europe—undoubtedly a very incomplete list, for it was confined in great measure to certain provinces concerning which I was able to obtain information. Each individual pound or measuring stick is from time to time copied; and at length the old one becomes destroyed. The measure of each copy is imperceptibly larger or smaller than its immediate prototype. If then these variations cannot, by gradual summation, produce a standard much smaller without that standard being destroyed as inconvenient while no such destruction would follow upon an increase of the standard, the average of the standards will slowly grow larger by Darwinian evolution. If there were a disposition on the part of owners of pounds to file them down, so as to make them lighter, though not enough to be noticed, then these filed pounds being copied, and the copies filed, there would be a gradual lightening of the pound by Lamarckian evolution. But it is very unlikely that either of these two modes has been a considerable factor in the actual evolution of weights and measures. As long as their circumstances are unchanged, human communities are exceedingly conservative. Nothing short of the despotism of a modern government with a modern police can cause a change in weights and measures. But from time to time changes occur which cause trade to take new routes. Business has to be adapted to new conditions; and under such influences we find all those habits of communities which are rendered unsuitable by the change become plastic enough. Then it is that a new pound or a new yard may be made which is a compromise between a desire to retain old ways and a desire to please new-comers.

In the evolution of science, a Darwinian mode of evolution might, for example, consist in this, that at every recall of a judgment to the mind—say, for example, a judgment in regard to some such delicate question as the marriage of the clergy—a slight fortuitous modification of the judgment might take place; the modified judgment would cause a corresponding modification of the belief-habit, so that the next recall would be influenced by this fortuitous modification, though it would depart more or less from it by a new fortuitous modification. If, however, by such summation of modifications an opinion quite untenable were reached, it would either be violently changed or would be associationally weak and not apt to be recalled. The effect of this would be in the long run that belief would move away from such untenable positions. It is possible that such a mode of influence may affect our instinctive feelings; but there can be nothing of this sort in science, which is controlled and exact. But another sort of Darwinian evolution undoubtedly does take place. We are studying over phenomena of which we have been unable to acquire any satisfactory account. Various tentative explanations recur to our minds from time to time, and at each occurrence are modified by omission, insertion, or change in the point of view, in an almost fortuitous way. Finally, one of these takes such an aspect that we are led to dismiss it as impossible. Then, all the energy of thought which had previously gone to the consideration of that becomes distributed among the other explanations, until finally one of them becomes greatly strengthened in our minds.

Lamarckian evolution might, for example, take the form of perpetually modifying our opinion in the effort to make that opinion represent the known facts as more and more observations came to be collected. This is all the time going on in regard, for example, to our estimate of the danger of infection of phthisis. Yet, after all, it does not play a prominent part in the evolution of science. The physical journals—say, for example, Poggendorff's [*Annalen der Physik*] and *Beiblätter*—publish each month a great number of new researches. Each of these is a distinct contribution to science. It represents some good, solid, well-trained labor of observation and inference. But as modifying what is already known, the average effect of the ordinary research may be said to be insignificant. Nevertheless, as these modifications are not fortuitous but are for the most part movements toward the truth—could they be rightly understood, all of them would be so—there is no doubt that from decade to decade, even without any splendid discoveries or great studies, science would advance very perceptibly. We see that it is so in branches of physics which remain for a long time without any decisive conquests. It was so, for example, in regard to the classification of the chemical elements in the lapse of time from Berzelius to Mendeléeff, as the valuable history of Venable [2] shows. This is an evolution of the Lamarckian type.

But this is not the way in which science mainly progresses. It advances by leaps; and the impulse for each leap is either some new observational resource, or some novel way of reasoning about the observations. Such novel way of reasoning might, perhaps, be considered as a new observational means, since it draws attention to relations between facts which would previously have been passed by unperceived.

[I] illustrate by the discoveries of Pasteur,[3] who began by applying the microscope to chemistry. He picked out the right- and left-handed crystals of tartaric acid. The two kinds have absolutely the same properties except in regard to direction of rotation of the plane of polarization and in their chemical relations to other "optically active" bodies. Since this method of picking out individual crystals was so slow, Pasteur looked for other means. Ferments of appropriate kinds were found to have the same effect. The microscope showed these were due to living organisms, which Pasteur began studying. At that time the medical world was dominated by Claude Bernard's dictum that a disease is not an entity but merely a sum of symptoms.[4] This was pure metaphysics which only barricaded inquiry in that direction. But that was a generation which attached great value to nominalistic metaphysics. Pasteur began with the phylloxera. He found it influenced the "optical activity" of the sugar. This pointed to a ferment and therefore to an entity. He began to extend the doctrine to other diseases. The medical men, dominated by the meta-

2 [*The Development of the Periodic Law* (Easton, Pa., 1896).]

3 [See *Oeuvres de Pasteur* (Paris, 1922), I, 83.]

4 [*Leçons de Pathologie expérimental*, 2ᵐᵉ Leçon (Paris, 1872).]

physics of Claude Bernard, raised all sorts of sophistical objections. But the method of cultures and inoculation proved the thing, and here we see new ideas connected with new observational methods and a fine example of the usual process of scientific evolution. It is not by insensible steps.

XX [SOME A PRIORI DICTA]

The last fifty years have taught the lesson of not trifling with facts and not trusting to principles and methods which are not logically founded upon facts and which serve only to exclude testimony from consideration.

Such, for example, was the dictum of Claude Bernard that a disease is not an entity—a purely metaphysical doctrine. But the observation of facts has taught us that a disease is in many, if not most, serious cases, just as much an entity as a human family consisting of father, mother, and children.

Such was the dictum of the old psychology which identified the soul with the ego, declared its absolute simplicity, and held that its faculties were mere names for logical divisions of human activity. This was all unadulterated fancy. The observation of facts has now taught us that the ego is a mere wave in the soul, a superficial and small feature, that the soul may contain several personalities and is as complex as the brain itself, and that the faculties, while not exactly definable and not absolutely fixed, are as real as are the different convolutions of the cortex.

Such were the dicta by means of which the internal criticism of historical documents was carried to such a height that it often amounted to the rejection of all the testimony that has come down to us, and the substitution for it of a dream spun out of the critic's brain. But archeological researches have shown that ancient testimony ought to be trusted in the main, with a small allowance for the changes in the meanings of words. When we are told that Pythagoras had a golden thigh, we are to remember that to the ancients gold did not mean a chemical element of atomic weight 197.5 and specific gravity 19.3, melting at 1045° C. and forming saline compounds of the types AuX and AuX_3. It meant something of metallic lustre, warmer in color than electrum and cooler than copper. Dr. Schliemann's discoveries were the first socdolager that "higher criticism" received. It has since got many others.

Such was the dictum of Laplace that stones do not come from heaven.

Such were the dicta by which everything of the nature of extraordinary powers connected with psychological states of which the hypnotic trance is an example were set down as tricks. At present, while the existence of telepathy cannot be said to be established, all scientific men are obliged by observed facts to admit that it presents at least a very serious problem requiring respectful treatment.

XXI [THE PAUCITY OF SCIENTIFIC KNOWLEDGE]

Persons who know science chiefly by its results—that is to say, have no acquaintance with it at all as a living inquiry—are apt to acquire the notion that the universe is now entirely explained in all its leading features; and that it is only here and there that the fabric of scientific knowledge betrays any rents.

But in point of fact, notwithstanding all that has been discovered since Newton's time, his saying that we are little children picking up pretty pebbles on the beach while the whole ocean lies before us unexplored remains substantially as true as ever, and will do so though we shovel up the pebbles by steam shovels and carry them off in carloads. An infinitesimal ratio may be multiplied indefinitely and remain infinitesimal still.

In the first place all that science has done is to study those relations between objects which were brought into prominence and conceiving which we had been endowed with some original knowledge in two instincts—the instinct of *feeding,* which brought with it elementary knowledge of mechanical forces, space, etc., and the instinct of *breeding,* which brought with it elementary knowledge of psychical motives, of time, etc. All the other relations of things concerning which we must suppose there is vast store of truth are for us merely the object of such false sciences as judicial astrology, palmistry, the doctrine of signatures, the doctrine of correspondences, magic, and the like.

In the next place, even within the very bounds to which our science is confined, it is altogether superficial and fragmentary. Want of knowledge of the constitution of matter and of electricity. The conservation of forces, as Helmholtz first enunciated it, untenable; whether it can be universally true in any sense is a difficult problem. To strengthen it Helmholtz greatly insisted on discontinuities—a most objectionable theory from every point of view. Mind quite as little understood as matter, and the relations between the two an enigma. The forces we know can be but a small part of all those that are operative. Our ignorance of small things and great, of distant times and of very slow operations. We are equally ignorant of very rapid performances which nevertheless we know to take place. Our science is altogether middlesized and mediocre. Its insignificance compared with the universe cannot be exaggerated.

XXII [THE UNCERTAINTY OF SCIENTIFIC RESULTS]

It is a great mistake to suppose that the mind of the active scientist is filled with propositions which, if not proved beyond all reasonable cavil, are at least extremely probable. On the contrary, he entertains hypotheses which are almost wildly incredible, and treats them with respect for the time being. Why does he do this? Simply because any scientific proposition whatever is always liable to be refuted and dropped at short notice. A hypothesis is something which looks as if it might be true and were true, and which is capable of verification or refutation by comparison with facts. The best hypothesis, in the sense of the one most recommending itself to the inquirer, is the one which can be the most readily refuted if it is false. This far outweighs the trifling merit of being likely. For after all, what is a *likely* hypothesis? It is one which falls in with our preconceived ideas. But these may be wrong. Their errors are just what the scientific man is out gunning for more particularly. But if a hypothesis can quickly and easily be cleared away so as to go toward leaving the field free for the main struggle, this is an immense advantage.

Retroduction goes upon the hope that there is sufficient affinity between the reasoner's mind and nature's to render guessing not altogether hopeless, provided each guess is checked by comparison with observation. It is true that agreement does not show the guess is right; but if it is wrong it must ultimately get found out. The effort should therefore be to make each hypothesis, which is practically no more than a question, as near an even bet as possible.

XXIII [THE ECONOMY OF RESEARCH]

Dr. Ernst Mach, who has one of the best faults a philosopher can have, that of riding his horse to death, does just this with his principle of Economy in science.[1] But of course there is a doctrine of the Economies of Research. One or two of its principles are easily made out. The value of knowledge is, for the purposes of science, in one sense absolute. It is not to be measured, it may be said, in money; in one sense that is true. But knowledge that leads to other knowledge is more valuable in proportion to the trouble it saves in the way of expenditure to get that other knowledge. Having a certain fund of energy, time, money, etc., all of which are merchant-

[1] [See e.g., the lecture on the "Economical Nature of Physical Inquiry" in the *Popular Scientific Lectures* (1895).]

able articles to spend upon research, the question is how much is to be allowed to each investigation; and *for us* the value of that investigation is the amount of money it will pay us to spend upon it. *Relatively,* therefore, knowledge, even of a purely scientific kind, has a money value.

This value increases with the fullness and precision of the information, but plainly it increases slower and slower as the knowledge becomes fuller and more precise. The cost of the information also increases with its fullness and accuracy, and increases faster and faster the more accurate and full it is. It therefore *may* be the case that it does not pay to get *any* information on a given subject; but, at any rate, it *must* be true that it does not pay (in any given state of science) to push the investigation beyond a certain point in fullness or precision.

If we have a number of studies in which we are interested, we should commence with the most remunerative and carry that forward until it becomes no more than equally remunerative with the commencement of another; carry both forward at such rates that they are equally remunerative until each is no more remunerative than a third, and so on.

If two or more kinds of knowledge are so related that one can replace the other so that the possession of one renders the other less profitable, this will diminish the investigation of either while increasing the investigation of all.

If two or more kinds of information are of use only as supplementing one another, that is, only when combined together, this will increase the investigation until there is little or no profit from the least profitable kind of research.

XXIV [THE FIRST RULE OF REASON] [1]

Upon this first, and in one sense this sole, rule of reason, that in order to learn you must desire to learn, and in so desiring not be satisfied with what you already incline to think,

1 [From unpaginated MS. "F. R. L.," *c.* 1899. (Originally published in *C.P.,* I, 56-58.)]

there follows one corollary which itself deserves to be inscribed upon every wall of the city of philosophy:

Do not block the way of inquiry.

Although it is better to be methodical in our investigations, and to consider the economics of research, yet there is no positive sin against logic in *trying* any theory which may come into our heads, so long as it is adopted in such a sense as to permit the investigation to go on unimpeded and undiscouraged. On the other hand, to set up a philosophy which barricades the road of further advance toward the truth is the one unpardonable offence in reasoning, as it is also the one to which metaphysicians have in all ages shown themselves the most addicted.

Let me call your attention to four familiar shapes in which this venomous error assails our knowledge:

The first is the shape of absolute assertion. That we can be sure of nothing in science is an ancient truth. The Academy taught it. Yet science has been infested with over-confident assertion, especially on the part of the third-rate and fourth-rate men, who have been more concerned with teaching than with learning, at all times. No doubt some of the geometries still teach as a self-evident truth the proposition that if two straight lines in one plane meet a third straight line so as to make the sum of the internal angles on one side less than two right angles those two lines will meet on that side if sufficiently prolonged. Euclid, whose logic was more careful, only reckoned this proposition as a *Postulate*, or arbitrary Hypothesis. Yet even he places among his axioms the proposition that a part is less than its whole, and falls into several conflicts with our most modern geometry in consequence. But why need we stop to consider cases where some subtilty of thought is required to see that the assertion is not warranted when every book which applies philosophy to the conduct of life lays down as positive certainty propositions which it is quite as easy to doubt as to believe?

The second bar which philosophers often set up across the roadway of inquiry lies in maintaining that this, that, and the other never can be known. When Auguste Comte was pressed to specify any matter of positive fact to the knowledge of which no man could by any possibility attain, he instanced the knowledge of the chemical composition of the fixed stars; and you may see his answer set down in the *Philosophie positive*.[2] But the ink was scarcely dry upon the printed page before the spectroscope was discovered and that which he had deemed absolutely unknowable was well on the way of getting ascertained. It is easy enough to mention a question the answer to which is not known to me today. But to aver that that answer will not be known tomorrow is somewhat risky; for oftentimes it is precisely the least expected truth which is turned up under the ploughshare of research. And when it comes to positive assertion that the truth never will be found out, that, in the light of the history of our times, seems to me more hazardous than the venture of Andrée.[3]

The third philosophical stratagem for cutting off inquiry consists in maintaining that this, that, or the other element of science is basic, ultimate, independent of aught else, and utterly inexplicable—not so much from any defect in our knowing as because there is nothing beneath it to know. The only type of reasoning by which such a conclusion could possibly be reached is *retroduction*. Now nothing justifies a retroductive inference except its affording an explanation of the facts. It is, however, no explanation at all of a fact to pronounce it *inexplicable*. That, therefore, is a conclusion which no reasoning can ever justify or excuse.

The last philosophical obstacle to the advance of knowledge which I intend to mention is the holding that this or that law or truth has found its last and perfect formulation—and especially that the ordinary and usual course of nature

2 [19me leçon.]

3 [In 1897 Salomon August Andrée attempted to fly over the polar regions in a balloon. He died in the attempt.]

never can be broken through. "Stones do not fall from heaven," said Laplace, although they had been falling upon inhabited ground every day from the earliest times. But there is no kind of inference which can lend the slightest probability to any such absolute denial of an unusual phenomenon.

XXV THE FIRST RULE OF LOGIC [1]

Certain methods of mathematical computation correct themselves; so that if an error be committed, it is only necessary to keep right on, and it will be corrected in the end. For instance, I want to extract the cube root of 2. The true answer is 1.25992105. . . . The rule is as follows:

Form a column of numbers, which for the sake of brevity we may call the A's. The first 3 A's are any 3 numbers taken at will. To form a new A, add the last two A's, triple the sum, add to this sum the last A but two, and set down the result as the next A. Now any A, the lower in the column the better, divided by the following A gives a fraction which increased by 1 is approximately $\sqrt[3]{2}$.

Correct Computation	Sum of Two	Triple	Erroneous Computation	Sum of Two	Triple
1			1		
0			0		
1	1	3	1	1	3
4	5	15	4	5	15
15	19	57	Error! 16	20	60
58	73	219	61	77	231
223	281	843	235	296	888
858	1081	3243	904	1139	3417
3301	4159	12477	3478	4382	13146
12700			13381		

$$1\frac{3301}{12700} \quad 1.2599213 \qquad\qquad 1\frac{3478}{13381} \quad 1.2599208$$

Error + .0000002 Error − .0000002

[1] [A portion of Lecture 3 on "Detached Ideas on Vitally Important Topics," 1898. (Originally published in *C.P.*, V, 399-400, 405.)]

You see the error committed in the second computation, though it seemed to multiply itself greatly, became substantially corrected in the end.

If you sit down to solve *ten* ordinary linear equations between ten unknown quantities, you will receive materials for a commentary upon the infallibility of mathematical processes. For you will almost infallibly get a wrong solution. I take it as a matter of course that you are not an expert professional computer. He will proceed according to a method which will correct his errors if he makes any.

This calls to mind one of the most wonderful features of reasoning and one of the most important philosophemes in the doctrine of science, of which, however, you will search in vain for any mention in any book I can think of; namely, that reasoning tends to correct itself, and the more so, the more wisely its plan is laid. Nay, it not only corrects its conclusions, it even corrects its premises. The theory of Aristotle is that a necessary conclusion is just equally as certain as its premises, while a probable conclusion is somewhat less so. Hence, he was driven to his strange distinction between what is better known to Nature and what is better known to us. But were every probable inference less certain than its premises, science, which piles inference upon inference, often quite deeply, would soon be in a bad way. Every astronomer, however, is familiar with the fact that the catalogue place of a fundamental star, which is the result of elaborate reasoning, is far more accurate than any of the observations from which it was deduced. . . .

Thus it is that inquiry of every type, fully carried out, has the vital power of self-correction and of growth. This is a property so deeply saturating its inmost nature that it may truly be said that there is but one thing needful for learning the truth, and that is a hearty and active desire to learn what is true. If you really want to learn the truth, you will, by however devious a path, be surely led into the way of truth, at last. No matter how erroneous your ideas of the method may be at first, you will be forced at length to correct them so long as your activity is moved by that sincere desire. Nay, no matter if you only half desire it, at first, that desire would at length conquer all others, could experience continue long enough. But the more veraciously truth is described [2] at the outset, the shorter by centuries will the road to it be.

2 [Probably, "But the more *voraciously* truth is *desired*" etc.—Ed.]

[THE LOGIC OF ABDUCTION]

I   [THE NATURE OF HYPOTHESIS] [1]

.   .   .   .

All our knowledge may be said to rest upon *observed facts*. It is true that there are psychological states which antecede our observing facts as such. Thus, it is a fact that I see an inkstand before me; but before I can say that I am obliged to have impressions of sense into which no idea of an inkstand, or of any separate object, or of an "I," or of seeing, enter at all; and it is true that my judging that I see an inkstand before me is the product of mental operations upon these impressions of sense. But it is only when the cognition has become worked up into a proposition, or judgment of a fact, that I can exercize any direct control over the process; and it is idle to discuss the "legitimacy" of that which cannot be controlled. Observations of fact have, therefore, to be accepted as they occur.

But observed facts relate exclusively to the particular circumstances that happened to exist when they were observed. They do not relate to any future occasions upon which we may be in doubt how we ought to act. They, therefore, do not, in themselves, contain any practical knowledge.

Such knowledge must involve additions to the facts observed. The making of those additions is an operation which we can control; and it is evidently a process during which error is liable to creep in.

Any proposition added to observed facts, tending to make them applicable in any way to other circumstances than those under which they were observed, may be called a hypothesis.

[1] [From "Hume on Miracles," *c.* 1901. (Originally published in *C.P.*, VI, 356-358.) The heading "The Logic of Abduction" has been supplied for this edition.—Ed.]

A hypothesis ought, at first, to be entertained interrogatively. Thereupon, it ought to be tested by experiment so far as practicable. There are two distinct processes, both of which may be performed rightly or wrongly. We may go wrong and be wasting time in so much as entertaining a hypothesis, even as a question. That is a subject for criticism in every case. There are some hypotheses which are of such a nature that they never can be tested at all. Whether such hypotheses ought to be entertained at all, and if so in what sense, is a serious question; . . . There are, moreover, many hypotheses in regard to which knowledge already in our possession may, at once, quite justifiably either raise them to the rank of opinions, or even positive beliefs, or cause their immediate rejection. This also is a matter to be considered. But it is the first process, that of entertaining the question, which will here be of foremost importance.

Before we go further, let us get the points stated above quite clear. By a *hypothesis,* I mean, not merely a supposition about an observed object, as when I suppose that a man is a Catholic priest because that would explain his dress, expression of countenance, and bearing, but also any other supposed truth from which would result such facts as have been observed, as when van't Hoff, having remarked that the osmotic pressure of one per cent solutions of a number of chemical substances was inversely proportional to their atomic weights, thought that perhaps the same relation would be found to exist between the same properties of any other chemical substance. The first starting of a hypothesis and the entertaining of it, whether as a simple interrogation or with any degree of confidence, is an inferential step which I propose to call *abduction.* This will include a preference for any one hypothesis over others which would equally explain the facts, so long as this preference is not based upon any previous knowledge bearing upon the truth of the hypotheses, nor on any testing of any of the hypotheses, after having admitted them on probation. I call all such inference by the peculiar name, *abduc-*

tion, because its legitimacy depends upon altogether different principles from those of other kinds of inference.

II [ON SELECTING HYPOTHESES] [1]

If we are to give the names of Deduction, Induction, and Abduction to the three grand classes of inference, then Deduction must include every attempt at mathematical demonstration, whether it relate to single occurrences or to "probabilities," that is, to statistical ratios; Induction must mean the operation that induces an assent, with or without quantitative modification, to a proposition already put forward, this assent or modified assent being regarded as the provisional result of a method that must ultimately bring the truth to light; while Abduction must cover all the operations by which theories and conceptions are engendered.

How is it that man ever came by any correct theories about nature? We know by Induction that man has correct theories; for they produce predictions that are fulfilled. But by what process of thought were they ever brought to his mind? A chemist notices a surprising phenomenon. Now if he has a high admiration of Mill's *Logic,* as many chemists have, he will remember that Mill tells him that he must work on the principle that, under precisely the same circumstances, like phenomena are produced. Why does he then not note that this phenomenon was produced on such a day of the week, the planets presenting a certain configuration, his daughter having on a blue dress, he having dreamed of a white horse the night before, the milkman having been late that morning, and so on? The answer will be that in early days chemists did use to attend to some such circumstances, but that they have learned better. How have they learned this? By an induction. Very well, that induction must have been based upon a theory which the induction verified. How was it that man was ever led to entertain that true theory? You cannot say that it hap-

1 [From the Eighth Lowell Lecture of 1903, entitled "How to Theorize." (Originally published in *C.P.,* V, 413-422.)]

pened by chance, because the possible theories, if not strictly innumerable, at any rate exceed a trillion—or the third power of a million; and therefore the chances are too overwhelmingly against the single true theory in the twenty or thirty thousand years during which man has been a thinking animal, ever having come into any man's head. Besides, you cannot seriously think that every little chicken that is hatched, has to rummage through all possible theories until it lights upon the good idea of picking up something and eating it. On the contrary, you think the chicken has an innate idea of doing this; that is to say, that it can think of this, but has no faculty of thinking anything else. The chicken you say pecks by instinct. But if you are going to think every poor chicken endowed with an innate tendency toward a positive truth, why should you think that to man alone this gift is denied? If you carefully consider with an unbiassed mind all the circumstances of the early history of science and all the other facts bearing on the question, which are far too various to be specifically alluded to in this lecture, I am quite sure that you must be brought to acknowledge that man's mind has a natural adaptation to imagining correct theories of some kinds, and in particular to correct theories about forces, without some glimmer of which he could not form social ties and consequently could not reproduce his kind. In short, the instincts conducive to assimilation of food, and the instincts conducive to reproduction, must have involved from the beginning certain tendencies to think truly about physics, on the one hand, and about psychics, on the other. It is somehow more than a mere figure of speech to say that nature fecundates the mind of man with ideas which, when those ideas grow up, will resemble their father, Nature.

But if that be so, it must be good reasoning to say that a given hypothesis is good, as a hypothesis, because it is a natural one, or one readily embraced by the human mind. It must concern logic in the highest degree to ascertain precisely how far and under what limitations this maxim may be held. For of all beliefs, none is more natural than the belief that it is natural for man to err. The logician ought to find out what the relation is between these two tendencies.

It behooves a man first of all to free his mind of those four idols of which Francis Bacon speaks in the first book of the *Novum Organum*. So much is the dictate of Ethics, itself. But after that, what? Descartes, as you know, maintained that if a man could only get a perfectly clear and distinct idea [2]—to which Leibniz added the third requirement that it should be adequate [3]—then that idea must be true. But this is far too severe. For never yet has any man attained to an apprehension perfectly clear and distinct, let alone its being adequate; and yet I suppose that true ideas have been entertained. Ordinary ideas of perception, which Descartes thought were most horribly confused, have nevertheless something in them that very nearly warrants their truth, if it does not quite so. "Seeing is believing," says the instinct of man.

The question is what theories and conceptions we *ought* to entertain. Now the word "ought" has no meaning except relatively to an *end*. That ought to be done which is conducive to a certain end. The inquiry therefore should begin with searching for the *end* of thinking. What do we think *for*? What is the physiological function of thought? If we say it is action, we must mean the government of action to some end. To what end? It must be something, good or admirable, regardless of any ulterior reason. This can only be the esthetically good. But what is esthetically good? Perhaps we may say the full expression of an idea? Thought, however, is in itself essentially of the nature of a sign. But a sign is not a sign unless it translates itself into another sign in which it is more fully developed. Thought requires achievement for its own development, and without this development it is nothing. Thought must live and grow in incessant new and higher translations, or it proves itself not to be genuine thought.

But the mind loses itself in such general questions and

[2] [*Meditations* III; *Method*, Pt. II; *Principles*, Pt. I, 30, 43, etc.]
[3] [Leibniz's *Nouveaux Essais*, Bk. II, Ch. 31; *Discours*, XXIV, XXV.]

seems to be floating in a limitless vacuity. It is of the very essence of thought and purpose that it should be special, just as truly as it is of the essence of either that it should be general. Yet it illustrates the point that the valuable idea must be eminently fruitful in special applications, while at the same time it is always growing to wider and wider alliances.

Classical antiquity was far too favorable to the sort of concept that was

fortis, et in se ipso totus, teres atque rotundus.[4]

I often meet with such theories in philosophical books, especially in the works of theological students and of others who draw their ideas from antiquity. Such is the circular theory, which assumes itself and returns into itself—the aristocratical theory which holds itself aloof from vulgar facts. Logic has not the least objection to such a view, so long as it maintains its self-sufficiency, keeps itself strictly to itself, as its nobility obliges it to do, makes no pretension of meddling with the world of experience, and does not ask anybody to assent to it.

Auguste Comte, at the other extreme, would condemn every theory that was not "verifiable." Like the majority of Comte's ideas, this is a bad interpretation of a *truth*. An explanatory hypothesis, that is to say, a conception which does not limit its purpose to enabling the mind to grasp into one a variety of facts, but which seeks to connect those facts with our general conceptions of the universe, ought, in one sense, to be *verifiable;* that is to say, it ought to be little more than a ligament of numberless possible predictions concerning future experience, so that if they fail, it fails. Thus, when Schliemann entertained the hypothesis that there really had been a city of Troy and a Trojan War, this meant to his mind among other things that when he should come to make excavations at Hissarlik he would probably find remains of a city with evidences of a civilization more or less answering to the descriptions of the *Iliad,* and which would correspond with other probable finds at Mycenae, Ithaca, and elsewhere. So

4 [Horace, *Satires,* II. 7. 86.]

understood, Comte's maxim is sound. Nothing but that *is* an explanatory hypothesis. But Comte's own notion of a *verifiable* hypothesis was that it must not suppose anything that you are not able directly to observe.[5] From such a rule it would be fair to infer that he would permit Mr. Schliemann to suppose he was going to find arms and utensils at Hissarlik, but would forbid him to suppose that they were either made or used by any human being, since no such beings could ever be detected by direct percept. He ought on the same principle to forbid us to suppose that a fossil skeleton had ever belonged to a living ichthyosaurus. This seems to be substantially the opinion of M. Poincaré at this day. The same doctrine would forbid us to believe in our memory of what happened at dinnertime today. I have for many years been an adherent of what is technically called Common Sense in philosophy, myself; and do not think that my Tychistic opinions conflict with that position; but I nevertheless think that such theories as that of Comte and Poincaré about verifiable hypotheses frequently deserve the most serious consideration; and the examination of them is never lost time; for it brings lessons not otherwise so easily learned. Of course with memory would have to go all opinions about everything not at this moment before our senses. You must not believe that you hear me speaking to you, but only that you hear certain sounds while you see before you a spot of black, white, and flesh color; and those sounds somehow seem to suggest certain ideas which you must not connect at all with the black and white spot. A man would have to devote years to training his mind to such habits of thought, and even then it is doubtful whether it would be possible. And what would be gained? If it would alter our beliefs as to what our sensuous experience is going to be, it would certainly be a change for the worse, since we do not find ourselves disappointed in any expectations due to common sense beliefs. If on the other hand it would not make any such difference, as I suppose it would not, why not allow us the harmless convenience of believing in these fictions, if they

[5] [*Cours de philosophie positive*, 28ᵐᵉ leçon.]

be fictions? Decidedly we must be allowed these ideas, if only as cement for the matter of our sensations. At the same time, I protest that such permission would not be at all enough. Comte, Poincaré, and Karl Pearson take what they consider to be the first impressions of sense, but which are really nothing of the sort, but are percepts that are products of psychical operations, and they separate these from all the intellectual part of our knowledge, and arbitrarily call the first *real* and the second *fictions.* These two words *real* and *fictive* bear no significations whatever except as marks of *good* and *bad.* But the truth is that what they call *bad* or *fictitious,* or *subjective,* the intellectual part of our knowledge, comprises all that is valuable on its own account, while what they mark *good,* or *real,* or *objective,* is nothing but the pretty vessel that carries the precious thought.

I can excuse a person who has lost a dear companion and whose reason is in danger of giving way under grief, for trying, on that account, to believe in a future life. I can more than excuse him because his usefulness is at stake, although I myself would not adopt a hypothesis, and would not even take it on probation, simply because the idea was pleasing to me. Without judging others, I should feel, for my own part, that that would be a crime against the integrity of the reason that God has lent to me. But if I had the choice between two hypotheses, the one more ideal and the other more materialistic, I should prefer to take the ideal one upon probation, simply because ideas are fruitful of consequences, while mere sensations are not so; so that the idealistic hypothesis would be the *more verifiable,* that is to say, would *predict more,* and could be put the more thoroughly to the test.

Upon this same principle, if two hypotheses present themselves, one of which can be satisfactorily tested in two or three days, while the testing of the other might occupy a month, the former should be tried first, even if its apparent likelihood is a good deal less.

It is a very grave mistake to attach much importance to the antecedent likelihood of hypotheses, except in extreme cases;

because likelihoods are mostly merely subjective, and have so little real value, that considering the remarkable opportunities which they will cause us to miss, in the long run attention to them does not pay. Every hypothesis should be put to the test by forcing it to make verifiable predictions. A hypothesis on which no verifiable predictions can be based should never be accepted, except with some mark attached to it to show that it is regarded as a mere convenient vehicle of thought—a mere matter of form.

In an extreme case, where the likelihood is of an unmistakably objective character, and is strongly supported by good inductions, I would allow it to cause the postponement of the testing of a hypothesis. For example, if a man came to me and pretended to be able to turn lead into gold, I should say to him, "My dear sir, I haven't time to make gold." But even then the likelihood would not weigh with me directly, as such, but because it would become a factor in what really is in all cases the leading consideration in Abduction, which is the question of Economy—Economy of money, time, thought, and energy.

It is Prof. Ernst Mach [6] who has done the most to show the importance in logic of the consideration of Economy although I had written a paper on the subject as early as 1878. But Mach goes altogether too far. For he allows thought no other value than that of economizing experiences. This cannot for an instant be admitted. Sensation, to my thinking, has no value whatever except as a vehicle of thought.

Proposals for hypotheses inundate us in an overwhelming flood, while the process of verification to which each one must be subjected before it can count as at all an item, even of likely knowledge, is so very costly in time, energy, and money —and consequently in ideas which might have been had for that time, energy, and money, that Economy would override every other consideration even if there were any other serious considerations. In fact there are no others. For abduction

[6] [See, e.g., "The Economical Nature of Physical Inquiry," in the *Popular Scientific Lectures* (1895).]

commits us to nothing. It merely causes a hypothesis to be set down upon our docket of cases to be tried.

I shall be asked, Do you really mean to say that we ought not to adopt any opinion whatever as an opinion until it has sustained the ordeal of furnishing a prediction that has been verified?

In order to answer that question, it will be requisite to inquire how an abduction can be justified, here understanding by abduction any mode or degree of acceptance of a proposition as a truth, because a fact or facts have been ascertained whose occurrence would necessarily or probably result in case that proposition were true. The abduction so defined amounts, you will remark, to observing a fact and then professing to say what idea it was that gave rise to that fact. One would think a man must be privy to the counsels of the Most High so to presume. The only justification possible, other than some such positive fact which would put quite another color upon the matter, is the justification of desperation. That is to say, that if he is not to say such things, he will be quite unable to know anything of positive fact.

In a general way, this justification certainly holds. If man had not had the gift, which every other animal has, of a mind adapted to his requirements, he not only could not have acquired any knowledge, but he could not have maintained his existence for a single generation. But he is provided with certain instincts, that is, with certain natural beliefs that are true. They relate in part to forces, in part to the action of minds. The manner in which he comes to have this knowledge seems to me tolerably clear. Certain uniformities, that is to say certain general ideas of action, prevail throughout the universe, and the reasoning mind is [it]self a product of this universe. These same laws are thus, by logical necessity, incorporated in his own being. For example, what we call straight lines are nothing but one out of an innumerable multitude of families of nonsingular lines such that through any two points there is one and one only. The particular family of lines called straight has no geometrical properties that distinguish it from any other of the innumerable families of lines of which there is one and one only through any two points. It is a law of *dynamics* that every dynamical relation between two points, no third point being concerned, except by combinations of such pairs, is altogether similar, except in quantity, to every such dynamical relation between any other two points on the same ray, or straight line. It is a consequence of this that a ray or straight line is the shortest distance between two points; whence, light appears to move along such lines; and that being the case, we recognize them by the eye, and call them straight. Thus, the faculty of sight naturally causes us to assign great prominence to such lines; and thus when we come to form a hypothesis about the motion of a particle left uninfluenced by any other, it becomes *natural* for us to suppose that it moves in a straight line. The reason this turns out true is, therefore, that this first law of motion is a corollary from a more general law which, governing all dynamics, governs light, and causes the idea of straightness to be a predominant one in our minds.

In this way, general considerations concerning the universe, strictly philosophical considerations, all but demonstrate that if the universe conforms, with any approach to accuracy, to certain highly pervasive laws, and if man's mind has been developed under the influence of those laws, it is to be expected that he should have a *natural light,* or *light of nature,* or *instinctive insight,* or genius, tending to make him guess those laws aright, or nearly aright. This conclusion is confirmed when we find that every species of animal is endowed with a similar genius. For they not only one and all have some correct notions of force, that is to say, some correct notions, though excessively narrow, of phenomena which we, with our broader conceptions, should call phenomena of force, and some similarly correct notions about the minds of their own kind and of other kinds, which are the two sufficient cotyledons of all our science, but they all have, furthermore, wonderful endowments of genius in other directions. Look at the little birds, of which all species are so nearly identical in their physique, and yet what various forms of genius do they not display in modelling their nests? This would be impossible unless the ideas that are naturally predominant in their minds were true. It would be too contrary to analogy to suppose that similar gifts were wanting to man. Nor does the proof stop here. The history of science, especially the early history of modern science, on which I had the honor of giving some lectures in this hall some years ago,[7] completes the proof by showing how few were the guesses that men of surpassing genius had to make before they rightly guessed the laws of nature. . . .

III [THE TESTING OF HYPOTHESES] [1]

The operation of testing a hypothesis by experiment, which consists in remarking that, if it is true, observations made under certain conditions ought to have certain results, and then causing those conditions to be fulfilled, and noting the results, and, if they are favorable, extending a certain confidence to the hypothesis, I call *induction*. For example, suppose that I have been led to surmise that among our colored population there is a greater tendency toward female births than among our whites. I say, if that be so, the last census must show it. I examine the last census report and find that, sure enough, there was a somewhat greater proportion of female births among colored births than among white births in that census year. To accord a certain faith to my hypothesis on that account is legitimate. It is a strong induction. I have taken all the births of that year as a sample of all the births of years in general, so long as general conditions remain as they were then. It is a very large sample, quite unnecessarily so, were it not that the excess of the one ratio over the other is quite small. All induction whatever may be regarded as the inference that throughout a whole class a ratio will have about

7 [In 1869.]

1 [Another excerpt from "Hume on Miracles." *C.P.*, VI, 358-364.—Ed.]

the same value that it has in a random sample of that class, provided the nature of the ratio for which the sample is to be examined is specified (or virtually specified) in advance of the examination. So long as the class sampled consists of units, and the ratio in question is a ratio between counts of occurrences, induction is a comparatively simple affair. But suppose we wish to test the hypothesis that a man is a Catholic priest, that is, has all the characters that are common to Catholic priests and peculiar to them. Now characters are not units, nor do they consist of units, nor can they be counted, in such a sense that one count is right and every other wrong. Characters have to be estimated according to their significance. The consequence is that there will be a certain element of guesswork in such an induction; so that I call it an *abductory induction*. I might say to myself, let me think of some other character that belongs to Catholic priests, beside those that I have remarked in this man, a character which I can ascertain whether he possesses or not. All Catholic priests are more or less familiar with Latin pronounced in the Italian manner. If, then, this man is a Catholic priest, and I make some remark in Latin which a person not accustomed to the Italian pronunciation would not at once understand, and I pronounce it in that way, then if that man is a Catholic priest he will be so surprised that he cannot but betray his understanding of it. I make such a remark; and I notice that he does understand it. But how much weight am I to attach to that test? After all, it does not touch an essential characteristic of a priest or even of a Catholic. It must be acknowledged that it is but a weak confirmation, and all the more so, because it is quite uncertain how much weight should be attached to it. Nevertheless, it does and ought to incline me to believe that the man is a Catholic priest. It is an induction, because it is a test of the hypothesis by means of a prediction, which has been verified. But it is only an abductory induction, because it was a sampling of the characters of priests to see what proportion of them this man possessed, when characters cannot be counted, nor even weighed, except by guess-work. It also partakes of the nature of abduction in involving an original suggestion; while typical induction has no originality in it, but only tests a suggestion already made.

In induction, it is not the fact predicted that in any degree necessitates the truth of the hypothesis or even renders it probable. It is the fact that it has been predicted successfully and that it is a haphazard specimen of all the predictions which might be based on the hypothesis and which constitute its practical truth. But it frequently happens that there are facts which, merely as facts, apart from the manner in which they have presented themselves, necessitate the truth, or the falsity, or the probability in some definite degree, of the hypothesis. For example, suppose the hypothesis to be that a man believes in the infallibility of the Pope. Then, if we ascertain in any way that he believes in the immaculate conception, in the confessional, and in prayers for the dead, or on the other hand that he disbelieves all or some of these things, either fact will be almost decisive of the truth or falsity of the proposition. Such inference is *deduction*. So if we ascertain that the man in question is a violent partisan in politics and in many other subjects. If, then, we find that he has given money toward a Catholic institution, we may fairly reason that such a man would not do that unless he believed in the Pope's infallibility. Or again, we might learn that he is one of five brothers whose opinions are identical on almost all subjects. If, then, we find that the other four all believe in the Pope's infallibility or all disbelieve it, this will affect our confidence in the hypothesis. This consideration will be strengthened by our general experience that while different members of a large family usually differ about most subjects, yet it mostly happens that they are either all Catholics or all Protestants. Those are four different varieties of deductive considerations which may legitimately influence our belief in a hypothesis.

These distinctions are perfectly clear in principle, which is all that is necessary, although it might sometimes be a nice question to say to which class a given inference belongs. It is to be remarked that, in pure abduction, it can never be justifiable to accept the hypothesis otherwise than as an interrogation. But as long as that condition is observed, no positive falsity is to be feared; and therefore the whole question of what one out of a number of possible hypotheses ought to be entertained becomes purely a question of economy.

Let us suppose that there are thirty-two different possible ways of explaining a set of phenomena. Then, thirty-one hypotheses must be rejected. The most economical procedure, when it is practicable, will be to find some observable fact which, under conditions easily brought about, would result from sixteen of the hypotheses and not from any of the other sixteen. Such an experiment, if it can be devised, at once halves the number of hypotheses. Or if the experiment might give any one of four results each of which would be the necessary consequence of the truth of any one of eight of the hypotheses, the single experiment would divide the number of admissible hypotheses by four. When such an experiment, or anything approaching such an experiment, is possible, it is clear that it is unwise to adopt any other course. But unfortunately, it commonly happens that this method becomes exhausted before the hypotheses are reduced to a single one, so that nothing remains but to test the remainder each by itself.

Now the testing of a hypothesis is usually more or less costly. Not infrequently the whole life's labor of a number of able men is required to disprove a single hypothesis and get rid of it. Meantime the number of possible hypotheses concerning the truth or falsity of which we really know nothing, or next to nothing, may be very great. In questions of physics there is sometimes an infinite multitude of such possible hypotheses. The question of economy is clearly a very grave one.

In very many questions, the situation before us is this: We shall do better to abandon the whole attempt to learn the truth, however urgent may be our need of ascertaining it, unless we can trust to the human mind's having such a power of guessing right that before very many hypotheses shall have been tried, intelligent guessing may be expected to lead us to the one which will support all tests, leaving the vast majority of possible hypotheses unexamined. Of course, it will be understood that in the testing process itself there need be no such assumption of mysterious guessing-powers. It is only in selecting the hypothesis to be tested that we are to be guided by that assumption.

If we subject the hypothesis, that the human mind has such a power in some degree, to inductive tests, we find that there are two classes of subjects in regard to which such an instinctive scent for the truth seems to be proved. One of these is in regard to the general modes of action [of] mechanical forces, including the doctrine of geometry; the other is in regard to the ways in which human beings and some quadrupeds think and feel. In fact, the two great branches of human science, physics and psychics, are but developments of that guessing-instinct under the corrective action of induction.

In those subjects, we may, with great confidence, follow the rule that that one of all admissible hypotheses which seems the simplest to the human mind ought to be taken up for examination first. Perhaps we cannot do better than to extend this rule to all subjects where a very simple hypothesis is at all admissible.

This rule has another advantage, which is that the simplest hypotheses are those of which the consequences are most readily deduced and compared with observation; so that, if they are wrong, they can be eliminated at less expense than any others.

This remark at once suggests another rule, namely, that if there be any hypothesis which we happen to be well provided with means for testing, or which, for any reason, promises not to detain us long, unless it be true, that hypothesis ought to be taken up early for examination. Sometimes, the very fact that a hypothesis is improbable recommends it for provisional acceptance on probation.

On the other hand, if one of the admissible hypotheses represents a marked probability of the nature of an objective fact, it may in the long run promote economy to give it an early trial. By an objective probability I mean one which could be used to guarantee an insurance company or gamester against loss, because it expresses the real fact that among occurrences of a certain genus a certain proportion are of a certain species. Such is the probability of one/six that a die will turn up any particular face. Such a probability must be distinguished from a mere likelihood which is nothing better than the expression of our preconceived ideas. The confusion between those two kinds of probability is one of the main sources of human errors, especially in abduction, in which yielding to judgments of likelihood is a fertile source of waste of time and energy.

In some departments of science, where experimentation is easy, the testing of hypotheses may be performed with some promptitude. In other departments, especially in ancient history, it will extend beyond a human life, so that for the individual the result of the abduction is all that he can hope to live to see. So long as the scientific hypothesis does not offer any particular dangers to the individual, he will do well to content himself with that hypothesis which the wise application of principles of economy recommends to undying scientific research. On the other hand, if there are such dangers, the individual may, as a scientific man, entertain one hypothesis for probation, while he allows probabilities greater weight in deciding upon what hypothesis he shall base his individual behaviour. Thus, in metaphysics, the maxim called Ockham's razor, to the effect that more elements must not be introduced into a hypothesis until it is absolutely proved that fewer are not sufficient, is a sound economic principle which ought to guide the scientific metaphysician. But centuries before it is absolutely proved that the simpler hypothesis is inadequate, it may have been made extremely probable that it is so, and the individual's behaviour may reasonably be based upon what the ultimate conclusion of science is likely to be.

In the department of ancient history, what is called "higher criticism"—that is to say, that particular color of non-textual criticism which has been dominant during the nineteenth

century, especially in Germany—has placed, and though it
has of late years retreated from many of its positions, still
continues to place, great reliance upon likelihoods. To such a
pitch is this carried that, although we can have no knowledge
of ancient history independent of Greek (and Latin) authors,
yet the critics do not hesitate utterly to reject narratives at-
tested sometimes by as many as a dozen ancient authorities—
all the testimony there is, at any rate—because the events
narrated do not seem to persons living in modern Germany to
be likely. I could write a whole book, and not an unentertain-
ing one, in illustration of this point. But scientific archaeology
has, in our day, subjected those hypotheses to objective tests;
and the uniform result has been to show that what seemed
likelihoods to German professors were all but quite uniformly
wrong and the ancient testimonies right. Thus the maxim of
exact logical analysis, that no regard at all, or very little indeed, ought to be paid to subjective likelihoods in abduction,
has been fully confirmed by inductive tests.

IV [PRAGMATISM—THE LOGIC OF ABDUCTION] [1]

If you carefully consider the question of pragmatism, you
will see that it is nothing else than the question of the logic of
abduction. That is, pragmatism proposes a certain maxim
which, if sound, must render needless any further rule as to
the admissibility of hypotheses to rank as hypotheses; that is
to say, as explanations of phenomena held as hopeful suggestions; and, furthermore, this is *all* that the maxim of
pragmatism really pretends to do, at least so far as it is confined to logic, and is not understood as a proposition in
psychology. For the maxim of pragmatism is that a conception can have no logical effect or import differing from that
of a second conception except so far as, taken in connection
with other conceptions and intentions, it might conceivably

[1] [From the seventh of "Lectures on Pragmatism," delivered at Harvard
University, 1903. (Originally published in *C.P.*, V, 121-124.)]

modify our practical conduct differently from that second conception. Now it is indisputable that no rule of abduction would be admitted by *any* philosopher which should prohibit on any formalistic grounds any inquiry as to how we ought in consistency to shape our practical conduct. Therefore, a maxim which looks only to possibly practical considerations will not need any supplement in order to exclude any hypotheses as inadmissible. What hypotheses it admits all philosophers would agree ought to be admitted. On the other hand, if it be true that nothing but such considerations has any logical effect or import whatever, it is plain that the maxim of pragmatism cannot cut off any kind of hypothesis which ought to be admitted. Thus, the maxim of pragmatism, if true, fully *covers* the entire logic of abduction. It remains to inquire whether this maxim may not have some *further* logical effect. If so, it must in some way affect inductive or deductive inference. But that pragmatism cannot interfere with induction is evident; because induction simply teaches us what we have to expect as a result of experimentation, and it is plain that any such expectation *may* conceivably concern practical conduct. In a certain sense it *must* affect *deduction*. Anything which gives a rule to abduction and so puts a limit upon admissible hypotheses will cut down *the premisses* of deduction, and thereby will render a *reductio ad absurdum* and other equivalent forms of deduction possible which would not otherwise have been possible. But here three remarks may be made. First, to affect the *premisses* of deduction is not to affect the logic of deduction. For in the process of deduction itself, no conception is introduced to which pragmatism could be supposed to object, except the acts of abstraction. Concerning that I have only time to say that pragmatism ought not to object to it. Secondly, no effect of pragmatism which *is consequent upon its effect on abduction* can go to show that pragmatism is anything more than a doctrine concerning the logic of abduction. Thirdly, if pragmatism is the doctrine that every conception is a conception of conceivable practical effects, it makes conception reach far beyond the practical. It allows any flight of imagination, provided this imagination ultimately alights upon a possible practical effect; and thus many hypotheses may seem at first glance to be excluded by the pragmatical maxim that are not really so excluded.

Admitting, then, that the question of Pragmatism is the question of Abduction, let us consider it under that form. What is good abduction? What should an explanatory hypothesis be to be worthy to rank as a hypothesis? Of course, it must explain the facts. But what other conditions ought it to fulfill to be good? The question of the goodness of anything is whether that thing fulfills its end. What, then, is the end of explanatory hypothesis? Its end is, through subjection to the test of experiment, to lead to the avoidance of all surprise and to the establishment of a habit of positive expectation that shall not be disappointed. Any hypothesis, therefore, may be admissible, in the absence of any special reasons to the contrary, provided it be capable of experimental verification, and only insofar as it is capable of such verification. This is approximately the doctrine of pragmatism. But just here a broad question opens out before us. What are we to understand by experimental verification? The answer to that involves the whole logic of induction.

Let me point out to you the different opinions which we actually find men holding today—perhaps not consistently, but thinking that they hold them—upon this subject. In the first place, we find men who maintain that no hypothesis ought to be admitted, even as a hypothesis, any further than its truth or its falsity is capable of being directly perceived. This, as well as I can make out, is what was in the mind of Auguste Comte,[2] who is generally assumed to have first formulated this maxim. Of course, this maxim of abduction supposes that, as people say, we "are to believe only what we actually see"; and there are well-known writers, and writers of no little intellectual force, who maintain that it is unscientific to make predictions—unscientific, therefore, to expect anything. One ought to restrict one's opinions to what one actually perceives.

[2] [See Cours de philosophie positive, 28ᵐᵉ leçon.]

I need hardly say that that position cannot be consistently maintained. It refutes itself, for it is *itself* an opinion relating to more than is actually in the field of momentary perception.

In the second place, there are those who hold that a theory which has sustained a number of experimental tests may be expected to sustain a number of other similar tests, and to have a general approximate truth, the justification of this being that this kind of inference must prove correct in the long run. . . . But these logicians refuse to admit that we can ever have a right to conclude definitely that a hypothesis is *exactly* true, that is that it should be able to sustain experimental tests in endless series; for, they urge, no hypothesis can be subjected to an endless series of tests. They are willing we should say that a theory is true, because, all our ideas being more or less vague and approximate, what we mean by saying that a theory is true can only be that it is very near true. But they will not allow us to say that anything put forth as an anticipation of experience should assert exactitude, because exactitude in experience would imply experiences in endless series, which is impossible.

In the third place, the great body of scientific men hold that it is too much to say that induction must be restricted to that for which there can be *positive* experimental evidence. They urge that the rationale of induction as it is understood by logicians of the second group, themselves, entitles us to hold a theory, provided it be such that if it involve any falsity, experiment must some day detect that falsity. We, therefore, have a right, they will say, to infer that something *never* will happen, provided it be of such a nature that it could not occur without being detected.

❦ XIV ❧

[THE ESSENCE OF MATHEMATICS] [1]

It was Benjamin Peirce, whose son I boast myself, that in 1870 first defined mathematics as "the science which draws necessary conclusions." [2] This was a hard saying at the time; but today, students of the philosophy of mathematics generally acknowledge its substantial correctness.

The common definition, among such people as ordinary schoolmasters, still is that mathematics is the science of quantity. As this is inevitably understood in English, it seems to be a misunderstanding of a definition which may be very old, [3] the original meaning being that mathematics is the science of *quantities,* that is, forms possessing quantity. We perceive that Euclid was aware that a large branch of geometry had nothing to do with measurement (unless as an aid in demonstrating); and, therefore, a Greek geometer of his age (early in the third century B.C.) or later could not define mathematics as the science of that which the abstract noun quantity expresses. A line, however, was classed as a quantity, or *quantum,* by Aristotle [4] and his followers; so that even perspective (which deals wholly with intersections and projections, not at all with lengths) could be said to be a science of quantities, "quantity" being taken in the concrete sense. That this was what was originally meant by the definition "Mathematics is

1 [A part of Chapter 3 of the "Minute Logic," dated January-February, 1902. (Originally published in *C.P.,* IV, 189-203.)]

2 ["Linear Associative Algebra" (1870), Sec. 1; see *American Journal of Mathematics,* IV (1881).]

3 From what is said by Proclus Diadochus, A.D. 485 [*Commentarii in Primum Euclidis Elementorum Librum,* Prologi pars prior, c. 12], it would seem that the Pythagoreans understood mathematics to be the answer to the two questions "how many?" and "how much?"

4 [*Metaphysica,* 1020a, 14-20.]

256

the science of quantity," is sufficiently shown by the circumstance that those writers who first enunciate it, about A.D. 500, that is Ammonius Hermiae [5] and Boethius,[6] make astronomy and music branches of mathematics; and it is confirmed by the reasons they give for doing so.[7] Even Philo of Alexandria (100 B.C.), who defines mathematics as the science of ideas furnished by sensation and reflection in respect to their necessary consequences, since he includes under mathematics, besides its more essential parts, the theory of numbers and geometry, also the practical arithmetic of the Greeks, geodesy, mechanics, optics (or projective geometry), music, and astronomy, must be said to take the word "mathematics" in a different sense from ours. That Aristotle did not regard mathematics as the science of quantity, in the modern abstract sense, is evidenced in various ways. The subjects of mathematics are, according to him, the how much and the continuous. (See *Metaph.* K iii 1061 a33). He referred the continuous to his category of *quantum;* and therefore he did make *quantum,* in a broad sense, the one object of mathematics.

Plato, in the sixth book of the *Republic,*[8] holds that the essential characteristic of mathematics lies in the peculiar kind and degree of its abstraction, greater than that of physics, but less than that of what we now call philosophy; and Aristotle [9] follows his master in this definition. It has ever since been the habit of metaphysicians to extol their own reasonings and conclusions as vastly more abstract and scientific than those of mathematics. It certainly would seem that problems about God, Freedom, and Immortality are more exalted than, for example, the question how many hours, minutes, and seconds would elapse before two couriers travelling under assumed conditions will come together; although I do not know that

[5] [In *Porphyrii Isogogen sine* v. *voces,* p. 5v., l.11 *et seq.*]

[6] [*De institutione arithmetica,* L.I, c.1.]

[7] I regret I have not noted the passage of Ammonius to which I refer. It is probably one of the excerpts given by Brandis. My MS. note states that he gives reasons showing this to be his meaning.

[8] 510c to the end; but in the *Laws* his notion is improved.

[9] [See *Metaphysica,* 1025 b1-1026 a33; 1060 b31-1061 b34.]

this has been proved. But that the methods of thought of the metaphysicians are, as a matter of historical fact, in any aspect, not far inferior to those of mathematics is simply an infatuation. One singular consequence of the notion which prevailed during the greater part of the history of philosophy, that metaphysical reasoning ought to be similar to that of mathematics, only more so, has been that sundry mathematicians have thought themselves, as mathematicians, qualified to discuss philosophy; and no worse metaphysics than theirs is to be found.

Kant [10] regarded mathematical propositions as synthetical judgments *a priori;* wherein there is this much truth, that they are not, for the most part, what he called analytical judgments; that is, the predicate is not, in the sense he intended, contained in the definition of the subject. But if the propositions of arithmetic, for example, are true cognitions, or even forms of cognition, this circumstance is quite aside from their mathematical truth. For all modern mathematicians agree with Plato and Aristotle that mathematics deals exclusively with hypothetical states of things, and asserts no matter of fact whatever; and further, that it is thus alone that the necessity of its conclusions is to be explained.[11] This is the true essence of mathematics; and my father's definition is in so far correct that it is impossible to reason necessarily concerning anything else than a pure hypothesis. Of course, I do not mean that if such pure hypothesis happened to be true of an actual state of things, the reasoning would thereby cease to be necessary. Only, it never would be known apodictically to be true of an actual state of things. Suppose a state of things of a perfectly definite, general description. That is, there must be no room for doubt as to whether anything, itself determinate, would or would not come under that description. And suppose, further, that this description refers to nothing occult—nothing that cannot be summoned up fully into the

10 [*Kritik der reinen Vernunft,* "Einleitung," B, § V.]

11 A view which J. S. Mill (*Logic* II, V, § 2) rather comically calls "the important doctrine of Dugald Stewart."

imagination. Assume, then, a range of possibilities equally definite and equally subject to the imagination; so that, so far as the given description of the supposed state of things is general, the different ways in which it might be made determinate could never introduce doubtful or occult features. The assumption, for example, must not refer to any matter of fact. For questions of fact are not within the purview of the imagination. Nor must it be such that, for example, it could lead us to ask whether the vowel *OO* can be imagined to be sounded on as high a pitch as the vowel *EE*. Perhaps it would have to be restricted to pure spatial, temporal, and logical relations. Be that as it may, the question whether in such a state of things, a certain other similarly definite state of things, equally a matter of the imagination, could or could not, in the assumed range of possibility, ever occur, would be one in reference to which one of the two answers, *Yes* and *No,* would be true, but never both. But all pertinent facts would be within the beck and call of the imagination; and consequently nothing but the operation of thought would be necessary to render the true answer. Nor, supposing the answer to cover the whole range of possibility assumed, could this be rendered otherwise than by reasoning that would be apodictic, general, and exact. No knowledge of what actually is, no *positive* knowledge, as we say, could result. On the other hand, to assert that any source of information that is restricted to actual facts could afford us a necessary knowledge, that is, knowledge relating to a whole general range of possibility, would be a flat contradiction in terms.

Mathematics is the study of what is true of hypothetical states of things. That is its essence and definition. Everything in it, therefore, beyond the first precepts for the construction of the hypotheses, has to be of the nature of apodictic inference. No doubt, we may reason imperfectly and jump at a conclusion; still, the conclusion so guessed at is, after all, that in a certain supposed state of things something would necessarily be true. Conversely, too, every apodictic inference is, strictly speaking, mathematics. But mathematics, as a serious science, has, over and above its essential character of being hypothetical, an accidental characteristic peculiarity—a *proprium,* as the Aristotelians used to say—which is of the greatest logical interest. Namely, while all the "philosophers" follow Aristotle in holding no demonstration to be thoroughly satisfactory except what they call a "direct" demonstration, or a "demonstration why"—by which they mean a demonstration which employs only general concepts and concludes nothing but what would be an item of a definition if all its terms were themselves distinctly defined—the mathematicians, on the contrary, entertain a contempt for that style of reasoning, and glory in what the philosophers stigmatize as "mere" indirect demonstrations, or "demonstrations that." Those propositions which can be deduced from others by reasoning of the kind that the philosophers extol are set down by mathematicians as "corollaries." That is to say, they are like those geometrical truths which Euclid did not deem worthy of particular mention, and which his editors inserted with a garland, or corolla, against each in the margin, implying perhaps that it was to them that such honor as might attach to these insignificant remarks was due. In the theorems, or at least in all the major theorems, a different kind of reasoning is demanded. Here, it will not do to confine oneself to general terms. It is necessary to set down, or to imagine, some individual and definite schema, or diagram—in geometry, a figure composed of lines with letters attached; in algebra an array of letters of which some are repeated. This schema is constructed so as to conform to a hypothesis set forth in general terms in the thesis of the theorem. Pains are taken so to construct it that there would be something closely similar in every possible state of things to which the hypothetical description in the thesis would be applicable, and furthermore to construct it so that it shall have no other characters which could influence the reasoning. How it can be that, although the reasoning is based upon the study of an individual schema, it is nevertheless necessary, that is, applicable, to all possible cases, is one of the questions we shall have to consider. Just now, I wish to point out that after the schema has been constructed according to the precept virtually contained in the thesis, the assertion of the theorem is not evidently true, even for the individual schema; nor will any amount of hard thinking of the philosophers' corollarial kind ever render it evident. Thinking in general terms is not enough. It is necessary that something should be *done*. In geometry, subsidiary lines are drawn. In algebra permissible transformations are made. Thereupon, the faculty of observation is called into play. Some relation between the parts of the schema is remarked. But would this relation subsist in every possible case? Mere corollarial reasoning will sometimes assure us of this. But, generally speaking, it may be necessary to draw distinct schemata to represent alternative possibilities. Theorematic reasoning invariably depends upon experimentation with individual schemata. We shall find that, in the last analysis, the same thing is true of the corollarial reasoning too; even the Aristotelian "demonstration why." Only in this case, the very words serve as schemata. Accordingly, we may say that corollarial, or "philosophical" reasoning is reasoning with words; while theorematic, or mathematical reasoning proper, is reasoning with specially constructed schemata.

Another characteristic of mathematical thought is the extraordinary use it makes of abstractions. Abstractions have been a favorite butt of ridicule in modern times. Now it is very easy to laugh at the old physician who is represented as answering the question, why opium puts people to sleep, by saying that it is because it has a dormative virtue. It is an answer that no doubt carries vagueness to its last extreme. Yet, invented as the story was to show how little meaning there might be in an abstraction, nevertheless the physician's answer does contain a truth that modern philosophy has generally denied: it does assert that there really is in opium *something* which explains its always putting people to sleep. This has, I say, been denied by modern philosophers generally. Not, of course, explicitly; but when they say that the different events of people going to sleep after taking opium have really

nothing in common, but only that the mind classes them together—and this is what they virtually do say in denying the
reality of generals—they do implicitly deny that there is any
true explanation of opium's generally putting people to sleep.

Look through the modern logical treatises, and you will
find that they almost all fall into one or other of two errors,
as I hold them to be; that of setting aside the doctrine of abstraction (in the sense in which an abstract noun marks an
abstraction) as a grammatical topic with which the logician
need not particularly concern himself; and that of confound-
ing abstraction, in this sense, with that operation of the mind
by which we pay attention to one feature of a percept to the
disregard of others. The two things are entirely disconnected.
The most ordinary fact of perception, such as "it is light," involves *precisive* abstraction, or *prescission*.[12] But *hypostatic*
abstraction, the abstraction which transforms "it is light" into
"there is light here," which is the sense which I shall commonly attach to the word abstraction (since *prescission* will
do for precisive abstraction) is a very special mode of thought.
It consists in taking a feature of a percept or percepts (after
it has already been prescinded from the other elements of the
percept), so as to take propositional form in a judgment (indeed, it may operate upon any judgment whatsoever), and in
conceiving this fact to consist in the relation between the subject of that judgment and another subject, which has a mode
of being that merely consists in the truth of propositions of
which the corresponding concrete term is the predicate. Thus,
we transform the proposition, "honey is sweet," into "honey
possesses sweetness." "Sweetness" might be called a fictitious
thing, in one sense. But since the mode of being attributed to
it *consists* in no more than the fact that some things are sweet,
and it is not pretended, or imagined, that it has any other

12 [According to Peirce, "abstraction" has two meanings—"the one the
contemplation of a form apart from matter, as when we think of *whiteness,* and the other the thinking of a nature *indifferenter,* or without regard to the differences of its individuals, as when we think of a *white*
thing, generally. The latter process is called, also, *precision* (or better, *prescission*)." *C.P.,* II, 428.—Ed.]

mode of being, there is, after all, no fiction. The only profession made is that we consider the fact of honey being sweet under the form of a relation; and so we really can. I have selected sweetness as an instance of one of the least useful of abstractions. Yet even this is convenient. It facilitates such thoughts as that the sweetness of honey is particularly cloying; that the sweetness of honey is something like the sweetness of a honeymoon; etc. Abstractions are particularly congenial to mathematics. Everyday life first, for example, found the need of that class of abstractions which we call *collections*. Instead of saying that some human beings are males and all the rest females, it was found convenient to say that *mankind* consists of the male *part* and the female *part*. The same thought makes classes of collections, such as pairs, leashes, quatrains, hands, weeks, dozens, baker's dozens, sonnets, scores, quires, hundreds, long hundreds, gross, reams, thousands, myriads, lacs, millions, milliards, milliasses, etc. These have suggested a great branch of mathematics.[13] Again, a point moves: it is by abstraction that the geometer says that it "describes a line." This line, though an abstraction, itself moves; and this is regarded as generating a surface; and so on. So likewise, when the analyst treats operations as themselves subjects of operations, a method whose utility will not be denied, this is another instance of abstraction. Maxwell's notion of a tension exercised upon lines of electrical force, transverse to them, is somewhat similar. These examples exhibit the great rolling billows of abstraction in the ocean of mathematical thought; but when we come to a minute examination of it, we shall find, in every department, incessant ripples of the same form of thought, of which the examples I have mentioned give no hint.

Another characteristic of mathematical thought is that it can have no success where it cannot generalize. One cannot,

[13] Of course, the moment a collection is recognized as an abstraction we have to admit that even a percept is an abstraction or represents an abstraction, if matter has parts. It therefore becomes difficult to maintain that all abstractions are fictions.

for example, deny that chess is mathematics, after a fashion; but, owing to the exceptions which everywhere confront the mathematician in this field—such as the limits of the board; the single steps of king, knight, and pawn; the finite number of squares; the peculiar modes of capture by pawns; the queening of pawns; castling—there results a mathematics whose wings are effectually clipped, and which can only run along the ground. Hence it is that a mathematician often finds what a chess-player might call a gambit to his advantage; exchanging a smaller problem that involves exceptions for a larger one free from them. Thus, rather than suppose that parallel lines, unlike all other pairs of straight lines in a plane, never meet, he supposes that they intersect at infinity. Rather than suppose that some equations have roots while others have not, he supplements real quantity by the infinitely greater realm of imaginary quantity. He tells us with ease how many inflexions a plane curve of any description has; but if we ask how many of these are real, and how many merely fictional, he is unable to say. He is perplexed by three-dimensional space, because not all pairs of straight lines intersect, and finds it to his advantage to use quaternions which represent a sort of four-fold continuum, in order to avoid the exception. It is because exceptions so hamper the mathematician that almost all the relations with which he chooses to deal are of the nature of correspondences; that is to say, such relations that for every relate there is the same number of correlates, and for every correlate the same number of relates.

Among the minor, yet striking characteristics of mathematics, may be mentioned the fleshless and skeletal build of its propositions; the peculiar difficulty, complication, and stress of its reasonings; the perfect exactitude of its results; their broad universality; their practical infallibility. It is easy to speak with precision upon a general theme. Only one must commonly surrender all ambition to be certain. It is equally easy to be certain. One has only to be sufficiently vague. It is not so difficult to be pretty precise and fairly certain at once about a very narrow subject. But to reunite, like mathematics, perfect exactitude and practical infallibility with unrestricted universality, is remarkable. But it is not hard to see that all these characters of mathematics are inevitable consequences of its being the study of hypothetical truth.

It is difficult to decide between the two definitions of mathematics; the one by its method, that of drawing necessary conclusions; the other by its aim and subject matter, as the study of hypothetical states of things. The former makes or seems to make the deduction of the consequences of hypotheses the sole business of the mathematician as such. But it cannot be denied that immense genius has been exercised in the mere framing of such general hypotheses as the field of imaginary quantity and the allied idea of Riemann's surface, in imagining non-Euclidian measurement, ideal numbers, the perfect liquid. Even the framing of the particular hypotheses of special problems almost always calls for good judgment and knowledge, and sometimes for great intellectual power, as in the case of Boole's logical algebra. Shall we exclude this work from the domain of mathematics? Perhaps the answer should be that, in the first place, whatever exercise of intellect may be called for in applying mathematics to a question not propounded in mathematical form [it] is certainly not pure mathematical thought; and in the second place, that the mere creation of a hypothesis may be a grand work of poietic [14] genius, but cannot be said to be scientific, inasmuch as that which it produces is neither true nor false, and therefore is not knowledge. This reply suggests the further remark that if mathematics is the study of purely imaginary states of things, poets must be great mathematicians, especially that class of poets who write novels of intricate and enigmatical plots. Even the reply which is obvious, that by *studying* imaginary states of things we mean *studying* what is true of them, perhaps does not fully meet the objection. The article "Mathematics" in the ninth edition of the *Encyclopaedia Britannica* [15] makes mathematics consist in the study of a particular sort of hy-

[14] [From ποιέω.]
[15] [By George Chrystal.]

potheses, namely, those that are exact, etc., as there set forth at some length. The article is well worthy of consideration.

The philosophical mathematician, Dr. Richard Dedekind,[16] holds mathematics to be a branch of logic. This would not result from my father's definition, which runs, not that mathematics is the science of *drawing* necessary conclusions—which would be deductive logic—but that it is the science which *draws* necessary conclusions. It is evident, and I know as a fact, that he had this distinction in view. At the time when he thought out this definition, he, a mathematician, and I, a logician, held daily discussions about a large subject which interested us both; and he was struck, as I was, with the contrary nature of his interest and mine in the same propositions. The logician does not care particularly about this or that hypothesis or its consequences, except so far as these things may throw a light upon the nature of reasoning. The mathematician is intensely interested in efficient methods of reasoning, with a view to their possible extension to new problems; but he does not, *qua* mathematician, trouble himself minutely to dissect those parts of this method whose correctness is a matter of course. The different aspects which the algebra of logic will assume for the two men is instructive in this respect. The mathematician asks what value this algebra has as a calculus. Can it be applied to unravelling a complicated question? Will it, at one stroke, produce a remote consequence? The logician does not wish the algebra to have that character. On the contrary, the greater number of distinct logical steps, into which the algebra breaks up an inference, will for him constitute a superiority of it over another which moves more swiftly to its conclusions. He demands that the algebra shall analyze a reasoning into its last elementary steps. Thus, that which is a merit to a logical algebra for one of these students is a demerit in the eyes of the other. The one studies the science of drawing conclusions, the other the science which draws necessary conclusions.

But, indeed, the difference between the two sciences is far

16 [*Was sind und was sollen die Zahlen*, Vorwort (1888).]

more than that between two points of view. Mathematics is purely hypothetical: it produces nothing but conditional propositions. Logic, on the contrary, is categorical in its assertions. True, it is not merely, or even mainly, a mere discovery of what really is, like metaphysics. It is a normative science. It thus has a strongly mathematical character, at least in its methodeutic division; for here it analyzes the problem of how, with given means, a required end is to be pursued. This is, at most, to say that it has to call in the aid of mathematics; that it has a mathematical branch. But so much may be said of every science. There is a mathematical logic, just as there is a mathematical optics and a mathematical economics. Mathematical logic is formal logic. Formal logic, however developed, is mathematics. Formal logic, however, is by no means the whole of logic, or even its principal part. It is hardly to be reckoned as a part of logic proper. Logic has to define its aim, and in doing so is even more dependent upon ethics, or the philosophy of aims, by far, than it is, in the methodeutic branch, upon mathematics. We shall soon come to understand how a student of ethics might well be tempted to make his science a branch of logic; as indeed, it pretty nearly was in the mind of Socrates. But this would be no truer a view than the other. Logic depends upon mathematics; still more intimately upon ethics; but its proper concern is with truths beyond the purview of either.

There are two characters of mathematics which have not yet been mentioned, because they are not exclusive characteristics of it. One of these, which need not detain us, is that mathematics is distinguished from all other sciences except only ethics, in standing in no need of ethics. Every other science, even logic—logic, especially—is in its early stages in danger of evaporating into airy nothingness, degenerating, as the Germans say, into an arachnoid [17] film, spun from the stuff that dreams are made of. There is no such danger for pure mathematics; for that is precisely what mathematics ought to be.

[17] [Originally "anachrioid."—Ed.]

The other character—and of particular interest it is to us just now—is that mathematics, along with ethics and logic alone of the sciences, has no need of any appeal to logic. No doubt, some reader may exclaim in dissent to this, on first hearing it said. Mathematics, they may say, is pre-eminently a science of reasoning. So it is; pre-eminently a science that reasons. But just as it is not necessary, in order to talk, to understand the theory of the formation of vowel sounds, so it is not necessary, in order to reason, to be in possession of the theory of reasoning. Otherwise, plainly, the science of logic could never be developed. The contrary objection would have more excuse, that no science stands in need of logic, since our natural power of reason is enough. Make of logic what the majority of treatises in the past have made of it, and a very common class of English and French books still make of it—that is to say, mainly formal logic, and that formal logic represented as an art of reasoning—and in my opinion, this objection is more than sound, for such logic is a great hindrance to right reasoning. It would, however, be aside from our present purpose to examine this objection minutely. I will content myself with saying that undoubtedly our natural power of reasoning is enough, in the same sense that it is enough, in order to obtain a wireless transatlantic telegraph, that men should be born. That is to say, it is bound to come sooner or later. But that does not make research into the nature of electricity needless for gaining such a telegraph. So likewise if the study of electricity had been pursued resolutely, even if no special attention had ever been paid to mathematics, the requisite mathematical ideas would surely have been evolved. Faraday, indeed, did evolve them without any acquaintance with mathematics. Still it would be far more economical to postpone electrical researches, to study mathematics by itself, and then to apply it to electricity, which was Maxwell's way. In this same manner, the various logical difficulties which arise in the course of every science except mathematics, ethics, and logic, will, no doubt, get worked out after a time, even though no special study of logic be made. But it would be far more economical to make first a systematic study of logic. If anybody should ask what are these logical difficulties which arise in all the sciences, he must have read the history of science very irreflectively. What was the famous controversy concerning the measure of force but a logical difficulty? What was the controversy between the uniformitarians and the catastrophists but a question of whether or not a given conclusion followed from acknowledged premisses? . . .

But it may be asked whether mathematics, ethics, and logic have not encountered similar difficulties. Are the doctrines of logic at all settled? Is the history of ethics anything but a history of controversy? Have no logical errors been committed by mathematicians? To that I reply, first, as to logic, that not only have the rank and file of writers on the subject been, as an eminent psychiatrist, Maudsley, declares, men of arrested brain-development, and not only have they generally lacked the most essential qualification for the study, namely mathematical training, but the main reason why logic is unsettled is that thirteen different opinions are current as to the true aim of the science. Now this is not a logical difficulty but an ethical difficulty; for ethics is the science of aims. Secondly, it is true that pure ethics has been, and always must be, a theatre of discussion, for the reason that its study consists in the gradual development of a distinct recognition of a satisfactory aim. It is a science of subtleties, no doubt; but it is not logic, but the development of the ideal, which really creates and resolves the problems of ethics. Thirdly, in mathematics errors of reasoning have occurred, nay, have passed unchallenged for thousands of years. This, however, was simply because they escaped notice. Never, in the whole history of the science, has a question whether a given conclusion followed *mathematically* from given premisses, when once started, failed to receive a speedy and unanimous reply. Very few have been even the apparent exceptions; and those few have been due to the fact that it is only within the last half century that mathematicians have come to have a perfectly clear recognition of what is mathematical soil and what foreign to mathematics. Perhaps the nearest approximation to an exception was the dispute about the use of divergent series. Here neither party was in possession of sufficient pure mathematical reasons covering the whole ground; and such reasons as they had were not only of an extra-mathematical kind, but were used to support more or less vague positions. It appeared then, as we all know now, that divergent series are of the utmost utility.[18]

Struck by this circumstance, and making an inference, of which it is sufficient to say that it was not mathematical, many of the old mathematicians pushed the use of divergent series beyond all reason. This was a case of mathematicians disputing about the validity of a kind of inference that is not mathematical. No doubt, a sound logic (such as has not hitherto been developed) would have shown clearly that that nonmathematical inference was not a sound one. But this is, I believe, the only instance in which any large party in the mathematical world ever proposed to rely, in mathematics, upon

[18] It would not be fair, however, to suppose that every reader will know this. Of course, there are many series so extravagantly divergent that no use at all can be made of them. But even when a series is divergent from the very start, some use might commonly be made of it, if the same information could not otherwise be obtained more easily. The reason is—or rather, one reason is—that most series, even when divergent, approximate at last somewhat to geometrical series, at least, for a considerable succession of terms. The series $\log (1 + x) = x - 1/2 x^2 + 1/3 x^3 - 1/4 x^4 +$, etc., is one that would not be judiciously employed in order to find the natural logarithm of 3, which is 1.0986, its successive terms being $2 - 2 + 8/3 - 4 + 32/5 - 32/3 +$, etc. Still, employing the common device of substituting for the last two terms that are to be used, say M and N, the expression $M/(1 - N/M)$, the succession of the first six values is 0.667, 1.143, 1.067, 1.128, 1.067, which do show some approximation to the value. The mean of the last two, which any professional computer would use (supposing him to use this series, at all) would be 1.098, which is not very wrong. Of course, the computer would practically use the series $\log 3 = 1 + 1/12 + 1/80 + 1/448 +$, etc., of which the terms written give the correct value to four places, if they are properly used.

unmathematical reasoning. My proposition is that true mathematical reasoning is so much more evident than it is possible to render any doctrine of logic proper—without just such reasoning—that an appeal in mathematics to logic could only embroil a situation. On the contrary, such difficulties as may arise concerning necessary reasoning have to be solved by the logician by reducing them to questions of mathematics. Upon those mathematical dicta, as we shall come clearly to see, the logician has ultimately to repose.